# TITCH HIKERS' GUIDE

Editor

Elspeth Pontin

Illustrated by children from Barton Hill Primary School,
Christ Church C.E. V.C. Primary School,
Greenfield Primary School,
& St. Werburghs Primary School

titch
hikers'
guide

freedom guides

# TITCH HIKERS' GUIDE, 11TH EDITION

## Edited by

Elspeth Pontin

## Researched by

Abi Pearse

## Contributions by

Ben Pontin, and Gillian Sweet Bartley.

## Advertising

Katie Watts

## Published by

Freedom Guides Limited
PO Box 2816, Bristol BS8 9EE

## Published

July 2009

## ISBN

978-0-9534648-7-6

## Cover design

karen painter design
karenpainter@blueyonder.co.uk

## Printed by

Cambrian Printers Ltd
www.cambrian-printers.co.uk

## Cover art courtesy of

Ibtisan (lion), Shakila (girls), Millie (school), Zobra (butterfly), Haatizah (boats), and Nabil (boy).

## Book orders

Email: books@titchhikers.co.uk

Tel: 0117 974 5471

## Special thanks to

- Our advertisers, wthout whom there would be no book.
- Borders in Clifton, Bristol.
- Nigel Vile, author of Kiddiwalks, Bristol & Bath.
- Pat from Arch House Deli, Clifton.
- Sophie Dawson, Cool Camping.
- Visit Bristol for the use of their maps.
- See also the acknowledgements at the back of the book.

First Published as Titch Hikers' Guide to Bristol by The National Childbirth Trust (Bristol Branch): First Edition 1983, revised editions 1985, 1987, 1989, 1992, 1994

Seventh Edition published by Titch Hikers' Guide Limited, 1998, revised edition 2001.

Ninth Edition published by Titch Hikers' Guide (UK) Limited, 2004

Tenth Edition published by Freedom Guides Limited, 2006

Although the Editor, writers and researchers have tried to make the information as accurate as possible, they accept no responsibility for any inconvenience sustained by any person using this book.

Freedom Guides Ltd is a member of Bristol Books & Publishers
www.bristolbooksandpublishers.co.uk

titch
hikers'
guide

# CONTENTS

# Welcome

Welcome to the latest edition of the Titch Hikers' Guide to Bristol. In it, we go back to the roots of when Titch Hikers' came into the world. The early editions of the book, the first of which appeared in 1983, were aimed at parents and carers of babies and young children. Our latest edition returns to this early years age group. We aim to guide people who are new to parenthood, or new to Bristol, through the wealth of services, activities and events the region offers.

This book has been produced by parents for parents, as it has been from the very beginning of the Titch Hikers' 'project'. All the entries are based on material supplied by parents and carers who volunteer information that is worth sharing with others. We do not think there is anything like it. It is unique because it is comprehensive, independent, and very reliable...and now, with the local children's art which we have commissioned, extremely vibrant and colourful!

Elspeth Pontin

July 2009

# How to use this Guide

The entries in this Guide focus on the period from pregnancy through to starting school. We have only included entries that have been recommended to us as being particularly suitable for this age range. (Ideas for older children can be found at www.titchhikers.co.uk.) While the entries in this guide have been fully researched, we do not guarantee the availability of any equipment for your child within the individual establishments. If you need something specific, we would always urge you to call first.

We have renamed the chapters to make them as specific as possible, but there are always overlaps and 'grey areas'. We recommend that you read the introductions to each chapter and have a look at our index if you are looking for something specific.

The maps in this Guide are for the purposes of general orientation only. They can be found in **Beaches**, **Family Holidays and Weekends Away**, and at the back of this book.

It is your responsibility to check the references of childcarers, entertainers, and any other people or businesses recommended in this Guide. Please do so at your discretion.

As Bristol is a city of change, we are always grateful for recommendations of people and places who we do not have, and for comments on things which may no longer be useful to readers. We have tried to ensure the accuracy of all material at time of going to press, but readers are urged to use the contact details provided to avoid disappointment.

Please check out our website at www.titchhikers.co.uk for updates and the times and dates of events, as they are released. Also look at the families section in Venue magazine www.venue.co.uk.

Remember - we only list recommendations. If you want to see something in the book, recommend it to us at info@titchhikers.co.uk

# earn+learn

**become an Early Years Professional and work towards Early Years Professional Status (EYPS).**

## Choose your route to success:

- **Validation Only pathway – Four month part time:** for those graduate practitioners employed in the early years sector and close to meeting the standards.
- **Short EPD pathway – Six month part time:** designed for graduates who are employed in the early years sector, but who have some gaps in their experience.
- **Long EPD pathway – Fifteen month part time:** for those working in the early years sector who have a foundation degree (or equivalent) and need to "top up" to an Honours Degree in Early Childhood Studies.
- **Full Training pathway – Twelve month full time:** for graduates with little or no experience of the early years sector. This pathway attracts an automatic tax-free bursary of £5,000 for every candidate. Limited places available for September 2009.

UWE has places available on all EYPS pathways starting in **September 2009**.

To find out more

**Telephone** 0117 32 84128
**E-mail** eyps@uwe.ac.uk

or click on
**www.uwe.ac.uk/eyps**

cwdc
Children's Workforce
Development Council

University of the
West of England

**UWE BRISTOL**

bettertogether

# Festivals & Events
## At a Glance

### March

Little Monster Baby & Toddler Show

### May

Royal Bath & West Show

Bristol Vegan Fayre

### June

St Werburgh's City Farm Festival

Beer Festival (Bitton Railway St)

Bristol Bike Fest

Bristol Festival of Nature

Love Parks week

Bristol's Biggest Bike Ride

Bristol Harbour Fun Run

### July

St Paul's Carnival

Truckfest

Keynsham Music Festival

Boogie for Brizzle

Trowbridge Festival

Boating Regatta

### August

Bristol Harbour Festival

Playday

Bristol International Balloon Fiesta

Bristol Children's Festival

Festival of the Tree

Bristol International Kite Festival

Turn the page for more details on each event.

### September

Gardening Show (Bath & West)

Organic Food Festival

Bristol Doors Open Day

Bath Children's Literature Festival

The Bristol Festival

### November

Encounters Film Festival

Firework Fiesta

Somerset Carnivals

**Little Monster** Baby & Toddler Show

## Bristol's Premier Baby & Toddler Event

Ashton Gate Stadium
Sunday March 28th 2010 10.00am - 4.00pm

**Everything you need for pregnancy, babies and toddlers**
Free facepainting & balloon modelling
Free goody bag for the first 500 families!!
Admission £3.00 for adults and kids go free!

And much more....

Visit **www.little-monster.co.uk** for more details

## March

Monster Baby Show

### Little Monster Baby & Toddler Show

www.little-monster.co.uk
Bristol Baby &Toddler Show, Dolman Exhibition Hall,
Ashton Gate Stadium, Bristol. BS3 2EJ
Show opening time: 10am-4pm.

Large baby and toddler show, featuring
everything related to pregnancy, babies
and toddlers. Great for shopping, new
products and for a wide range of advice on
pregnancy and childcare. Lots of activities to
keep children entertained, including balloon
modelling and free face painting. Approx
£3 entry fee (cheaper if book in advance).
Accompanied children under 16 FREE.

See Advert on p.vii

## May

Royal Bath & West Show

Bristol Vegan Fayre

### Royal Bath & West Show

www.bathandwest.com, 01749 822222

Agricultural show with lots of interesting trade
stands. For all ages. Children get in FREE
when adult tickets (approx £17) are bought in
advance!

### Bristol Vegan Fayre

www.veganfayre.co.uk, 0117 923 9053

By the Waterside. Stalls, entertainers,
fantastic line up of talks and demos. It doesn't
matter if you follow a Vegan diet or not. Buy
your advance weekend ticket online.

## June

Bristol Vegan Fayre (see May)

Beer Festival (Bitton Railway St)

Bristol Bike Fest

Bristol Festival of Nature

Love Parks week

Bristol's Biggest Bike Ride

Glastonbury Festival

Bristol Harbour Fun Run

### Beer Festival at Bitton Railway

www.avonvalleyrailway.org, 0117 932 5538

Sample local, and UK wide, ales. FREE

### Bristol Bike Fest

www.bristolbikefest.com, 0117 9532698

Mountain bike event at Ashton Court Estate.

### Bristol Festival of Nature

www.festivalofnature.org, 0117 370 0971

The UK's biggest celebration of the natural
world. Takes place at Bristol Harbourside.
Download brochure online. FREE

### Love Parks Week

www.loveparksweek.org.uk

Celebrating the nation's parks and green
spaces. Visit the Bristol Parks website for
more information nearer the week
and look out for a very special
event at Blaise Castle Estate. FREE

### Bristol's Biggest Bike Ride

www.bristol.gov.uk, 0117 9036701

All ages and abilities cycle on a traffic
free Portway, as well as venturing into the
beautiful countryside beyond. Register online
or call number above.

## July

St Paul's Carnival

Truckfest

Keynsham Music Festival

Boogie for Brizzle

Trowbridge Festival

Boating Regatta

### St Paul's Carnival

www.stpaulscarnival.co.uk, 0117 944 4176

Music, dance and costumes. The annual carnival started in the 60s. It aims to promote cultural & community development in St Paul's.

### Truckfest

www.truckfest.co.uk

Trucking heaven at Bath & West Showground, Shepton Mallett. Starts at 9am.

Tickets: Approx £12 adult, £6 child, £30 family (2+2)

### Keynsham Music Festival

www.keynshammusicfestival.co.uk

A variety of music, creative workshops and children's activities. FREE (but take a small donation).

### Boogie for Brizzle

www.bristolzoo.org.uk, 0117 974 7307

A true Bristol occasion at Bristol Zoo. Relaxed, festival feel, bringing together Bristol's music talent, children's entertainment, and much more. Children's activities - 4pm, music - 6pm
Tickets (advance): Approx £10 adult, £6 child, £26 family.

### Boating Regatta

www.bristol.gov.uk

This event will consist of numberous pulling boats, sail boats, canoes and motorboats taking part in various races. FREE

## August

Bristol Harbour Festival

Playday

Bristol International Balloon Fiesta

Bristol Children's Festival

Festival of the Tree

Bristol International Kite Festival

### Bristol Harbour Festival

www.bristol-city.gov.uk/harbourfestival

The city's most spectacular waterside event. Excellent children's activities.

### Playday

College Green, www.playday.org.uk

Annual celebration of children's right to play. Lots of child friendly activities.

### Bristol International Balloon Fiesta

www.bristolfiesta.co.uk

150 hot air balloons go up at 6am and 6pm.

### Bristol Children's Festival

www.childrensworldcharity.org

Fun activities for under 12's at Bristol Downs (between Stoke Road & Saville Rd) 11am-5pm

### Festival of the Tree

www.forestry.gov.uk

Week of exciting events and activities that celebrate trees and their uses. Approx £8 adult, £3 child.

## Bristol International Kite Festival

www.kite-festival.org.uk/whats-on

Colourful kites at Ashton Court Estate. FREE

## September

Gardening Show (Bath & West)

Organic Food Festival

Bristol Doors Open Day

Bath Children's Literature Festival

The Bristol Festival

## Bath & West Gardening Show

www.bathandwest.com
01749 822222/822200 (office hours)

Garden displays, flowers, fruit and vegetables, TV celebrities, top gardening experts, and much more.

## Organic Food Festival

www.organicfoodfairs.co.uk

Harbourside event with tempting treats!

## Bristol Doors Open Day

www.visitbristol.co.uk
10am-4pm, various locations.

Your chance to peek inside some of Bristol's most fascinating architecturally and historically important buildings, many of which are not normally open to the general public.

Brochures will be available at local libraries, the Tourist Information Centres, and many other locations.

The event is FREE.

## Bath Children's Literature Festival

www.bathkidslitfest.co.uk
01225 463362, info@bathkidslitfest.co.uk

The biggest and best celebration of children's books. Have a look at their excellent website.

## The Bristol Festival

Lloyds Amphitheatre, BS1 5DB
www.thebristolfestival.org

The community festival is a showcase of talent from the Southwest region. Expect circus shows, art exhibitions, cabaret, art.

## November

Encounters

Firework Fiesta

Somerset Carnivals

## Encounters

www.encounters-festival.org.uk

Short film festival including animation. Takes place around the harbourside.

## Firework Fiesta

www.visitbristol.co.uk

Bonfire and fireworks at Bristol Downs.

## Somerset Carnivals

www.somersetcarnivals.co.uk

Impressive illuminated processions. Various locations, including Bridgwater, Burnham-On-Sea, Chard, Illminster, Glastonbury, North Petherton, Shepton Mallet, Wells, Weston-Super-Mare and Yeovil. Well worth a visit!

# Pregnancy & Birth

## Contents

This section is all about the wellbeing of Mum or Mum-to-be, taking her from pregnancy through to the post birth period. It looks at the support she may receive during and after her pregnancy, where to have scans and tests, choices over where to have her baby, and good exercise classes for this time.

For general healthcare and therapists specialising in the pregnancy, birth and postnatal period, see **Family Health**.

For birth pools, TENS machines and more see **Shopping & Services.**

Contact the local NCT for antenatal through to early days courses: **www.bristolnct.ik.com**

**For antenatal classes and postnatal workshops, see Courses for Parents.**

### Good Website:

www.borntogether.ning.com

A place for parents and parents-to-be to find help, health and fun.

# Pregnancy

Bristol has many services available to women during their pregnancy.

This section covers:
Midwives, Doulas, Maternity Nurses, Scans and Tests, Antenatal Exercise and Relaxation.

Also see our review of "Beautiful Birth" by local practitioner Suzanne Yates (on page 12).

## Health in Pregnancy

There are many books available about health and wellbeing during pregnancy; just visit the appropriate section in your local bookshop or library and have a browse. Your midwife and GP will also advise you on aspects such as what foods to avoid in pregnancy.

Taking regular and appropriate exercise is recommended while pregnant and Bristol has many opportunities for exercise to suit any budget. (You can find out more about these later in this chapter.)

Many women will be apprehensive about the birth itself and especially the pain of labour. Antenatal and birth preparation classes provide a chance to discuss concerns, see **Courses for Parents** page 13.

**Antenatal Depression:** Experienced by about 10% of women some who will never have been depressed before. The symptoms to look out for are similar to those for postnatal depression (see page 9). If you think you are suffering from antenatal depression, do seek medical advice, there is a lot out there to help you and you should not feel ashamed. It is not only mothers-to-be that suffer from depression but also fathers-to-be. See **Advice & Support**.

## MATERNITY RIGHTS

For details about maternity rights, see **Advice and Support** Chapter.

Make sure that you claim your one-off maternity payment.
See **Advice & Support**

## PREGNANCY SUPPORT

### MIDWIVES

As soon as you think that you are pregnant you can contact your GP who will then inform you of your nearest midwives.

Antenatal care has been designed to help ensure that expectant mothers and their babies remain healthy throughout the duration of the pregnancy. This is most commonly shared between your GP and midwife. In Bristol, there is the opportunity to go with a community or independent midwife for your antenatal care.

Your first midwife appointment is usually between the 8th and 12th weeks of pregnancy. Some women, because of health problems or difficulties with previous pregnancies, may need to see an obstetrician. Your midwife or GP will be able to advise you.

See **Courses for Parents** for Antenatal and Birth Preparation Classes.

### Community Midwives

Working for the NHS and usually based at your local surgery or clinic. They provide care and advice during pregnancy and for the first ten days after birth. If you are planning a home birth, they will also deliver your baby. Community midwives in Bristol work in teams so you will probably see more than one midwife during your pregnancy.

### Independent Midwives

Qualified, regulated midwives who have chosen to work outside the NHS in a self-employed capacity, whilst still supporting its aims and ideals. They care for women during pregnancy, birth and afterwards and liaise with other healthcare professionals if necessary. In Bristol, bookings are only taken for planned homebirths although, if necessary, midwives can accompany their client into all hospitals. Contact practices for costs.

### Bristol Birth Practice
0117 9090475, www.bristolbirth.co.uk
Covering Bristol, Bath and surrounding area.

### Sue Learner
58 Bellevue Crescent, Cliftonwood, BS8 4TF
0117 927 6131
Covering central Bristol.

## DOULAS

Doula means "woman servant or caregiver". A doula will offer emotional and practical support to women and their families before, during and after birth. Contact:

### Alphabet Childcare
www.alphabet-childcare.co.uk, 0117 9625588

### Bristol Doulas
www.bristoldoulas.co.uk, 07889 258853

### Night Nannies
www.nightnannies.com, 0117 9394845

### Positive Birth - Bath
www.positivebirth.org

## MATERNITY NURSES

Usually employed just before and immediately after you have a baby to care for the newborn and sometimes the mother. May be a qualified nanny with experience with young babies, a qualified nurse, midwife or health visitor. Usually working on a short-term contract (from 2wks-6mths) living with the family. Book early as they can be in short supply.

**Advantages:**

- On call 24 hrs a day up to 6 days a week
- Help with all aspects of baby's care, even during the night
- Encourage sleeping and feeding routines
- Self-employed so you don't need to arrange their tax and national insurance.

### Alphabet Childcare
www.alphabet-childcare.co.uk, 0117 9625588

### Nannies & Childcare
www.nanniesandchildcare.co.uk, 0117 9442893

### Night Nannies
www.nightnannies.com, 0117 9394845

# SCANS & TESTS

In Bristol, any antenatal scans and tests are carried out at St Michael's hospital, Southmead hospital (see contact details below), or the private Spire hospital (the nuchal translucency scan is only available privately). Your midwife or GP will give you details of the various scans and tests that you may have. At 18-20 weeks an ultrasound scan checks your baby's growth and development and how many babies you are carrying! You may also wish to ask the sex of the baby. For a small fee you can buy ultrasound pictures.

**Southmead Hospital**
Southmead Road, Westbury-On-Trym, Bristol
0117 950 5050

**St. Michael's Hospital**
St. Michael's Hill, Southwell Street, Bristol
0117 923 0000

## PRIVATE SCANS
**Bristol Pregnancy Scans**
The Spire Health Clinic, 116 Pembroke Rd, BS8 3EW
0117 3171300, www.bristolpregnancyscans.co.uk

Pregnancy services including early antenatal scans, nuchal translucency (OSCAR scan), fetal wellbeing scans, amniocentesis and chorionic villus sampling (CVS). You can also have a 4D fetal wellbeing scan where you can take home a DVD of your baby in 3D.

See **Advert** opposite.

### Useful Website:
**ARC (Antenatal Results and Choices)**
020 7631 0285, www.arc-uk.org

Offers information and support throughout antenatal testing and when serious abnormalities are diagnosed.

For other support contacts and groups, see **Advice & Support**

# EXERCISE & RELAXATION

## FITBALL

### Kingsdown Sports Centre
Kingsdown Sports Centre, Portland Street, BS2 8HL
0117 9031633, www.everyoneactive.co.uk
Bus routes: 20, 21, 22, 23
Every Sunday. 5.30-6.30pm

Pre and Post Natal Fitball.

## PERSONAL TRAINING

### Saskia French Postnatal Fitness
07903128949, ffrenchfitness@gmail.com

See full entry under **Postnatal** in this chapter.

### KREES Personal Training
07920 032 513, kirsten_rees@yahoo.co.uk

See full entry under **Postnatal** in this chapter.

## RELAXATION

### Back in Action Float
42-43 College Green, BS1 5SH
0117 922 6377, www.backinaction.co.uk/bristol
Float Centre - 01173 169 619
Monday to Thursday - 10am-9pm
Friday and Saturday - 10am-7pm
Sunday – by advance booking only.
(Walk in floats available during store opening hours - subject to availability. Out of store hours - by appointment only)

Flotation is an excellent way to achieve deep relaxation, promoting stress relief and recovery from a variety of injuries. As well as assisting healing, promoting general well-being and self-improvement. See also **Family Health**, and their Advert in **Shopping & Services** (page 29) for information about hiring a mobiliser.

# Bristol **Pregnancy Scans**

**0117 980 4070**
www.bristolpregnancyscans.co.uk

## Pregnancy is a very special time for the mother to be, and for all of her family.

The fun and excitement of seeing the developing baby on a scan is one of the high points of antenatal care, and at Bristol Pregnancy Scans we provide top quality, expert scans at varying stages of pregnancy. We have been providing scans in pregnancy since 2000, at The Glen Hospital, Bristol and more recently from The Spire Women's Health Clinic, on Pembroke Road, Clifton.

The scans available are:

### The OSCAR test
This is offered to women between 11 and 14 weeks of pregnancy, to assess the risk of their baby having Down's syndrome.

### Dating scans
Performed at 7-12 weeks, to date a pregnancy and provide an estimated date for delivery (EDD).

### Fetal normality scans
At 20 weeks, to check the vital anatomy of the baby (and check the sex, if requested).

### 4D fetal Wellbeing Scans
To check that the baby is growing well, and provide a DVD of the baby in 3D for you to take home. You can bring your chosen music on a CD if you wish, which will be used as the background music to your DVD.

### Reassurance and growth scans
Can be performed at any time in pregnancy. If you have been told you have a 'low placenta' we recommend a scan at 36 weeks.

### Amniocentesis or chorionic villus sampling
These are the invasive, diagnostic tests which can detect or rule out a chromosomal abnormality. If you wish to have a private amniocentesis or CVS, this can be performed at Bristol Pregnancy Scans.

All the scans are performed by Consultant Obstetricians and Gynaecologists or Midwife Sonographers with post graduate qualifications. All have completed Fetal Medicine Foundation training.

We use the most up to date ultrasound machines, in comfortable surroundings, with time to look at your baby. We encourage clients to bring a family member or two and pictures of each scan are provided as a record to take home.

We recommend you keep your midwife informed of your visit to the clinic.

## For appointments & further information please give us a call on 0117 980 4070 or 0117 317 1300

**Spire** Bristol Hospital

## SWIMMING

### Free swimming for pregnant women

Bristol Community Sport
www.bristol-city.gov.uk/sport

This is a great opportunity to maintain fitness and relax during your pregnancy. In order to receive your free swims, you need to purchase an Everyone Active Discount Card, which costs £3.50 per year for Bristol residents and £30 for non-residents. You also need to fill in an application form for the Everyone Active Discount Card. This can be downloaded from the Council website or you can collect one from your nearest Everyone Active swimming pool. Take your completed form to any of the Everyone Active centres or pools for processing and they can take you to the next step in obtaining an Everyone Active Discount Card. You will need to take proof of residency and your National Health Service Card with you - this proves your eligibility for the scheme.

#### Participating pools:

Bishopsworth Swimming Pool - 0117 903 1600

Bristol South Swimming Pool - 0117 903 1618

Easton Leisure Centre - 0117 903 1628

Henbury Leisure Centre - 0117 353 2555

Horfield Leisure Centre - 0117 903 1643

Jubilee Swimming Pool - 0117 903 1607

### PreNatal Swimming Class at Horfield Leisure Centre

Dorian Road, Horfield, Bristol, BS7 0XW
0117 9031643

Prenatal class every Monday from 10am-10.55am.

See more swimming in **Get Physical** chapter.

For birthing pools, TENS machines, and all birthing equipment, see **Shopping & Services.**

## Tips

If you are having emotional difficulties during or after your pregnancy, don't suffer in silence. See **Advice & Support.**

Try aromatherapy to help with pregnancy ailments, relaxation, and labour, also refexology and acupuncture. See p. 237 for a list of practitioners.

Don't let pelvic pain in pregnancy make your life a misery. Christine Andrew is a Chiropractor who specialises in this area. There are also sessions at the hydrotherapy pool. See Purely Active below and **Family Health.**

### AquaNatal

Physiotherapy Department, Bristol Royal Infirmary, Upper Maudlin Street, Bristol BS2 8HW
07847 786866, www.purelyactive.com
£40 for four consecutive classes, Thur pm

Low-impact, water-based, gentle toning and strengthening exercise suitable for expectant mothers. Designed to improve core strength and ease pregnancy related pelvis and low back pain. Aqua natal is suitable for all pregnant women from 16 weeks right up to 40 weeks.

Classes aim to be fun, relaxing and a great opportunity to meet other expectant mums!

# PILATES

### Purely Active

Physiotherapy Department, Bristol Royal Infirmary, Upper Maudlin Street, Bristol BS2 8HW
07847 786866, www.purelyactive.com
Thur 5.15pm. £69 for the first six sessions including a 1:1, thereafter £35 for 5 classes

Purely Active also run physiotherapy sessions in the hydrotherapy pool at the BRI, contact for details or see **Family Health** (p.238).

### Simply Pilates

Garden Studio, 21 All Saints Rd, BS8 2JL
0117 942 6809, 07980 236948
www.simply-pilates.co.uk
info@simply-pilates.co.uk

Bristol's first fully equipped and dedicated Pilates studio offering equipment and mat classes. Pilates works on the deep core muscles which support the spine and the joints, improving posture and realigning muscles. Helpful during and after pregnancy.

# YOGA

### Antenatal Yoga Classes with Sally

St Georges Community Centre,St George, Bristol
0780 389 6268
Thu 5.30pm-6.45pm. 6 week course
A gentle class for all stages of pregnancy that combines relaxation, stretching and breathing.

### Bristol City Yoga

16 Backfields Lane, Bristol, BS2 8QW
0117 924 4414, www.bristolcityyoga.co.uk
Mon 9.30–11am with Dominique or Wed 5.45–7.15pm with Laura Gilmore. £64 for 8 weeks. Drop-in.
Helps maintain wellbeing throughout pregnancy, and prepare for the birth and beyond.

### Chris Fielder

Avon Cottage, White Hart Steps, BS8 4TQ
0117 929 4894
Day and evening classes from her home. Birth preparation sessions also available, see p.15.

### Dominique Ker

c/o Relaxation Centre, All Saints Rd, Clifton
0117 968 6030, sakoilsky@msn.com
Evening antenatal yoga classes. Advance booking essential. Also see Bristol City Yoga.

### Jane Roberts

St Annes Park Children's Centre, Lichfield Rd
0117 3778768, janerobertsyoga@yahoo.co.uk

### Jessica Eveleigh

07818 407 796, www.relaxedbirthandparenting.com
Fitness4Less, The Pithay, All Saints St, BS1 and
The Berkeley Centre, 3 Berkeley Square, Clifton, BS8

Also see **Courses for Parents** for more on Relaxed Birth and Parenting.

### Somalotus

Gasworks Studio, 27 Narroways Road, St Werburghs
Nicole: 07733 226 410, www.somalotus.com

### Tessa Sanderson

St Michael's Church, Gloucester Road
www.damayoga.com 0117 9023766
Tuesdays 6-7.30pm

### Vivien Tallis

07801550842, yogaplus@live.co.uk
Classes will held in Redland/Bishopston - Fishponds - Lawrence Weston and Knowle West
Friendly, informal classes.

### Yoga Frankie

Relaxation Centre, 9 All Saints Rd, Clifton
0117 942 9598, 07890 996 782
www.yogafrankie.co.uk, info@yogafrankie.co.uk
Mon 2-3.30pm. £8 per session, £32 block of 5
Small, friendly classes that run throughout most of the year. There is no need to book or to bring any equipment.

### Yoga Sara

10-12 Picton Street Bristol BS6 5QA
07789 501884, www.yogasara.co.uk
Wed 10-11.30am. £8 per session, £32 block of 5
For everyone from complete beginners to seasoned practitioners at all stages of pregnancy. Drop-in (yoga mats supplied).

### Yoga West

Denmark Place, Bishopston
0117 9243330, www.yogawest.co.uk
Classes are suitable for beginners onwards. No booking required.

It is always a good idea when pregnant to consult your midwife or GP before trying any new form of exercise or relaxation.

# Birth

Choosing where you give birth should be about what is best for you and your family.

In Bristol, you have the choice of giving birth at home or in hospital. In both instances you will be attended by a midwife. Although birthing in a hospital is still the more common option there have been many moves by the Government to take birth back into the home. This is based on the premise that home birth is as safe as hospital birth for most women.

If you choose to give birth in hospital, there is now the option of either the midwife-led or the consultant-led units at both St. Michael's and Southmead hospitals. If you opt for the midwife-led birthing suite, there is the option of a water birth (although use of it cannot be guaranteed due to demand on the day).

Choices for Bristol should increase in the future, with plans for community birthing centres, see www.birthcentrebristol.org.uk

## HOME BIRTHS

### Bristol Home Birth Group

The Gasworks Studio, 27 Narroways Road, St Werburghs, BS2 9TS www.bristolhomebirth.org.uk Welcome a £3 donation to help cover costs. A variety of drinks and snacks will be included. Concessions available. 1st Sunday of month, 7-9pm

Offering encouragement, information and support for parents and parents-to-be who would like their children born at home. A range of topics are discussed at meetings, with an experienced midwife and occasional guests to share specific expertise.

## HOSPITAL BIRTHS

### Southmead Hospital
0117 950 5050

### St. Michael's Hospital
St. Michael's Hill, BS2 8EG
0117 923 0000

Both have neonatal intensive care units.

## REGISTERING THE BIRTH

If parents are married when the baby is born, either parent may register the birth. If the baby's parents are not married, and they want the father's details to be included in the register, both parents should attend the office together to register the birth. If the parents are not married, it is not necessary to have the father's details in the register. If his details are not entered at the time of registration, there are special procedures for them to be added later if required. There may be other options in some cases. Contact a registrar for details.

### Main Office: Bristol
The Old Council House, Corn Street, BS1 1JG (Entrance on Broad Street)
Tel for an appointment: 0117 922 2800
9am-4pm Mon, Tue, Thur, Fri
10am-4pm Wed (late night opening 5-7.30pm.)
Sat 9.45-11.15am
**By appointment only**

### Southmead Hospital
Monks Park Lodge, BS10 5NB
Tel for an appointment: 0117 922 2800
10am-3.30pm Mon to Fri.
**By appointment only**

For maternity bras, breast pumps and more see **Shopping & Services.**

# After the Birth

Some women are fortunate, having straightforward births with bodies that bounce back very quickly. For others, things are not that straightforward. A difficult birth can leave mothers feeling drained and in discomfort. A new baby, particularly for first time parents, can also induce anxieties. Sometimes just getting out and involved with local parent groups, see **Parent and Baby/Toddler**, or taking some time out for yourself can help.

This part of the chapter lists people and places that you can contact for postnatal support, relaxation or other therapy.

## HELP & SUPPORT

### Health visitors

These are nurses, based at local clinics, with training in child development, health education and the social aspects of health. They visit you at home after your baby is ten days' old and stay in touch with you until your child starts school. They advise on all aspects of childcare including feeding, sleeping, crying and behaviour problems. Your health visitor performs your child's developmental checks.

### Doulas & Maternity Nurses

See page 3.

### Independent Support

**Dominique Ker**
0117 968 6030, sakoilsky@msn.com

Counsellor (also in practice with Relate) offering women and couples the chance to go through their birth experience, particularly if it was difficult or having a negative impact on their relationship or that with their baby.

**Elspeth Pontin**
0117 9745471, elspethpontin@aol.com

Chartered Psychologist working with mother-infant attachment difficulties.

### NCT Postnatal Support

08704 448 707, www.bristolnct.ik.com
www.nctpregnancyandbabycare.com

If you are a member of the NCT, a local member will contact you before or soon after your baby is born. It will be a mother who knows what is happening locally and will be happy to chat. Also see the NCT Early Days Courses. Full details in **Courses for Parents**.

## Postnatal Depression

**Postnatal Depression:** Affects 10% of women. Symptoms include anxiety/panic attacks, fatigue, feeling low, sleeplessness, and irritability, aches and pains and fears of unknown cause. Your health visitor will use a questionnaire/scale after the birth to detect signs of postnatal depression, but it can occur at any time. It can also occur in fathers. Talk to your GP or Health Visitor if you think you may be suffering. Also see **Advice & Support** and Tips over the page.

## Breastfeeding Support

If you have difficulties breastfeeding, you can contact your midwife, health visitor or NCT breastfeeding counsellor for help and support.

### NCT Breastfeeding Counsellors

0300 330 0771 any day between 8am and 10pm.
www.bristolnct.ik.com,
www.nctpregnancyandbabycare.com

Contact for details of local breastfeeding counsellors. Also, see the NCT newsletter (available to members and in Bristol libraries). If you fancy becoming a breastfeeding counsellor, see **New Opportunities**.

### La Leche League

0845 1202918, www.laleche.org.uk

La leche league is an international organization run by experienced and well trained mothers. If you are pregnant or breastfeeding and looking for some help or information about breastfeeding, find the numbers of your local La Leche Legue leader at www.bristollll. blogspot.com or call the National Helpline 0845 120 2918. There are also monthly meetings and informal coffee mornings. One phone call can make a difference.

### Support Groups at Children's Centre

Brentry & Henbury Children's Centre, Brentry Primary School, Brentry Lane, BS10 6RG
0117 9593800/9593900
www.bhchildrenscentre.org.uk
Wed 11.30-1pm

### Breastfeeding Support Groups

For a list of breastfeeding support groups in Bristol, South Gloucestershire, and North Somerset, go to: www.avon.nhs.uk/kris

## Tips

If you think you may be suffering from postnatal depression or are not bonding with your child, there are various groups listed in this book that may help. Try one of the mum & baby swimming groups, a postnatal yoga classes, Story Dance (p.120) or try baby massage. If you need to talk to someone, see the practitioners mentioned on page 9 or **Advice & Support**.

## Night Nannies

### Alphabet Childcare

www.alphabet-childcare.co.uk, 0117 9625588
See full entry in **Childcare**.

### Nannies & Childcare

www.nanniesandchildcare.co.uk, 0117 9442893
See full entry in **Childcare**.

### Night Nannies

www.nightnannies.com, 0117 9394845

Night Nannies ensures that the first few weeks of motherhood really are spent in a rosy glow rather than a haze of sleeplessness. Your Night Nanny will come to look after your baby overnight, encouraging him to sleep through when he is old enough and enabling you to sleep peacefully, and additionally offering help and advice on breast feeding, weaning and many other babyhood issues. Night Nannies can also teach older babies to overcome bad sleep habits. Each Night Nanny is interviewed by Camilla Rabey who also checks all references and qualifications and ensures you get the perfect night nanny.

*"I cannot speak highly enough of the Night Nannies service. From our initial phone enquiry to the 'night nanny' who came to our house, the care, professionalism and level of support has been fantastic. Exactly the right level of input was provided to match our needs with absolutely no element of judgement but, instead, it was like having a highly experienced friend by our side. Best of all, when our night nanny left we felt we had the skills, tools and confidence we needed to carry on our parenting journey with much more enjoyment than before – the result, a happy baby and very happy parents!"*

# EXERCISE & RELAXATION

## YOGA

Postnatal yoga sessions are different to other yoga classes. They are genuinely run for mums and babies together and that means that feeding, changing a nappy, crying, and putting your baby down for a sleep, are often part of the experience. The main focus of the classes is on postnatal recovery (pelvic floor and abdominal strength, pelvic stability, relaxing as a parent, and other useful practices). Babies from 0-1yr are involved as much as possible.

### Bristol City Yoga
16 Backfields Lane, Bristol, BS2 8QW
0117 924 4414, www.bristolcityyoga.co.uk
Strengthening and relaxing for Mums with movement to support development and ease ailments for Babies.

### Leonie de Mearns
0117 966 3145, babyoga@gmail.com
Various locations across Bristol, 6 week courses
Gentle postnatal stretches, meditation, baby games, singing and shiatsu massage.

### Yoga Frankie
22 The Yard, St Werburghs, Bristol
07890 996 782, www.yogafrankie.co.uk
Thur 2-3.30pm. Book in advance.
Block of 6 classes £45

### Postnatal Yoga Classes with Sally
St Georges Community Centre, St George, Bristol
0780 389 6268
Postnatal yoga for mums and babies.

## PILATES

### Purely Active
Purely Active, Physiotherapy Department, Bristol Royal Infirmary, Upper Maudlin Street, BS2 8HW
07847 786866, www.purelyactive.com
£35 for 5 classes

### Simply Pilates
Garden Studio, 21 All Saints Rd, BS8 2JL
0117 942 6809, 07980 236948
www.simply-pilates.co.uk, info@simply-pilates.co.uk
For 6 weeks-6 months post delivery.

The class focuses on basic core muscle including abdominal/pelvic floor tone and spinal flexibility.

Also see **KREES Personal Training** page 12.

## POSTNATAL EXERCISE

Many of the Leisure Centres in Bristol have classes especially tailored to the postnatal period. See our Leisure Centre list in **Get Physical**. If you want to be listed below, or you can recommend someone, please get in touch with us.

### Horfield Leisure Centre
Dorian Road, Horfield, Bristol, BS7 0XW
0117 9031643
Offers the following classes:

### Post Natal Exercise
Mon 11-11.55am, Weds 10-11am
Build your fitness levels after pregnancy. Gentle cardiovascular and toning exercises are used. New babies are welcome and a creche is available for toddlers. Advanced booking for the creche is required. Please check with your GP before joining the class.

### Post Natal Spinning
Fri 9-9.45am
A ride specifically designed to get new mums back in gear! Bring your child to the studio.

Check out more classes at
The Berkeley Centre
www.theberkeleycentre.co.uk

## Kingsdown Sports Centre

Portland Street, Kingsdown, Bristol, BS2 8HL
0117 9426582
Offers the following class:
**Pre and Post Natal Fitball**
Every Sunday, 5.30pm-6.30pm

## Saskia French Postnatal Fitness

07903128949, ffrenchfitness@gmail.com

Saskia is a mobile personal trainer working in and around the Bristol area, specialising in ante- and post-natal fitness and health. Her sessions are built around a relaxed and fun environment where clients are encouraged to work at their own pace that will help them achieve their fitness goals. As a mum of two, Saskia is passionate about encouraging new mums to regain fitness and strength following pregnancy and labour. She also offers discounted personal training sessions for post-natal mums (babies/children welcome) built around their lifestyle and family commitments.

### Easton Community Centre

Kiburn Street
Mon 10-11am and Wed 11am-12pm.
£4.90 pay as you go. £24.50 for 6 sessions.

### Berkeley Centre

3 Berkeley Square, Clifton
www.theberkeleycentre.co.uk
Wed 1-2pm (starting Aug 2009)
£7.50 Pay as you go. £39 for 6 sessions

## KREES Personal Training

07920 032 513, kirsten_rees@yahoo.co.uk

Kirsten is a well recommended personal trainer as well as being a mum herself. She offers pre - and postnatal training, from 1:1 to group sessions. She also runs a Pilates group for mums and babies at Hope Chapel in Hotwells, with time after for a cup of tea and a chat with other mums. Contact for more details.

# A Review of "Beautiful Birth"

Author: Suzanne Yates
(Carroll & Brown. £12.99)

Suzanne has been working to support mothers, their partners, and babies since 1989. She is the founder of Well Mother (www.wellmother.org) whose aim is to support parents and babies by promoting the use of bodywork, especially massage, shiatsu and exercise.

The book is beautifully written and inspirational. Suzanne emphasies how 'one size does not fit all' so don't think this book is about preaching about how you should give birth. It describes in depth the application of practical tools such as visualisation, breathing, physical preparation and massage. These practical exercises and the detailed description make it quite unlike any other book that I have read to date. The book will increase your awareness of the stages involved in labour, as well as making the most of this special period. You will almost certainly find that the tools described throughout this book will not just be beneficial for the birth, but indeed you will take them with you through life.

PRACTICAL TECHNIQUES that can help you achieve a
HAPPIER and MORE NATURAL labour and delivery

# Beautiful BIRTH

SUZANNE YATES

# Courses for Parents & Carers

## Contents

There are many courses in this chapter that are aimed at preparing parents-to-be for birth and life with a baby. Courses do not stop there, however, and areas like first aid help parents and carers with children of all ages.

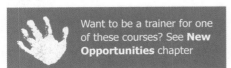
Want to be a trainer for one of these courses? See **New Opportunities** chapter

# ANTENATAL CLASSES

Antenatal classes are designed to prepare parents for the experience of birth and the task of looking after their new baby. They also provide a chance to meet other parents. Classes may be provided by your midwife or independent practitioners and the NCT. If this is not your first pregnancy, there are also often refresher courses, though these are less common to find.

If you are planning on booking an Independent Midwife see **Pregnancy & Birth** chapter (page 2) and contact the midwife direct to see what they are offering.

## Content of Antenatal Classes

There are many different kinds of classes but the topics covered will be fairly similar:

- Physical and emotional effects of having a baby
- Looking after yourself and your baby during pregnancy, including exercises and tips on nutrition
- Screenings and check-ups you can attend during the ante-natal period
- What to expect in labour and childbirth
- Relaxation and pain relief options
- Effective breathing techniques for a smooth delivery
- Medical procedures involved
- Caring for your baby after the birth

## NHS Classes

0844 243 6946, www.nhs.uk

These are usually quite large classes, taught by midwives (this may or may not be the midwife that you eventually have for the birth) and will probably be free.

## Tip

Antenatal classes fill up quickly so make sure you book early in your pregnancy.

*'Best of all I liked the practical aspects – how to bathe and change a baby, when to go to the hospital or call the midwife.'*

## National Childbirth Trust Bristol

0844 243 6946, www.bristolnct.org.uk
bookings3e@nct.org.uk

Antenatal classes help prepare you for labour, your baby's birth and early parenthood. NCT antenatal classes are usually provided in the evening for the pregnant woman and her partner (which may be the baby's father or another supporting person, such as mother or friend). Classes may be held in a home or in a public venue and usually start at 30 weeks.

# BIRTH PREPARATION CLASSES

These vary in their content. Please do contact the class directly to find out if it covers what you need.

### Birthing Awareness

0117 973 3965, 07833 146 576
www.birthingfromwithin.com

Offer expectant parents and birth partners a holistic and individual approach to pregnancy, birth and parenthood. The workshops offer practice in proven pain-coping strategies, practical information on birth choices, exploration with birth art to meet your beliefs, fears and hopes, what to expect from parenthood, and a resource & reference pack.

### Birthology

www.birthology.co.uk, mitch@birthology.co.uk

Excellent private birth and parenting preparation classes in your own home.

### Bristol City Yoga

16 Backfields Lane, Bristol, BS2 8QW
0117 924 4414, www.bristolcityyoga.co.uk

Birth Rehearsals. A unique session to prepare women and their birth partner for labour.

*"My husband keeps saying how much more confident and comfortable he feels about the birth after the session. Thank you so much!" Bristol City Yoga Mum*

### Chris Fielder
Avon Cottage, White Hart Steps, BS8 4TQ
0117 929 4894
Runs a series of birth preparation sessions for women and their partners. Also see **Pregnancy and Birth**.

### Dominique Ker
07969204763, sakoilsky@msn.com
Runs Relaxed Birth and Parenting (see below) and Active Birth workshops on a sat or in an evening every month for couples or pregnant women and their partners and/or birth attendants. Based on the work of Janet Balaskas.

### Frankie Duggan
22 The Yard, St Werburghs
£40 per couple, 10am-1pm
Yoga for birth preparation sessions. These are longer sessions (usually a half day at the weekend) which focus on using yoga practices to prepare for labour and birth. They are designed for women and their birthing partners as an opportunity to rehearse the birthing journey together. They are practical sessions with time devoted to physical, mental and emotional preparedness for both mother and birth partner. They cover positions and movement for labour, breathing, positions for resting, visualisation and more. The sessions are informal and run according to demand.

### Relaxed Birth & Parenting
Jessica Eveleigh on 07818 407 796
www.relaxedbirthandparenting.com
Relaxed Birth and Parenting offers pregnancy yoga and birth preparation classes, birth preparation workshops for couples and much more, empowering you to have the most joyful and loving experience of birth and parenting possible.

With venues across Bristol and North Somerset, Relaxed Birth and Parenting weekly pregnancy groups will prepare you physically and emotionally for birth and beyond with yoga-based exercises, active birth preparation, breathing, visualisation and relaxation.
They also simply offer you a space to just 'be' and honour your pregnancy, and to meet and share your experiences with other mums-to-be.

Meanwhile, the regular one-day workshops for pregnant women and their birth attendants/partners look at all the different ways to support the physiology of birth, with a body-mind focus and place particular emphasis on how your birth partner can best support you in labour.

Relaxed Birth and Parenting practitioners also offer doula services, ante- and postnatal one-to-one sessions, and postnatal groups and support. (For more about doulas, see page 3).

### Vivien Tallis
yogaplus@live.co.uk or 07801550842
Classes held in Redland/Bishopston, Fishponds, Lawrence Weston & Knowle West. These are friendly, informal classes covering a wide range of issues relating to home and hospital birth.

### Well Mother
24 Dunkerry Road, Windmill Hill, BS3 4LB
0117 963 2306, www.wellmother.org
Massage and shiatsu for pregnancy and birth. Birth preparation & exercise.

# POSTNATAL WORKSHOPS

### NCT Early Days Courses
0844 243 6946 or by email bookings3e@nct.org.uk. www.bristolnct.org.uk

This six-week Early Days course for new mums is about how mums are as well as their baby. Designed to encourage them to focus on their own needs as mothers, just for a short while each week, they will be able to explore issues in more depth than they may otherwise, using a range of fun, thought-provoking activities. Classes currently run in North Somerset, South Gloucestershire, Bath, Redland, St Werburghs, but there will soon be mum and baby groups, courses for couples, and also evening courses aimed at second time mums. Book by contacting Sarah at the address above. Or find out more by looking at the Bristol NCT website.

### Relaxed Birth & Parenting
Jessica Eveleigh on 07818 407 796
www.relaxedbirthandparenting.com

Full details above.

# BABY MASSAGE & REFLEXOLOGY

Baby massage is thought to boost the baby's immune system, stimulate circulation, improve digestion and reduce colic. It also helps with physical and emotional development, sleep, and parent-baby bonding.

## BABY MASSAGE

### Anne Badger

39 Leighton Road, Southville, Bristol. BS3 1NS
0117 963 6557, annebadger@madasafish.co.uk

Classes run over 4 weeks and teach parents/carers how to massage their baby, and techniques for dealing with baby discomforts such as colic. Friendly and informal. Also baby shiatsu. These are all helpful for bonding, understanding your baby, and helping with the usual baby discomforts such as wind, digestive difficulties, and difficulty settling. Anne also has experience in working with babies and children with special needs.

### Bristol City Yoga

16 Backfields Lane, Bristol, BS2 8QW
0117 924 4414, www.bristolcityyoga.co.uk

5 week courses for parents/carers and their babies from birth to pre-crawling. Sessions include baby massage, & music and movement. Parents/carers massage their babies whilst being taught step-by-step massage routines, combining Swedish massage, yoga and reflexology techniques.

*"I now massage Heidi before bath- she just loves the touch and it's our most calm and precious time together"*
*Bristol City Yoga Mum*

### Christine Lamont

07929 309522, www.relax-ology.me.uk

Classes run weekly for 3 weeks and last 1 hour. Small, relaxed classes, which teach parents/carers baby massage techniques. Cost includes small bottle of massage oil and booklet.

### Hobbs Holistic Health

The Chiron Centre, 130 Westbury Road, Westbury-on-Trym, Bristol, BS9 3AL
07966 383371 / 07974 465955
www.hobbsholistichealth.co.uk

Baby massage classes.

### Jayne Moffat, CIMI

014546 14390

Baby massage classes in outer NW Bristol. Home sessions offered.

### Jocasta Crofts

0117 929 0009 deva-shanti@hotmail.com

Classes aimed at babies 0-12 months. Also offers teaching to parents to massage their child at any age. Sessions include a mixture of Indian massage, Swedish massage, baby yoga and reflexology.

### Louise Morgan

Therapy Centre, Chruch Road, Redfield
07779 234144 www.louise-morgan.co.uk

Offers individual or group sessions for parents/carers and their babies (from 7 weeks). Sessions last 1 hour. Oil or lotion is provided during sesssions and parents/carers are taught which oils to use, how to use essential oils with your baby and how massage can be beneficial for common baby complaints. Contact for prices.

### Samantha Pupuca

0117 9323530, sampupuca@googlemail.com

Provides 4 week courses £28, (including massage oil and handouts). Each session lasts 1hr. Classes teach how to massage your baby, which includes combination of Swedish, Indian and Reflexology techniques. Classes currently based in Hanham and Bitton.

### Sarah Presley

0117 956 0414 or 07887 984540

Baby massage sessions in your own home. Also body massage, Indian Head massage & Reiki for pregnant mums and new mums!

### Teresa Bultitude, CIMI

0117 949 8428, tbultitude@blueyonder.co.uk

Baby massage in Oldland Common, Warmley, Longwell Green, Kingswood and surrounding areas.

## BABY REFLEXOLOGY

### This Little Piggy

07989 964 7775 Claire Collins
www.this-little-piggy.co.uk
claire.collins@blueyonder.co.uk

Classes aimed at babies and toddlers up to the age of 2½ years. Parents are taught how to do simple yet effective reflexology on their own children. Classes are taught by 2 qualified reflexologists, and run monthly on Thursday mornings 10:30am.

### Helen Varley Reflexology

0845 370 4774 / 07972 368943
www.helenvarleyreflexology.co.uk
helenvarleyreflexology@hotmail.co.uk

Teaches parents/carers how to give their babies calming, soothing baby reflex treatment. Sessions held at locations in Horfield and Redland, and run over 4 weeks for 1 hour. Home sessions (max 4 people) also offered.

For more on keeping healthy during and after birth, see **Pregnancy and Birth** chapter

# FIRST AID COURSES

## Alphabet Childcare

184a Henleaze Rd, Henleaze, BS9 4NE
0117 962 5588, www.alphabet-childcare.co.uk
alphabet@btconnect.com

Alphabet Childcare are one of the longest established Childcare Agencies in Bristol and as such are encouraging anyone who cares for or works with children to consider doing a Paediatric First Aid Course to equip themselves with a comprehensive range of skills to enable them to respond calmly and confidently in the event of a child becoming unwell or injuring themselves.

Alphabet Childcare are running their course at their office in Henleaze for anyone who is interested. It is open to all and participants do not need to be registered with the Agency to book a place – up until now they have had parents / grandparents / Nannies / Childminders / Au Pairs / Social Workers / Youth Workers & Teachers on the course which is in line with the Statutory Framework for the Early Years Foundation Stage (EYFS) and meets the criteria for Ofsted registration.

The Courses generally run on consecutive Saturdays from 9.30am – 4.30pm or Week-day evenings fro 6.30 – 9.30pm & the cost is £70 + vat.

It is also possible for a group ( 6 + ) to get together and book a course to suit their requirements, either at the Alphabet Childcare office or at their own home / venue.

Alphabet Childcare are also happy to negotiate to provide the course as an extension of the Introduction to Childminding course.

There is no "exam" at the end as assessment is ongoing throughout and the Certificates are presented at the end of the second day.

If you have any queries please do not hesitate to contact Alphabet Childcare at the address on the previous page.

### St John Ambulance (Avon)

0117 963 0195
www.sja.org.uk

An **Early Years First Aid Course** is among their extensive range of courses at their training centre in Bedminster.

If a group of mums want to arrange for a course to be delivered at one of their homes or at another venue and they only wanted to learn first aid for babies, 0 – 12mths or children 1 – puberty this course can also be delivered (2 hours).

**For mums with new babies (0 – 12mths)**
St John Ambulance has also delivered FREE 1½ hour **Baby Resuscitation** courses. This course includes: managing an incident, recovery position, CPR and choking. It is delivered through a lot of Health centres. Mums or dads who would like to attend this free course should talk to their health visitor to find out if it is being provided in their area. Not all health centres are involved with this scheme.

# WEANING & HEALTHY EATING

*Weaning Courses for Parents & Carers*

### Alphabet Childcare South West Ltd
184A Henleaze Rd, Henleaze, BS9 4NE
0117 962 5588

The Weaning Workshops cover weaning and diet in the first year, including the way allergies, introduction of lumpy food & finger food could be covered. This is a practical & informal session with plenty of demonstrations on how to prepare healthy food.

*Health & Wellbeing Courses for Parents & Carers*

### Hartcliffe Health & Environment Action Group
The Gatehouse Centre, Hareclive Rd, BS13 9JN
0117 946 5285, www.hheag.org.uk

Health related and environmental projects for people in the BS13 area of Bristol.

### Knowle West Health Association
40a Park St, Bristol, BS1 5JG
0117 9262987, www.bristolfolkhouse.co.uk

Classes cover aspects of health and wellbeing. For residents of Knowle West.

# Parentline Plus

www.parentlineplus.org.uk, 0808 800 2222

When parenting's just too hard, you can't always wait for things to get better. Parentline Plus, are available 24 hours a day, seven days a week.

They believe that all parents want to do the best they can for their children - but know that parenting is as difficult as it is rewarding, especially in today's climate of less money and less job security.

Also look out for parenting courses run through Parentline Plus.

# Shopping & Services

## Contents

Like it or loathe it, shopping is an essential ingredient to most of our lives, yet it is not always the most relaxing experience with a baby or toddler in tow. However, knowing the location of the nearest toilets, changing mats, feeding rooms, lifts and refuelling stations can make the outing a little easier.

Shopping areas such as Cabot Circus, the Mall at Cribbs Causeway, Clifton Village, and Gloucester Road provide Bristol with a wide selection of shops along with good facilities for parents with small children. And if you can't get out of the house, many big and small names offer mail order and internet shopping. This chapter includes listings of the major high street names, but our main aim is to focus on the many independent retailers in Bristol, who offer interesting products, in-depth knowledge and a personal service.

Titch Hikers' Discount - see your exclusive 10% discount in JoJo Maman Bébé on p.25.

For book shops see **Reading & Storytelling.**

# SHOPPING CENTRES

Details of the individually recommended shops are listed throughout this chapter.

### Cabot Circus

Bristol. BS2 9AB
0117 9529 360, www.cabotcircus.com
Mon-Sat 10am-8pm & Sun 11am-5pm.

Newly opened shopping centre, with wide selection of shops, restaurants and 'Cinema de Lux'. Large car park located next to centre (just off M32 /Newfoundland St). Child parking spaces on ground, second, third and fourth floors.

### The Mall Bristol, (formerly 'The Galleries').

25 Union Gallery, Broadmead, Bristol. BS1 3XD
0117 929 0569, www.themall.co.uk

Mon-Sat 9am-6pm & Sun 11am-5pm.
Car park open for one hour after shops close.

### The Mall at Cribbs Causeway

Bristol, BS34 5DG
0117 903 0303, www.mallcribbs.com
Mon-Fri 9:30am-9pm, Sat 9am-8pm, Sun 11am-5pm. Bank Holidays 10am-6pm
John Lewis opening hours vary.
Jct 17, M5

Wide selection of shops and children's play zone, crèche and party centre, located at 'The Avenue', on upper mall level. Crèche open Mon-Fri 10am-8pm, Sat 9am-7pm & Sun 10:30am-5pm . For further information call: 0117 915 58 02.

---

### Factory Outlets

Many well known high street stores selling discontinued lines with great reductions.

**Bicester Village**
50 Pringle Drive, Oxon, OX26 6WD
01869 323200, www.bicestervillage.com

**Clarks Village**
Farm Rd, Street, Somerset, BA16 0BB
01458 840064, www.clarksvillage.co.uk

---

# SUPERMARKETS

Over recent years, supermarkets have increased their non-food ranges significantly. Many of them now offer a one-stop shop for all your needs, stocking maternity wear, nursery equipment, clothing, toys and books. Some stock food ranges specifically manufactured for children. See Supermarket table overleaf.

## ONLINE SHOPPING

Several supermarkets offer an internet shopping and delivery service which can be very useful at any time, not least during the last few weeks of pregnancy and early months with a newborn. Most charge around £5 for delivery, although some waive this charge if you spend above a certain amount.

# Tips

The following tips may help you when ordering your groceries online:

• Ordering online can take a while at first, so place your first order when you've got a bit of time on your hands and you will reap the rewards as you build up your own personal shopping list. It's best to make a list before you start.

• If you have enough storage, it can be cost effective to buy household items in bulk.

• You sometimes need to know the weights/sizes of products that you buy.

• Many supermarkets now do a plastic bag-free option. Your shopping will be delivered in crates for you to unpack.

# DEPARTMENT AND LARGER STORES SUMMARY TABLE

For stores at The Mall or The Mall Bristol, the facilities shown are in addition to those at the shopping centre. All stores have nearby parking and can accomodate single and double buggies

| Department Store | Mail Order | Internet Shopping | Branch Location | Facilities | Clothing (Age Range) | Shoes | Maternity wear | Maternity Underwear | Children's Furniture | Nursery Equipment | Toys | Outdoor Toys | Computer Games | Books |
|---|---|---|---|---|---|---|---|---|---|---|---|---|---|---|
| BHS www.bhs.co.uk | | ✓ | The Mall 0117 950 9493 | Baby change, toilets, car park | 0-14 | ✓ | | | | | | | | |
| | | | Broadmead 0117 929 2261 | Baby change, toilets, cafe | 0-14 | ✓ | | | | | | | | |
| Woolworths www.woolworths.co.uk | | | Online only | | 0-16 | ✓ | | | ✓ | ✓ | ✓ | ✓ | ✓ | ✓ |
| Boots (Larger Branches) www.boots.com | | ✓ | The Mall 0117 950 9744 | Car park | 0-4 | | | | | web | ✓ | ✓ | ✓ | |
| (Boots Parenting Club - money off vouchers etc) | | | Broadmead 0117 929 3631 | Baby change, car park | 0-4 | | | | | web | ✓ | ✓ | ✓ | |
| | | | Avon Meads 0117 972 8056 | Baby change, toilets, car park | 0-4 | | | | | web | ✓ | ✓ | ✓ | |
| | | | Eastgate 0117 952 2413 | Baby change, car park | 0-4 | | | | | | | | | |
| Debenhams www.debenhams.com | ✓ | ✓ | Broadmead 08445 616161 | Baby change, toilets, café | 0-14 | ✓ | | | | | ✓ | ✓ | ✓ | ✓ |
| House of Fraser www.houseoffraser.co.uk | | ✓ | Cabot Circus 0844 8003710 | Baby change, toilets, café | 0-10 | | | | ✓ | | | | | |
| Ikea www.ikea.co.uk | | | Eastville 0845 355 2264 | Baby change, toilets, car park, café | | | | | ✓ | | ✓ | | | |
| John Lewis www.johnlewis.com | | ✓ | The Mall 0117 959 1100 | Baby change, toilets, car park, café | 0-14 | ✓ | | | ✓ | ✓ | ✓ | ✓ | ✓ | ✓ |
| Marks & Spencer marksandspencer.com | ✓ | ✓ | Broadmead 0117 927 2000 | Baby change, toilets, café | 0-12 | ✓ | | | ✓ | ✓ | | ✓ | ✓ | ✓ |
| | | | The Mall 0117 904 4444 | Baby change, toilets, car park, café | 0-12 | ✓ | | | ✓ | ✓ | | ✓ | ✓ | ✓ |
| Mothercare World www.mothercare.com | ✓ | ✓ | Avon Meads 0117 971 9815 | Baby change, toilets, car park | 0-8 | ✓ | ✓ | ✓ | ✓ | ✓ | ✓ | ✓ | | ✓ |
| | | | Eastville 0117 951 8200 | Baby change, toilets, car park | 0-8 | ✓ | ✓ | ✓ | ✓ | ✓ | ✓ | ✓ | | ✓ |
| TK Maxx www.tkmaxx.com | | ✓ | The Galleries 0117 930 4404 | Car park | 0+ | ✓ | | | | | | ✓ | ✓ | ✓ |
| | | | Cribbs 0117 950 8081 | Car park | 0+ | ✓ | | | | | | ✓ | ✓ | ✓ |

# LARGE SUPERMARKETS

| Supermarket | Mail Order | Internet Shopping | Branch Location | Facilities | Clothing (Age Range) | Late opening | Shoes | Maternity wear | Maternity Underwear | Nursery Equipment | Toys | Books | Computer Games |
|---|---|---|---|---|---|---|---|---|---|---|---|---|---|
| Asda<br>www.asda.co.uk | | ✓ | Cribbs Causeway<br>0117 317 2400 | Toilets, baby changing, café, parking | 0-15 | ✓ | ✓ | ✓ | ✓ | ✓ | ✓ | ✓ | ✓ |
| | | | Longwell Green<br>0117 960 3947 | Toilets, baby changing, parking | 0-15 | ✓ | ✓ | ✓ | ✓ | ✓ | ✓ | ✓ | ✓ |
| | | | Bedminster<br>0117 923 1563 | Toilets, baby changing, parking | 0-15 | ✓ | | | | | ✓ | ✓ | ✓ |
| | | | Whitchurch<br>01275 839 431 | Toilets, baby changing, parking | 0-15 | ✓ | | | | | ✓ | ✓ | ✓ |
| Tesco<br>www.tesco.com | ✓ | ✓ | Brislington<br>0117 991 7400 | Toilets, baby changing, café, parking | 0-13 | ✓ | ✓ | ✓ | ✓ | | ✓ | ✓ | ✓ |
| | | | Eastgate Centre<br>0117 912 7400 | Toilets, baby changing, parking | 0-13 | ✓ | ✓ | ✓ | | | ✓ | ✓ | ✓ |
| Sainsburys<br>www.sainsbury.co.uk | | ✓ | Ashton Gate<br>0117 966 3064 | Toilets, baby changing, café, parking | 0-13 | | | | | | ✓ | ✓ | ✓ |
| | | | Castle Court<br>0117 977 4887 | Toilets, baby changing, café, parking | 0-10 | ✓ | | | | | ✓ | ✓ | ✓ |
| | | | Filton<br>0117 923 6459 | Toilets, baby changing, café, parking | 0-13 | | | | | | ✓ | ✓ | ✓ |

N.B There are smaller branches of Tesco, Sainsburys, as well as Waitrose and many others, in most local districts.

**Soil Association**
the heart of organic food & farming

The Soil Association Organic Food Festival takes place in September every year. See **Events** at the start of this book and check: www.titchhikers.co.uk for dates and times as we are told them.

# MARKETS

Bristol has its fair share of markets where bargains and quality produce can be bought. Crowded markets can make the manoeuvring of buggies and toddlers difficult but children of any age can enjoy the atmosphere, colours and sounds. Non-regular markets and sales are usually advertised in the local press.

## BRISTOL MARKETS

### Abbots Leigh Market

Village Hall, Church Rd
www.abbotsleigh.org.uk
Every second Sat in the month. 10am-12pm.

Buy quality food direct from local producers.

### Craft Market

Corn St, BS1 1LJ
Fri 10am-5pm, Sat 10am-4pm

Crafts including glass and jewellery.

### Eastville Market

Eastgate Shopping Centre, Eastgate Rd, BS5 6XY
0117 935 4913 / 0117 934 9870
Fri and Sun 9am until 3pm

Varied range of inexpensive goods, with an emphasis on clothes and fabrics.

### Slow Food Market

Corn St, Bristol, BS1 1JQ
1st Sun of the month, 10am-3pm.

Run in conjunction with Bristol City Council markets. Slow food is about good food production. This market is a monthly treat for everyone who loves real food.

### St Nicholas' Market

St Nicholas St/Corn St, BS1 1LJ
0117 922 4017
Mon-Sat 9.30am-5pm & open 1st Sun of the month.

This is an indoor and outdoor market, situated in the Glass Arcade and the Corn Exchange, selling a wide variety of goods.

### The Farmers' Market

Corn St, Bristol. BS1 1JQ
Wed 9.30am-2.30pm

Local farm produce including dairy, meat, fruit and veg, as well as wines and preserves.

# ORGANIC & SPECIALIST FOODSTORES

In recent years, the demand for organic food has grown enormously and many parents are keen to give their children organic food from weaning onwards. While nearly all supermarkets sell organic food in their fresh, frozen and packaged sections, the local companies listed over the page have good, organic food either on their premises or delivered to your door.

Soil Association
the heart of organic food & farming

### Soil Association

Bristol House, 40-56 Victoria Street, Bristol, BS1 6BY
0117 314 5000
www.soilassociation.org

The Soil Association has a wealth of information on organic food and healthy living. It sells the Organic Directory, listing all organic outlets, which is also on their consumer website www.soilassociation.org.

## Also see:

**www.organic-supermarket.co.uk**

Here you will find one big searchable list of organic food, natural food, and other organic goods, available from suppliers in the UK.

### Bib & Tucker

34 Thingwall Park, Fishponds, BS16 2AE
077612 78031, www.bibandtucker.info

Homecooked children's food, prepared, frozen and delivered to your door, within the Bristol area. Ingredients include organic fruit and vegetables along with free range locally sourced meat. Order over the phone or through their website. Party food and celebration cakes also available.

### Earthbound

8 Abbotsford Rd, Cotham, BS6 6JX
0117 904 2260
Mon-Sat 9am-6pm

Friendly store specialising in locally produced organic foods. Sells a wide range of fresh fruit and veg, basic and luxury organic groceries, wholefoods and fair trade products.

### Harvest Natural Foods

11 Gloucester Road, Bishopston, BS7 8AA
0117 942 5997, www.harvest-bristol.coop
Mon-Sat 9am-6pm

This workers' co-operative sells a wide range of organic products including bread, fresh fruit and veg, beers and wines, suitable for vegans. They also stock a wide range of gluten-free products and have a delicatessen.

### Riverford Organic Vegetables

0845 600 2311, www.riverford.co.uk

This Devon-based company was one of the first to start delivering organic vegetable boxes to customers' doors. Predominantly seasonal vegetables grown locally, although they do import from France and Spain (nothing via air freight). Boxes start from £8.35 up to £16.45. Order ad hoc or on a regular basis.

### Somerset Organics

Gilcombe Farm, Bruton, Somerset
01749 813710, www.somersetorganics.co.uk

Delivery of a wide range of fresh organic meat, cheese, fish, juices, chutneys & butter to your door. Minimum order £40, deliveries cost £14 for orders below £100 & £8.50 for orders over £100, to any UK address.

### Southville Deli

262 North St, Bedminster, BS3 1JA
0117 966 4507, www.southvilledeli.com
Mon-Sat 9am-5.30pm

Organic whole foods, ground coffee, herbal teas, preserves, goat milk, and a range of baby products including Tushies nappies. "A wonderful shop in the heart of South Bristol."

### Stone Age Organics

01823 432 488, www.stoneage-organics.co.uk

Boxes of 100% organic vegetables priced from £6-£11. Also sells organic Lamb.

### Stoneground Health Foods

5 The Mall, Clifton Village, BS8 4DP
0117 974 1260   Mon-Fri 9am-5pm, Sat 9am-3pm

Combination of organic, GM free and natural products, 100% vegetarian. Sells fruit, veg, dairy products and dry goods. Take-away sandwiches, home-made soup, jacket potatoes, smoothies and fresh juice.

### The Bay Tree

176 Henleaze Rd, Henleaze, BS9 4NE
0117 962 1115   Mon-Sat 9am-5pm

Stocks a wide variety of natural, organic and gluten-free foods as well as supplements, natural toiletries, Bach Flower and other homeopathic remedies.

### Viva Oliva

30 Oxford St, Totterdown, BS3 4RJ
0117 940 7419, 07967 202625   Mon-Sat 10am-6pm

Friendly delicatessen stocks a variety of Mediterranean delights including breads, olives, sundried tomatoes, handmade sauces and pestos, authentic preserves, cheeses and meats. "The stuffed vine leaves are a must!"

# Maternity & Baby

There are good ranges of maternity wear available, at varying prices, in the outlets listed below. There are several fastenings designed to accommodate your growing bump and it is a good idea to try, before buying, to find the most comfortable one for you. Well-fitting, comfortable, maternity underwear is a necessary expense during your pregnancy, to support your changing shape. Your bra size can change dramatically during pregnancy and most stockists offer a measuring service. Also see Department Stores, Supermarkets and Nearly New for maternity clothing.

## MAIL ORDER MATERNITY WEAR

If you would like the privacy and convenience of trying your maternity clothes at home before buying, try the companies listed below. All offer maternity wear ordering and delivery

**Argos Additions**
0845 304 0008, www.additionsdirect.co.uk

**Blooming Marvellous**
0845 458 7406, www.bloomingmarvellous.co.uk

**Cecily Plum**
www.cecilyplum.com

**Crave Maternity**
0844 800 0478, www.cravematernity.co.uk

**JoJo Maman Bébé**
0871 423 5656, www.jojomamanbebe.co.uk

**Isabella Oliver**
0844 844 0448 www.isabellaoliver.com

**Mamas & Papas**
www.mamasandpapas.co.uk

**Mamas Feels Good**
0845 268 2000, www.mamafeelsgood.com

**NCT Maternity Sales**
0845 8100 100, www.nctshop.co.uk

**Next**
0845 600 7000, www.next.co.uk

**Vertbaudet**
0845 270 0270, www.vertbaudet.co.uk

## HIGH STREET MATERNITY WEAR

**Asda**
Maternity wear stocked at their Cribbs Causeway and Longwell Green branches.

**Blooming Marvellous**
5 Saracan Street, Bath, BA1 5BR
0845 458 7425, www.bloomingmarvellous.co.uk
Wide range of maternity wear.

**Born**
64 Gloucester Rd, Bishopston, BS7 8BH
0117 924 5080, www.borndirect.com
Lovely, independent shop. Stocks Bravado range of maternity underwear and feeding tops. See Advert on page 27.

**Dorothy Perkins**
39, George White Street, Bristol, BS1 3BA
0117 927 3790
The Mall, Cribbs Causeway 0117 950 7665
Good range of trousers, jeans, dresses, tops and swimwear in sizes 8 to 22. No underwear.

## SHOPPING & SERVICES

### H&M
The Mall, Cribbs Causeway
0117 950 9590
www.hm.com
Inexpensive maternity wear in sizes 8 to 20.

### JoJo Mamam Bébé
www.jojomamambebe.co.uk/clifton
8-10 Clifton Down Road, Clifton, Bristol. BS8 4AD
0117 923 9957
High quality maternity clothing & pregnancy and nursing products. See Titch Hikers' special discount code on page 25.

### John Lewis
The Mall, Cribbs Causeway
0117 959 1100
Maternity and feeding bras, with a measuring service available. No maternity clothes.

### Mamas & Papas
Eastgate Retail Park, Eastgate Road, Bristol. BS5 6XX
0845 268 2000, www.mamasandpapas.co.uk
Good range of maternity and baby clothing. Also stock wide range of nursery equipment.

### Mothercare World
The Eastgate Centre, Eastville, BS12
0117 951 8200
& Avon Meads, St Philips Causeway
0117 971 9815
For Hours & Facilities see Children's Clothing

Both stores have a wide range of maternity wear in sizes from 8 to 22. Swimming costumes and bras (measuring service). Also see Children's Clothes in this chapter

### Next Clearance
Abbeywood Retail Park, Station Rd, Filton
0117 906 2280, www.next.co.uk
Mon-Fri 9.30am-8pm, Sat 9am-6pm, Sun 11am-5pm

End-of-season and clearance maternity wear at up to 50% off original price.

### Venus Maternity & Baby
56 The Mall, Clifton Village, Bristol, BS8 4JG
0117 973 6400, www.venus-maternity.com

Venus maternity wear offers a range of fashions for all occasions along with swimwear, underwear, baby and child clothing, and mum & baby gift ideas. Visit the shop or buy online.

## BIRTHING POOLS & MATERNITY EQUIPMENT

### BORN in water
01225 868961 or Mobile: 07894 034406
www.borninwater.co.uk

All the equipment that you could need to set up your water birth, including pool, floor padding, stool for use in the pool, floatation pillow, birthing ball, and a breastfeeding pillow. Also TENS machines and more. For hire or purchase.

### The Good Birth Company
www.thegoodbirth.co.uk

An independent agent covering the West Country. Choose from a range of equipment, they will deliver to your home. Informative brochure available and friendly service.

### NCT Electric Breast Pump Hire

If you are having difficulties breastfeeding or have a sick baby, you can hire an NCT hospital grade electric breast pump from one of three agents in Bristol:

Eva Fernandes (BORN, Gloucester Rd)
07886 001802 / 0117 924 5080

Helen Phillips (St Andrews) 0117 924 4899

Martina Whitley (Westbury-on-Trym) 0117 962 9081

Contact for pricing.

### NCT Valley Cushion Hire
See: www.nctpregnancyandbabycare.com/in-your-area/bristol/postnatal

The NCT have agents who hire valley cushions for use in the first few weeks after birth. See the above website for contact details.

### ObTENS
53 Linden Rd, Westbury Park, BS6 7RW
0117 924 1982
www.obtens.co.uk, obtens@btinternet.com

ObTENS hire out TENS machines for drug-free pain relief during labour. Hire for a six week period around the baby's due date costs £19.

# REAL NAPPIES

After the move away from washable nappies to disposables, the trend is now reversing. Modern washable nappies are different from the old-fashioned Terry toweling ones and there are several types to choose from. Dinky Diapers offers a nappy laundering service. Contact for more details.

## Boo coo

7 Station Rd, Pill, BS20 0AB
01275 373735, www.boocoo.co.uk
nfo@boocoo.co.uk

A friendly, local business run by washable nappy users with a vast experience of cloth nappies. They sell a select range of easy to use modern washables at competitive prices. Their website has cost comparisons and they offer local demos and hire kits so you can try before you buy! Also local agents who can advise mums from their home (cover the Bristol, North Somerset, South Glos area). (No laundry service provided.)

## Born

64 Gloucester Rd, Bishopston, BS7 8BH
0117 924 5080, www.borndirect.com
Mon-Sat 9.30am-5.30pm

Stock a large range of cotton nappies and accessories. See **Advert** below and other entries in this section.

## Dinky Diapers

Unit 2, 13 Wellsway, Keynsham, Bristol, BS31 1HS
0117 986 6167, Shop: 01291 427262
www.dinkydiapers.co.uk

Under new management. All-cotton nappies are delivered to homes in Bristol and Bath. A special lined bin for storing soiled nappies is provided. Monthly service costs £36-80, (includes weekly collection, delivery and nappy rental). A 4-week trial with demonstration is £34. Also sells Tushies, Moltex and Ecover refillable products.

Also see **Jack & Jill Toyshop**, page 35.

# NURSERY EQUIPMENT

The independent retailers listed in this section offer a great choice of nursery equipment including prams, car seats and cots. They often stock more unusual brands compared to the high street names and can often offer more flexibility in terms of colours or fabrics.

See also Department Stores, and for repair services, see the Services section of this chapter.

## Baby & Co

21 Temple Street, Keynsham, BS31 1HF
0117 986 8184, www.babyandco.com
Mon-Sat 9am-5pm

Large range of prams, highchairs, cots, car seats, bedding and toys.

## Back in Action

42-43 College Green, Bristol, BS1 5SH
0117 922 6377, www.backinaction.co.uk/bristol
Tue-Sun 10am-4pm

Back in Action stocks wonderful products all carefully designed to relieve or prevent back pain. There is a wide range of furniture for babies and children, including Stokke and Tripp Trapp. See **Advert** opposite.

## Born

64 Gloucester Rd, Bishopston, BS7 8BH
0117 924 5080, www.borndirect.com
Mon-Sat 9.30am-5.30pm

Stockist of Stokke children's furniture, Tripp Trapp high chair, Sleepi Cot, Sleepy Care changing table and the Xplory pushchair and Bugaboo buggy. Also stocks slings and backpacks. See **Advert** on previous page.

# ALSO TRY

### Dinky Inc

138 Whiteladies Rd, Bristol, BS8 2RS
0117 973 1255 www.dinkyinc.co.uk,

### TinyTots Kids Shop

Abbotswood Shopping Centre, Yate
01454 314 174

# NEARLY NEW

Children grow so quickly that most clothes, toys and nursery equipment are outgrown before they're outworn. The shops listed in this section specialise in buying and selling good quality, nearly new children's items. This is an ideal way to recycle, save and generate some cash, whilst clearing some space.

**Remember to check all second hand goods for safety before you buy.**

## CAR BOOT SALES

www.bristol-city.gov.uk

Toys and other items can be bought cheaply at Car Boot Sales which are held across Bristol. Some are held regularly, others on an ad hoc basis and are mostly advertised in the local press. Bristol City Council has a trading standards leaflet to read if you trade at car boot sales.

## As New Toys and Togs

99 High Street, Staple Hill, BS16 5FH
0117 940 1214, www.asnewtoys.co.uk
Mon-Sat 9am-5pm

An Aladdin's Cave stocking second hand toys (disinfected and tested for safety), children's clothes, maternity wear and equipment. Also has new equipment, toys and books. Buys selected items from clients with 50% commission. 0-11yrs.

## Caterpillars

8 Alexandra Rd, Clevedon
01275 876 966
Tues-Sat 10am-4.30pm, Wed closes 1pm

High quality second hand nursery equipment, toys & children's clothes. 0-10 yrs.

## NCT Sales

www.bristolnct.org.uk

The Bristol branch of the NCT organise nearly new sales on a regular basis. They sell clothes, toys, books, nursery equipment, prams, washable nappies and maternity wear.

## "... an amazing experience, a sense of relaxation unmatched by anything I've ever done before."

**Book a float today**

- Expectant mothers often comment on the deep connection they feel with their baby.
- Relieve aching muscles and stiff joints whilst taking in vital minerals.
- Floatation has been highly rated as a useful pregnanay therapy.
- Regular floating can make natural childbirth easier.

Our **Mobiliser™** normalises your sacro-illiac after birth.
**Free first use!**

**Tripp Trapp®**
The chair that grows with your child

Float as a couple or
on your own

Wonderful products

Easy to find

Fabulous furniture

The seller receives 70% commission on sales, with 30% going to the NCT. Sales are busy and you usually need to go early to get the bargains. Members are allowed in slightly before non-members. Look at the website for more details.

## Quality Nearly New Sales

Details of how to become a seller can be found at www.longwellgreenprimaryschool.co.uk

For more information about the sale and future dates email qualitynearlynewsale@live.co.uk

The Quality Neary New Sale at Longwell Green School takes place twice a year, April and September. It offers items for sale from Birth up to 11 years of age. Including nursery equipment, toys, books and games. Outside equipment bikes, swings and slides.

## Roundabout

14 North View, Westbury Park
0117 373 9147
Mon-Sat 9.30am-5pm

A small shop filled with second hand clothing for 0-12yrs, books, toys, nursery equipment and maternity wear. Commission is 50% on all sales. "Good quality second hand shop with friendly, helpful staff — well worth a visit."

## Designer Factory Outlets

Many well known high street stores selling discontinued lines with great reductions.

### Bridgend Designer Outlet

The Derwen, Bridgend, South Wales, CF32 9SU
01656 665 700
www.bridgenddesigneroutlet.com

### Swindon Designer Outlet

Kemble Drive, Swindon, SN2 2DY
01793 507600
www.swindondesigneroutlet.com

Children's fun workshops at both the above venues during school holidays.

# Children

From basic vests to exclusive party wear, the shops listed have a wide selection of children's clothing to suit all budgets. Also look at our Factory Outlets, Markets, Department Stores, and Nearly New Sales listings.

## INDEPENDENT CLOTHES SHOPS

### Bishopston Trading Company

193 Gloucester Rd, Bishopston
0117 924 5598
www.bishopstontrading.co.uk
Mon-Sat 9.30am-5.30pm

Workers co-operative set up to create employment in South Indian village of KV Kuppam. Fair trade shop with play area. Specialises in natural fabrics and organic handloom cotton in a range of colours in sizes from 0-13yrs. Also see Mail Order below.

### Born

64 Gloucester Rd, Bishopston, BS7 8BH
0845 1302676
www.borndirect.com
Mon-Sat 9.30am-5.30pm

Most of the products in this shop are natural, organic and fairly traded. They stock a large range of cotton nappies and accessories, soft leather shoes, organic cotton and fairtraded clothing/toys along with a practical range of high quality outdoor wear. Also see their advertisement on page 27, along with their entries in Nursery Equipment, Maternity Wear, and Real Nappies sub-chapters.

### Dinky Inc

138 Whiteladies Rd, Clifton, BS8 2RS
0117 973 125
www.dinkyinc.co.uk

New to Bristol. Dinky Inc stocks children's clothing from The Ryde, Little Green Radicals and their own lovingly handprinted range. Also various baby accessories such as neoprene bibs, lunch totes etc. Most ranges up to age 6.

## Eskimo Kids

36 The Mall, Clifton, BS8 4DS
07545 171041, www.eskimokids.co.uk

New concept store in Clifton Village. Offers
a small but attractive range of clothing. See
entry under Toys and Hairdressers.

## Oranges and Lemons

20 Princess Victoria Street, Clifton, BS8 4BP
0117 973 7370
www.orangesandlemons-bristol.co.uk

Mon-Sat 9am-5.30pm

Wide range of designer clothing, shoes and
accessories, including Baby Dior, Diesel and
O'Neill. Excellent quality clothes, 0-12yrs.
Has recently launched an online shop.

## TinyTots Kids Shop

Abbotswood Shopping Centre, Yate
01454 314 174

Mon-Fri 9am-4pm, Wed 1pm, Sat 9am-12am.

Sells designer and well known chainstore
clothing for 0-8yrs at discount prices.

## Venus Maternity & Baby

56 The Mall, Clifton Village, Bristol, BS8 4JG
0117 973 6400, www.venus-maternity.com

Mon-Sat 10-5:30am & Sun 12-4pm.

Offers range of designer baby and child
clothing. Helpful and friendly staff.

## Zebra Children's Clothing

17 High Street, Portishead,
01275 397397, www.zebrachildren.co.uk

Well recommended children's shop, selling
a wide range of contemporary children's
clothing, accessories and gifts. Something to
suit most tastes and budgets.

## Also try...

### Jack & Jill Toyshop

192 Wells Rd, Totterdown, BS4 2AX
0117 9588860, www.jackandjilltoyshop.co.uk

Jack & Jill Toyshop sells clothes up to the age
of 3 years. Also see entry under Toys.

Zebra
Fabulous clothes
& accessories for
children

17 High Street, Portishead
Tel: (01275) 397 397

ME TOO · PETIT BATEAU · crocs · moto · MinyMo · oilily · LelliKelly · PHISTER & PHILINA · Emile et Rose · And more...

# LIST OF HIGH STREET SHOPS

## Adams Childrenswear
The Mall Bristol, Broadmead, BS1 3XB
0117 922 1034, www.adams.co.uk

## Baby Gap & Gap Kids
The Mall, Cribbs Causeway
0117 950 9698 Baby Gap
0117 950 9667 Gap Kids

30-32 Broadmead, BS1 3HA
0117 922 0657

Mon-Fri 9.30am-6pm, Sat 9am-6pm, Sun 11am-5pm

## H&M
www.hm.com
The Mall, Cribbs Causeway
0117 950 9590

Broadmead Gallery, Broadmead, Bristol.
0117 922 6657
Mon-Sat 9am-5:30pm, Thu 7pm

Unit SU1 5B Cabots Circus, Bristol. BS1 3BD
0117 927 7116

## Matalan
www.matalan.co.uk, 0845 330 3330
Unit 1, Brislington Retail Park, BS4 5NG
Unit 1, Abbey Retail Park, Filton, BS12 7JL
& Locking Castle District Centre, Weston-Super-Mare, BS22 0BE

Stock inexpensive range of baby & children's clothes, shoes & accessories.

## Monsoon
www.monsoon.co.uk
Kids' store, The Mall, Cribbs Causeway
0117 750 0753

Unit 13B, Cabot Circus, Broadmead
0117 927 7551

Mon-Sat 10am-8pm, Sun 11am-5pm

## Mothercare World
www.mothercare.com
The Eastgate Centre, Eastville, BS12
0117 951 8200

Mon-Fri 9.30am-8pm, Sat 9am-6pm, Sun 11am-5pm

Avon Meads, St Philips Causeway
0117 971 9815

Mon-Fri 9.30am-8pm, Sat 9am-6pm, Sun 11am-5pm

Large range of reasonably priced baby and children's wear. Clothes from 0-8yrs, school wear to 11yrs. Also see Nursery Equipment, Toys and Maternity Wear sub-chapters.

## Next
www.next.co.uk
Unit 22, Brigstow St, Cabot Circus, Bristol. BS1 3AX
0844 844 5133
Mon-Sat 9:30am-8pm & Sun 11am-5pm

The Mall, Cribbs Causeway
0117 950 9033

## Next Clearance
Abbeywood Retail Park, Station Rd, Filton
0117 906 2280

Mon-Fri 9.30am-8pm, Sat 9am-6pm, Sun 11am-5pm

End of season and clearance stock from Next and Next Directory. Prices are up to 50% off original selling price. Children's clothing and shoes available from birth upwards.

## Peacocks
50-60 The Horsefair, BS1 3EY
0117 927 9583, www.peacocks.co.uk
Mon-Sat 9am-5.30pm

Large selection of reasonably priced clothing, from 0-15yrs. Branches in Bedminster, Gloucester Road, Keynsham, Nailsea and Weston-super-Mare.

# CHILDREN'S SHOES

There are a wide range of shoes available from birth, suited to each stage of your child's development. When learning to walk, children use the feel of the floor to balance, so it is best to wait until they are walking confidently before buying their first pair of proper walking shoes. It is important to check the fit of your child's shoes frequently (good shoe shops will be happy to do so). Most shops below will have trained shoe fitters but do ask if you are in doubt. Also see Department Stores p.21.

## Bahoo
52, The mall, Clifton, BS8 4JG
0117 973 4808
Mon-Sat 10am-5pm

Family run children's shop, providing mainly modern, funky styles. Stock wide range of styles including school shoes and trainers. Also stock some accessories and toys.

## Clarks Shoes

The Mall, Cribbs Causeway - 0117 959 2290
& 35 Broadmead, BS1 8EU - 0117 929 0992
Mon-Sat 9.30am-5.30pm, Sun 11am-5pm

### Clarks at Mothercare World

The Eastgate Centre, Eastville- 0117 951 9917
& Avon Meads, St Philips Causeway - 0117 971 9860

### Thomas Ford

The Clarks Shop, Kingschase Shopping Centre,
Kingswood, BS15 2LP
0117 961 3807. Mon-Sat 9am-5.30pm

## The Handmade Shoe Company

64 Colston Street, BS1 5AZ
0117 921 4247 (call for opening hours)

Handmade shoes starting at size 4, available
in standard sizes and made to measure. Baby
shoes available (not handmade).

## KBK Shoes

203 Cheltenham Road, Cotham, BS6 5QX
0117 924 3707, www.kbkshoes.com
Mon-Fri 9.30am-6pm, Sat 9am-6pm

Sells Dr Martens and Birkenstock sandals in
summer. Will measure children's feet.

## Kids at Clinks

At Charles Clinkard, The Mall, Cribbs Causeway
0117 959 2484, www.charlesclinkard.co.uk

A good selection of baby shoes (size 0) and
shoes starting at size 2. Brands include Clarks,
Start-Rite, Kickers, Hush Puppies, Timberland,
Babybotte, Buckle My Shoe and many more.

## Oranges and Lemons

20 Princess Victoria Street, Clifton, BS8 4BP
0117 973 7370, www.orangesandlemons-bristol.
co.uk
Mon-Sat 9am-5.30pm

Shoes stocked from newborn upwards
including O'Neill trainers and sandals.

## Solelution

1-2 Boyce's Av, Clifton, BS8
0117 973 8350, www.solelution.co.uk
Mon-Sat 9am-5.30pm

Newly refurbished. Good range of Start-rite
and Clarks shoes and trainers. Also dance
shoes.

# UNIFORMS

Most department stores and supermarkets sell
school uniforms and offer good value ranges.
Below are specialist stockists.

## National School Wear Centres

22 Gloucester Rd Nth, Filton Park, BS7 0SF
0117 969 8551
www.n-sc.co.uk
Mon-Fri 9am-5pm, Sat 10am-3pm

Sells generic and some North Bristol State
school uniforms. Also clothing for Cubs,
Brownies, ballet, bowling and sports wear.

## School Togs Nailsea Ltd

110 High St, Nailsea, BS48 1AH
01275 857 491
Mon-Fri 9am-5.30pm, Sat 9am-5pm

Comprehensive range of uniforms for local
schools, along with school sports, Scouts,
Guides & dance clothing. 4-16yrs.

## Ikon (UK) Ltd

190 Henleaze Rd, Bristol, BS9 4NE
0117 962 0011
www.ikonsports.com
sales@ikonsports.com
Mon-Fri 9am-5pm, Sat 10am-5pm

Stock range of sporting equipment/clothing
and local Scout/school uniforms. There is a
good stock level, but anything new or unusual
can be sourced. Online ordering available.

# DANCEWEAR

### Cavalier Dancewear

45 Deanery Rd, Warmley, BS15 9JB
0117 940 5677
Mon-Fri 10.30-5pm, Closed Wed, Sat 10am-4pm

Good range of clothing and shoes for ballet, tap and jazz. Also stocks fancy dress and party wear. Sizes from 2yrs.

### Dance World

52 Bedminster Parade, Bedminster, BS3 4HS
0117 953 7941, www.danceworld.ltd.uk
Mon-Sat 9am-5.30pm (9:30am during holidays).

Extensive range of dancewear and dance shoes for ballet, tap and salsa from 3yrs.

### Dancewell

60 Cotham Hill, Bristol, BS6 6JX
0117 973 0120, www.dancewell.com
Mon-Sat 9am-5pm

Supplying Bristol's dancers for 40 years. Dancewear and shoes for all types of dance from 2yrs.

### Kathy's Dancewear

Alexandra Park, Fishponds, BS16 2BG
0117 965 5660
www.dancestation.org.uk
admin@dancestation.org.uk
Mon-Sat 8:30am-9pm & Sat 9am-5pm

Good range of ballet, tap, modern & jazz dance wear, plus shoes & leotards. From 2yrs.

### Weston Dancewear

32a-34 Orchard St, Weston-super-Mare, BS23 1RQ
01934 419818
Mon-Sat 9am-5pm

Large range of dancewear, gym leotards and shoes for ballet, tap, modern and jazz, from 2+yrs.

Also see entry for **Solelution** above.

# FANCY DRESS

Many children love to dress up and once they start school there are often costumes to be made. If you want to try your hand at dress-making, the art and craft stores below will give you loads of ideas. However, below are some quicker solutions to your needs. Remember many of the super hero costumes can be found in such shops as Asda.

### Christmas Steps Joke Shop

47 Colston St, Bristol, BS1 5AX
0117 926 4703, www.fundirect2u.com
Tue-Sat 10am-5pm (4.30pm costume hire)

Jokes, wigs, magic tricks and a range of costumes and accessories for children. Costume hire for older teens and adults only.

### Dauphine's of Bristol

7 Cleeve Road, Downend, Bristol, BS16 6AD
0117 956 6556

Mon-Sat 9am-5pm

Sells wigs along with face painting and theatre make-up. There are make-up courses for children.

### Partysmartys

PO Box 155, Portishead, BS20 8WR
01275 818971, 07918 667 843
partysmartys@yahoo.co.uk, www.partysmartys.co.uk

Fran has a beautiful range of fancy dress clothes to purchase, for both girls and boys up to 8 years old. Also see Fran's entry and Advert in **Parties.**

### Starlite Costumes

275-277 Lodge Causeway, Fishponds, BS16 3RA
0117 958 4668

Mon-Sat 9.30am-5.30pm, Wed closed

Quality fancy dress hire, theatrical costumes and wigs. Costume sizes from 18 months to adult. Face paints and novelties.

 Jack & Jill Toyshop also do dressing up clothes. See entry opposite.

# TOYS

Toys can be purchased from a number of places including department stores and Nearly New Sales, charity shops and online. The shops listed below are the best independent shops that we have in Bristol.

## Bristol Guild of Applied Art

68-70 Park Street, BS1 5JY
0117 926 5548, www.bristolguild.co.uk
Mon-Sat 9:30am-5:30pm.

Large store selling a wide variety of gifts, household goods and furniture (including Tripp Trap highchairs). The toy department sells toys, games and puzzles for all ages. The store is not buggy friendly, with lots of stairs, but staff are happy to mind buggies on the ground floor. Good quality gifts and toys.

## Enkla

21 Broad St, Bath, BA1 5LN
01225 339789, www.enkla.co.uk
Mon-Sat 10am-5.30pm, Sun 11am-4pm

The shop looks at childhood through work, rest and play. There are toys to help with gardening, cooking and cleaning along with a range of lighting, storage and bedding. Most of the age range 3-13yrs, with some lovely gifts for babies.

## The Entertainer

www.theentertainer.com
The Galleries, Broadmead, BS1
0117 934 9522

Unit 77, Level 3, Cabot Circus, BS1 3AG
0117 929 4698

Toys for all ages (up to adult!) with 6,000 lines. Also branches in Keynsham, Yate and Midsomer Norton. Mail or internet ordering available. Call 01494 737002 for a catalogue.

**Jack and Jill TOY SHOP**

192 Wells Road, Totterdown, Bristol, BS4 2AX

0117 958 8860

jackandjilltoyshop@gmail.com

## Eskimo Kids

36 The Mall, Clifton, BS8 4DS
07545 171041, www.eskimokids.co.uk

Brand new concept store stocking a good range of quality toys including Playmobil, art and craft materials, nice present ideas, clothes and more. Also see Hairdressers.

## Jack & Jill Toyshop

192 Wells Road, Totterdown, BS4 2AX
0117 958 8860, www.jackandjilltoyshop.co.uk

Jack & Jill Toyshop is an independent, family run business which specialises in traditional and educational toys. Due to a recent expansion of the shop, children now have the space to try out some of the toys, games, books and puzzles for sale in the shop. An extremely friendly shop where the staff are really helpful in suggesting ideas for that special little person. It isn't difficult to imagine why it was recently awarded the 'Best Toddler and Baby Shop' from Little Monster 'Bristol's Best' Awards.

### Just So

12 Regent Street, Clifton, BS8 4HG
0117 974 3600, www.justso-online.co.uk
Mon-Sat 9.30am-5.30pm

61 Henleaze Road, Bristol. BS9 4JT
0117 962 8205

A traditional shop with helpful staff. You will find high quality toys, books, dressing up clothes and puppets. It also sells a select range of baby clothes as well as Tripp Trapp high chairs, soft shoes and blankets. 0-11yrs.

### Playfull

87 Gloucester Rd, BS7 8AS
0117 944 6767
Mon-Sat 9.30am-5.30pm

This shop sells a wide range of natural toys, puzzles, gifts and some craft materials. They have handmade wooden toys suitable from birth. There is a small play area for children to test the toys! Mail order is also available.

### Revillo Toys

5:15 Paintworks, Bath Road, BS4 3EH
0117  9723195, www.revilotoys.co.uk

Wonderful selection of wooden toys. Shop online or visit the shop.

### Totally Toys

109 Gloucester Rd, Bishopston, BS7 8AT
0117 942 3833

Mon-Sat 9am-5.30pm

Friendly shop stocking major brands of toys including Brio, Lego, Play Mobil, Galt and TP (outdoor equipment). Good range of pocket money toys, party bag items as well as play tables for children to use while you browse.

## Also try...

### Early Learning Centre

www.elc.co.uk
The Mall, Cribbs Causeway, The Mall Broadmead, and Eastgate Retail Park

Tuesday Playtime (2+yrs)
10am-11am, The Galleries, 10am-11.30am, The Mall

**Toys R Us -** Cribbs Causeway
0117 959 1430, www.toysrus.co.uk

# OUTSIDE ACTIVITY TOYS

### Child's Play Activity Toys

The Close, Inglesbatch, Bath, BA2 9DZ
01225 314123, www.childsplayatc.co.uk
Opening hours vary, please call for details

Stocks mainly TP Activity toys, climbing frames with wooden and galvanised metal frames. There is a good range of trampolines, equipment for tennis, indoor play and giant garden games. Larger orders delivered free.

### Eastermead Activity Toy Centre

Eastermead Farm, Eastermead Lane, Banwell, BS29
01934 823926, www.eastermead-activity-toys.co.uk
Mon-Sat 9am-5pm, Sunday am by arrangement

Stocks TP galvanised climbing frames. Also has a wide range of wooden toddler toys including garages, castles, farms and dolls houses. Stocks sledges and ride-on tractors. Will deliver locally.

# BIKES

Purchasing your child's first bike is an exciting occasion. The following bicycle shops come well recommended.

### Blackboy Cycles

180 Whiteladies Road, Clifton, Bristol BS8 2XU
0117 9731420 www.blackboycycles.co.uk

### Fred Baker

www.fredbakercycles.co.uk
144 Cheltenham Road, Bristol BS6 5RL
0117 924 9610 &
292 Lodge Causeway, Bristol BS16 3RD
0117 965 5510

See **Advert** in **Travelling Around**.

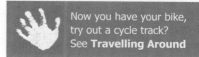

Now you have your bike, try out a cycle track?
See **Travelling Around**

# ARTS & CRAFT SHOPS

## B Delicious

2 Triangle South, Clifton, Bristol. BS8 1EY
0117 929 1789 (Opening times vary).

Creative fun with beads and feathers, ready made, made to order or even made by you!

## Children's Scrapstore

The Proving House, Sevier St, St Werburghs, BS2 9LB
0117 908 5644, www.childrensscrapstore.co.uk
Mon-Sat 10am-5pm.

Registered charity who re-use safe, clean waste for play purposes. Also see **Art, Craft and Cookery.**

## Craft Works (Bristol) Ltd

355-357 Gloucester Rd, BS7 8TG
0117 942 1644, www.craftworksbristol.co.uk
Mon-Fri 9am-6pm, Sat 9am-5pm

Everything for the craft lover including kids crafts, fine art, needle craft and creative craft.

## Creativity

7/9 Worrall Rd, Clifton, BS8 2UF
0117 973 1710, www.creativitycraftsuppliers.co.uk
Mon-Sat 9am-5.30pm

A lovely local shop selling a vast range of creative products including decorative mirrors, paints, beads, glass and silk paints, and more.

## Evangeline's

58-61 St Nicholas Market, Bristol, BS1 1LJ
0117 925 7170, www.evangelines.co.uk
Mon-Sat 9.30am-5pm (also postal service).

Small shop stocking most things for those with a flair for arts & crafts. They sell glass paints, beads, origami paper and much more.

## Harold Hockey

170-174 Whiteladies Road, Clifton, Bristol. BS8 2XU
0117 973 5988, www.haroldhockey.com
Mon-Sat 8.45am-5.30

Packed with all things artistic, from easels to sketchpads, pens, cards and picture frames.

Also a good selection of puzzles and games, cards and stocking or party bag fillers.

## Hobbycraft

Centaurus Road, Cribbs Causeway, BS34 5TS
0117 959 7100 / 0845 051 6524
www.hobbycraft.co.uk
Mon-Fri 9am-8pm, Sat 9am-6pm, Sun 11am-5pm

Superstore packed with craft and art materials for children through to professionals! Occasional in-store demonstrations.

## Rajani's Superstore Ltd

Fishponds Trading Estate, Maggs Lane, BS5 7EW
0117 958 5801 / 0800 630 0050, www.rajanis.co.uk
Mon-Sat 9am-6pm, Sun 10am-4pm.

Here you will find artists' materials at very reasonable prices: paints, canvasses, brushes and frames. You will also be amazed at the other household bargains in this huge store.

# MUSIC SHOPS

The shops below all sell a selection of musical instruments.

### Bristol Music Shop/Hobgoblin

30 College Green, Bristol
0117 929 0390
Mon-Sat 9.30am-5.30pm

### Clevedon Music Shop

19 Alexandra Rd, Clevedon, BS21 7QH
01275 342 090
Mon-Sat 9.30am-5.30pm
Road is opposite pier, café Scarlett's on corner.

### Mickleburgh

1-9 Stokes Croft, Bristol, BS1 3PL
0117 924 1151
www.mickleburgh.co.uk, mail@mickleburgh.co.uk
Mon-Sat 9am-5.30pm

Also see **Mail Order** opposite for recorders.

# HOBBY TOYS & KITES

### Al's Hobbies

438-440 Gloucester Rd, BS7 8TX
0117 944 1144
Tue-Sat 9.30am-5pm

For all hobby and modelling enthusiasts. Large stacks of balsa wood, building materials, paints, clay, brushes, model kits. From 8+yrs.

### Bristol Kite Store

39A Cotham Hill, Redland, BS6 6JY
0117 974 5010, www.kitestore.co.uk
Mon-Fri 10am-6pm, Sat 9.30am-5.30pm

Wide range of kites and kite surfing equipment, DIY Kites and spare parts. Also frisbees, yo-yos, juggling and circus equipment, books & videos. From 3yrs. Online ordering available.

# MAIL ORDER

This is a selection of recommended and mainly regionally based mail order companies where you can order via the internet or by phoning for a catalogue. Many of the places already listed in this chapter also offer online shopping (we have not relisted them here), and this is sure to only increase. It is also always worth asking a shop (particularly if they are independent) if they will post something that is of particular interest to you.

### Boden (& Mini Boden)

0845 677 5000, www.boden.co.uk

Mail order baby / childrens wear and accesories.

### Cox and Cox

0870 442 4787, www.coxandcox.co.uk

Unusual and exciting selection of ideas for children's birthday presents and parties. They have a range of games, activities, toys and party bags suitable for different ages. Order online or via the catalogue.

### Ethos Baby Care

19 The Praedium, Bristol. BS6 6WB
www.ethosbaby.com

Stocks natural products for baby: 100% natural cotton nappies, organic cotton clothing, sleeping bags, natural baby care products and wooden toys. For mum: a range of books and maternity pillows.

### The Great Little Trading Company

0845 848 6000, www.gltc.co.uk

Sells a wide range of good quality childrens clothing, toys, bedroom furniture and accessories. Great for unusual gift ideas.

### Green Child of Mine

www.greenchildofmine.com

Contemporary clothing for children. Organic and fair-trade.

## Letterbox

0844 888 6000. www.letterbox.co.uk
Original and colourful durable gifts and toys
for babies through to young teens.

## Look at My Crazy Shoes

0800 731 4885, www.lookatmycrazyshoes.com

Company selling bright fun shoes. Sizes start
from infants to UK adult size 3.

## Partysmartys

PO Box 155, Portishead, BS20 8WR
01275 818971, 07918 667 843
partysmartys@yahoo.co.uk
www.partysmartys.co.uk

Everything you could need for that special
party, whether that is a birthday, Christening,
or some other occasion. See more about
Partysmartys in **Parties** chapter.

## Raindrops

01730 810031, www.raindrops.co.uk

"There is no such thing as bad weather,
just inappropriate clothing." Raindrops sells
good quality Scandinavian outdoor clothing.
Products include dungarees and jackets,
camouflage trousers, wellie boots, ski kit,
thermals and swim wear — everything you
need come rain, snow or shine. Sizes range
from 6mths to 13yrs.

## Saunders Recorders

0117 973 5149, www.saundrecs.co.uk

Specialist dealer in recorders & recorder
music. Shop now closed. Mail order only.

## Wise Owl Toys

www.wiseowltoys.co.uk, 01305 266311

Educational toys, games and puzzles
supporting the National Curriculum and the
Early Learning Goals, for ages 0-14 yrs.

For maternity wear that you can order
online, see page 25 of this chapter.

# SERVICES

## LATE NIGHT PHARMACIES

Pharmacies have a rota for opening outside
normal retail hours. Details can be found in
the Bristol Evening Post or by calling NHS
Direct.

### NHS Direct

0845 606 46 47
www.nhsdirect.nhs.uk

Gives out of hours pharmacies in your area.

### Asda Walmart

Highwood Lane, Cribbs Causeway
0117 979 0426
Mon opens 8am, Tue-Sat 24hrs,
Sun 10am-4pm

### Boots The Chemists

19 St Augustines Parade, (near to Hippodrome)
0117 927 6311
Mon-Sat 8am-7pm, Sun closed

59 Broadmead, Bristol City Centre
0117 929 3631
Mon-Sat 8:15am-6pm, (Tues opens 8:45am & Thurs
closes 7pm).

Upper Mall, Cribbs Causeway
0117 950 9744
Mon-Fri 9:30am-9pm, Sat 8:30am-8pm & Sun
10:30am-5:30pm.

### Morrisons

www.morrisons.co.uk

688-718 Fishponds Road, Fishponds
0117 965 3014
Mon-Sat 8.30am-8.00pm, Sun 10am-4pm

### Sainsbury's

www.sainsburys.co.uk
Sainsbury's, Winterstoke Road, Ashton
0117 953 7273
Mon-Fri 8am-10pm, Sat 7.30am-10pm,
Sun 10am-4pm

Fox Den Road, Stoke Gifford, S Glos
0117 923 6459
Mon-Sat 8am-8pm, Sun 10am-4pm

### Tesco

www.tesco.com
Callington Road, Brislington, BS4 5AY
0117 991 7400
Mon-Sat 8.30am-8pm, Sun 10am-4pm

Eastgate Centre, Eastville, BS5 6XU
0117 951 1156
Mon-Sat 8am-8pm, Sun 10am-4pm

# EQUIPMENT REPAIR

The companies listed here can repair prams and buggies. For problems with other baby equipment it is probably best to contact your supplier or go direct to the manufacturer. For the safety of you and your child, car seats should be replaced and not repaired.

## Baby & Co

21 Temple Street, Keynsham, BS31 1HF
0117 986 8184, www.babyandco.com
Mon-Sat 9am-5pm

The workshop, which is on the premises, can repair all major makes of prams/buggies and carries many spare parts. If available, buggies can be loaned to you.

## John Lewis

The Mall, Cribbs Causeway, BS34
0117 959 1100

Will arrange for the repair of any pram or buggy bought at John Lewis.

## Mothercare World

Eastgate Centre, Eastville, BS5 6XZ
0117 951 8200
Mon-Fri 9.30am-8pm, Sat 9am-6pm, Sun 11am-5pm

Most types of prams and buggies can be repaired here. The repair man is in the store on Mon, Wed and Fri. You must book your repair in advance.

# BESPOKE JEWELLERY

## Smallprint

Victoria Wilkes, Smallprint
0117 9029348/07787 938729
www.smallp.co.uk
victoria@smallp.co.uk

Beautiful pieces of individually handcrafted and engraved jewellery that captures your child's fingerprint, drawing or hand and feet impression forever in pure polished silver.

See Victoria's Advert on page 37.

# PHOTOGRAPHERS

The photographers listed here have been recommended for their expertise in children's photography.

## Burntfish Photography

www.burntfish.co.uk, helen@burntfish.co.uk
07989 854380

Helen is an independent, professional photographer, based in Bristol, and available for both organised groups (eg playgroups, nurseries etc) and individual sittings. She offers a high quality, personal service specialising in fun and informal child, family and pet portraits.

## Lisa Gault Photography

Studio 9a, Clevedon Craft Centre, Moor Lane, Clevedon, North Somerset, BS21 6TD
01275 341366, www.lisagaultphotography.co.uk

Lisa will photograph you and your family anywhere you feel comfortable, therefore achieving really natural, fun photographs.

## Looking Glass Photography

Mobile studio
07962 440037, www.lookingglassphotography.co.uk

Vicki is a mobile photographer specialising in family, couple, baby, children and pregnancy photography. She has 11 years experience and promises a high-quality yet inexpensive photographic service. There is no sitting fee and you will also be able to view your photographs on the day, which means that your pictures or canvasses will be with you so much sooner. She is highly recommended.

## Snappy Families

0117 9246238, www.snappyfamilies.co.uk

Clare Swayne combines photographing children and families with teaching French and Spanish. She offers a relaxed experience, believing in photographing families in situations in which they feel comfortable. She is available for parties and comes highly recommended.

*Looking Glass*
PHOTOGRAPHY
07962440037

**Professional Photographs
taken in the comfort of your own home**

* **Vicki Brown** specialises in:
  Babies, Children, Families, Couples & Pregnancy.
  * The professional mobile studio
    that comes to your home.
    * A whole range of poses, sets, outfits & moods.
    * High quality yet inexpensive results.
      * Contemporary Stretched Canvases,
        Glass Blocks, Watch Me Grow, Vouchers, etc.

**No Sitting Fee**

www.lookingglassphotography.co.uk

## Also recommended

### James Nicholas Photography

27 Pool Road, Kingswood, Bristol
0117 985 9520
www.jamesnicholasphotography.co.uk
Mon-Fri 9am-7:30pm, Sat 9a,-6pm, closed Sun.

Variety of photo/portrait sessions. Cater for all ages from babies to grandparents.

### Mark Simmons

The Fire Station, 82-84 York Rd, Bedminster, BS3
0117 914 0999
www.marksimmonsphotography.co.uk
Appointment only

Mark is an established Bristol portrait photographer with a warm, spacious and comfortable studio. He is friendly, relaxed and favours an informal style of portraiture. See website for examples of his work.

### Michael Rich Studios

3 Prospect Lane, Frampton Cotterell, BS36 2DR
01454 778816, www.richphotos.com

Mike offers free sittings for children under 12 months and does a 'watch me grow' scheme.

### James Owens Studios

Charlton Studio, 18 Charlton Road, Keynsham
0117 986 5114, www.jamesowens.co.uk

A family-run photographic studio with 25 years experience. Examples of previous work are shown on the website.

### Paul Burns Photography

72 Shirehampton Road, Bristol, BS9 2DU
0117 968 6300
www.paulburns.co.uk

Photographs for all occasions. Friendly family-run business. Contemporary style portraits from a photographer with a royal warrant!

### Phil McCheyne Photographers

5 St. Austell Close, Nailsea, Bristol, BS48 2US
01275 858 545
Flexible opening times

Specialises in school, nursery and playgroup photography along with portraits and passport photos.

### Portrait Place

Debenhams, 1-5 St James Barton, Broadmead
0117 922 5960

## HAIRDRESSERS

Many salons are happy to cut children's hair (even if your little one is not quite so keen). The salons listed below are all especially family friendly.

### Eskimo Kids

36 The Mall, Clifton, BS8 4DS
07545 171041
www.eskimokids.co.uk
Monday to Saturday 9.30am to 5.30pm and late night Thursday until 7.00pm.

New concept store in Clifton Village. Specialises in haircuts for parents and children. The hair salon provides a haven for kids where they can choose their themed seats and watch DVDs or play on the latest games consoles. Buggy parking, baby changing, drinks and a kiddie friendly waiting area. It is possible to book your appointment via their website. Also see their entry under Toys.

### Hairy Monsters

180 Henleaze Rd, Henleaze, BS9 4NE
0117 962 8184
www.hairymonsters.com
Contact for opening hours and pricing

Specialist family hair salon where children can read, play computer games, or watch DVDs while having their hair cut.

## Also recommended

### Bonomini

22 Alma Vale Road, Clifton, BS8 2HY
0117 923 9169, www.bonominihair.co.uk
£14 U5's, £18 5-9yrs, £27 10-14yrs

### Illusions Hair

22 Gloucester Road, The Promenade, Bishopston, Bristol, BS7 8AE
0117 907 7447

U4's £7.70, 4-8yrs £12.10

### Jon Hurst Hairdressing

18 Cotham Hill, Cotham, Bristol, BS6 6LF
0117 373 0044
Mon-Fri: 10am-7pm Sat: 9am-5pm

Offering a relaxed atmosphere for your baby's first haircut.

### Nitty Gritty

020 7229 7775, www.nittygritty.co.uk

This company, created and run by three mums, may not be regionally based but their chemical-free Head Lice Solution and Repellent Spray comes with loads of recommendations. The award-winning NitFree Comb really does effectively remove head lice, nits and eggs. At last, a non-toxic solution to ridding your family of head lice!

### Moda Hairdressing

205a Gloucester Rd, Bishopston
0117 924 1006

Approx £6 preschool, £10 5+yrs to adult

### Pride Hair and Beauty Salon

236 Stapleton Rd, Easton, BS5 0NT
0117 951 9518

Approx £11.50 girls, £7 infants & boys under 12yrs

### Supercuts

The Mall, Cribbs Causeway
0117 959 2597
Mon-Fri 10am-9pm, Sat 9am-7pm, Sun 11am-5pm

7 Union Gallery, Broadmead
0117 929 2184

Approx £7.95 U8's, £11.95 over 8's

### The Business Hair Studio

69 Islington Road, Southville, BS3
0117 966 6618

# Bristol Visitor Attractions

## Contents

Why not travel around Bristol by bus, bike, train or boat? See Travelling Around.

According to the Council, 10 million tourists visit Bristol's attractions each year. This tells only part of the story, for Bristol is different from some other tourist centres. Main attractions, like the suspension bridge and the Downs, are enjoyed every day by locals, while those running Brunel's ss Great Britain and At-Bristol are fully aware that it is families a walk or a bus ride away which keep them ticking. Go out and enjoy what people travel great distances to experience.

### Summer Activities ☀

Look out for all the great
Summer Events listed in this Section

### Winter Activities

Look out for Santa Trains, ice rinks, & more

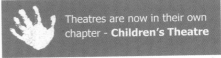

Theatres are now in their own chapter - **Children's Theatre**

## VISITOR INFORMATION CENTRES

Bristol has three excellent tourist information points, the harbourside being the largest. Each offer advice, accommodation, booking, maps, guides, leaflets and brochures. Their website also has excellent coverage of seasonal events:

www.visitbristol.co.uk, 0333 321 0101

### Bristol Visitor Information Harbourside

Explore-At-Bristol, Harbourside, Bristol, BS1 5DB
Mon-Sun: 10am-5pm

Services available include: general advice and enquiries, accommodation booking service, maps and guidebooks, leaflets and brochures.

### Bristol International Airport

Bristol Visitor Information, BIA
Opening hours vary

Services available: general advice and enquiries, accommodation booking, leaflets and brochures.

### Broadmead Information Point

Ground Floor, The Mall Galleries
Mon-Sat 9am-5.30pm, Sun 11am-4pm

Services available include: general advice and enquiries, leaflets and brochures.

## SIGHTSEEING TOURS

### Bristol City Sightseeing Tour

0870 4440654 information hotline
www.bristolvisitor.co.uk, www.city-sightseeing.com
Easter-Sep: 10am-6pm, last bus 4pm
Call for prices, U5's FREE, one child free per adult passenger. Tour takes 75 mins.

Tickets can be bought on the bus or from Bristol Tourist Information Centre and the Travel Bristol Information Centre. This open-top, live guide, sightseeing bus takes in all the major attractions: including at-Bristol, Bristol Zoo, Brunel's ss Great Britain, and Clifton Village. Discounts on a number of attractions on presentation of your bus ticket. Hop on and off the bus at any of the stops en route.

*Bristol Highlights at 11am*

Saturdays until late September

Leisurely 2 hour walk. Departs Tourist Information Centre, Harbourside (next to @ Bristol). £3.50 (under 12's FREE).

## Pirate Pete

Call Pete on 07950 566 483, www.piratewalks.co.uk
2pm, Sat & Sun all year. Always call for availability
£3.50 adult, £2.50 child, £8 family (2+2)
60 mins. Meet outside @Bristol in Millennium Square.

Walking tour of Bristol's maritime history. 'Pirate Pete' is truly dynamic and will tailor the walk according to the specific group.

Walks are wheelchair and pushchair friendly

## Bristol Packet

Brunel's ss Great Britain Car Park, Wapping Wharf, BS1 6UN
0117 9268157, www.bristolpacket.co.uk
Open all year, daily in school holidays, weekends only during term-time.
Call or see website for full range of prices.

Bristol Packet offers a variety of educational-based river adventures on one of their four boats. These include city dock tours with commentary, trips under the Clifton Suspension Bridge and lunch and afternoon tea cruises to local, child friendly pubs and Beese's tea gardens. Leaves from Brunel's ss Great Britain & Bristol Packet Pontoon, Watershed.

## Bristol Ferry Boat Company

M.B Tempora, Welsh Back, BS1 4SP
0117 9273416, www.bristolferry.com
Daily ferry service. Public trips at various times throughout the year.
Call or see website for more information.

In addition to the timetabled ferry service, there are numerous public trips and events. Boats are heated in Winter.

*Summer Trips*

Festival of Nature Trips (June), Beese's Cream Tea Cruises.

*Winter Trips*

Sail with Santa!

## The Matthew

Great Western Dock, Gas Ferry Rd, BS1 6TY
0117 9276868, www.matthew.co.uk
March-Sep. Call or see website for more information

Reconstruction of the 15th century boat John Cabot discovered Newfoundland in. Harbour cruises. Also available for private charter. Disabled and buggy access is limited.

## Tangaroa

Merchant's Row, Wapping Wharf, BS1 6JN
0776 479 4435
www.tangaroa-sailing.com
Trips from £25 per adult, £10 per child. Call or see
website for more information.

Tangaroa is a wooden sailing ship which is
available for adventures in and around Bristol.
A variety of trips are available - or if there is
a large group of you (8-12), you can design
your own.

*Also see Travelling Around
for more boat and ferry trips,
train rides and more..*

CAPTAIN **cecily** (ADD YOUR NAME!)

# LANDMARKS

## Bristol Cathedral

College Green, Bristol
0117 926 4879, www.bristol-cathedral.co.uk
Daily 8am-6pm  FREE (donations welcome). Charge
for some events.

Bristol Cathedral welcomes visitors young
and old, and a look-in holds more for children
than you might first expect. The awesome
size of the building is impressive and the
animals, stain glass windows and gruesome
gargoyles provide plenty of entertainment.
An experienced children's guide is available.
The cathedral staff encourage kids to draw
many of the features and also hold regular
brass rubbing events and other workshops,
including music, drama, environmental science
and craft. A tour list can be downloaded from
the website.

## Cabot Tower

Brandon Hill Park, off Park Street, Bristol
0117 922 3719
Daily 8am-½hr before dusk (4pm winter, 7pm
summer)  FREE

At over 32.4 metres high on top of a high hill,
this tower offers one of the best panoramic
views of Bristol. It was built in 1897 to
celebrate John Cabot's voyage to America in
1497. There is a winding staircase that takes
you to the top. Very young children may find
the climb tricky but there are secure viewing
areas. The gardens are great for exploring.
**Cabot Tower is currently closed and
should reopen late 2009.**

Also see **Parks and Play Areas** for the
superb Brandon Hill Park.

great days out!

**FREE** return visits for a year*

BRUNEL'S
ss GREAT BRITAIN

A TRUE STORY

Visit ssgreatbritain.org
for what's on!

*excludes schools, groups and venue hire.
Reg. charity no. 262158

# Brunel's ss Great Britain for pre-schoolers – – a review

By The Titch Hikers' Team

There is something about the sight of Brunel's ss Great Britain, looming majestically in the Bristol harbourside, that catches the imagination of young children more than many other landmarks in Bristol. In fact, so impressive a sight it is from the outside that you might forget that there could be anything more inside. But once you visit this symbol of Bristol's seafaring heritage, and realise what a place of incredible interest it is to young maritime explorers, you will more than likely find yourself compelled to visit time and time again.

What is really special about a visit to Brunel's ss Great Britain is that children of all ages are made to feel especially welcome as they are encouraged to touch, smell, hear, see and really feel what life would have been like for Victorian passengers and crew onboard the ship. It is so good for children to be able to use all their senses in this way, getting involved in the action rather than having to simply observe.

The two Titch Hikers' investigators we recently took with us, Anna and Gabriel (both aged 4), enjoyed running around underneath the ship, marvelling at how they could be underwater without getting wet. They showed tireless enthusiasm for setting off the steam whistle, boundless excitement as they flung from cabin to cabin seeing what new scene would greet them, and an inspiring imagination as they 'played ship' climbing in the ship's bunks and exploring the ship's kitchen.

"I loved the sick bowl', exclaimed Gabriel, without putting us off our hot chocolate and home made cakes in the dockyard café during our visit. "See if you can find the ship's cat", challenges Anna. And William, aged 7, adds "there's a surprise in the loo" (and there is indeed). In fact, there really is something to impress and intrigue visitors of all tastes. Should you need more prompts, visitors are provided with a useful sheet of ideas to help you make the most of your visit, there is a superb guide book with lots of practical suggestions, an audio tour, and enthusiastic, kind staff and volunteers to assist you throughout your journey.

## Need to know:

The ship is pushchair and wheelchair friendly, with lifts giving access to the Drydock, throughout the museum, and into the ship itself. There are also baby changing facilities in the museum, the ship and the café.

Many events aimed at the under-fives take place throughout the year. These ooze creativity. Check out our website www.titchhikers.co.uk or see: www.ssgreatbritain.org

Brunel's ss Great Britain receives no local or central government funding. It therefore relies on the sale of admission tickets. See their listing on page 48 to find out about pricing and opening hours.

## Clifton Observatory and Caves

Clifton Down, Bristol
0117 974 1242
Daily: 10.30am-5pm summer only, occasionally closed due to adverse weather, phone first
£1 adults, 50p children (£2 and £1 for both Obscura and Caves). Access from the Clifton side.

The Observatory houses a Camera Obscura installed in 1829. In fine weather a rotating mirror in the roof reflects the panorama outside. From the Observatory a steep stepped passage through the rock leads to a viewing platform which give splendid views of the Bridge and Gorge. Buggies can be left at the kiosk, which sells ice creams.

## Clifton Suspension Bridge

0117 974 4664
www.clifton-suspension-bridge.org.uk
Guided tours every sunday afternoon (Easter Sun-mid Sep). Meet at toll booth at Clifton end of bridge (3pm). Lasts 45 mins. FREE

One of the world's greatest bridges and it's on our doorstep. It was designed by the Victorian engineer Isambard Kingdom Brunel, although he never lived to see it finished in 1864. Its spectacular setting over the Avon Gorge has made it the symbol of Bristol and the subject of many school projects! Visit the website or phone for details.

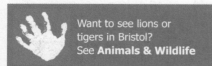
Want to see lions or tigers in Bristol?
See **Animals & Wildlife**

# THE DOCKSIDE

The City has a distinguished history of maritime activity and consequently, this is a fascinating and lively area of Bristol with a lot to offer parents and children of all ages. Largely traffic-free, it is ideal for walking and family cycling. Parking is ample and located at Brunel's ss Great Britain and At-Bristol. Cafes and restaurants are on both sides of the harbour.

## Bristol Ferry Boat Company

See **Travelling Around** and page 44.

## Bristol Harbour Railway

See **Travelling Around** section

## Brunel's ss Great Britain

Great Western Dock Yard, Gas Ferry Road, BS1 6TY
0117 926 0680, www.ssgreatbritain.org
Open daily 10am (except 24/25 Dec) - 4pm (Jan/Nov/Dec), 4.30pm (Feb/Mar), 5.30pm (Apr-Oct), 4.30pm (last week Oct)
£10.95 adult, £5.95 child, £30 family (2+3) or £20 (1+3), U4's FREE (approx prices). Keep your ticket for free entry for 12 mths after purchase.

Brunel's masterpiece of ship design has been wonderfully restored throughout. Go "under water" to stand below the ship's impressive hull and propeller, step back in time in the Dockyard Museum and try your hand at preparing the ship for sail, steering her on a westerly course, or climbing above the rigging to the crow's nest. On board, explore cabins and crew quarters. A choice of audio guides bring the ship to life. See our review of Brunel's ss Great Britain on page 47.

*Events*

Lots of exciting events throughout the year including Mr Brunel visiting the ship in person, art & craft workshops, the wonderful Dream Boats, and children's ship trails. Visit the excellent website or call prior to visiting.

### The Matthew

Moored next to Brunel's ss Great Britain.
(See full entry on page 44)

# MUSEUMS & GALLERIES

## Arnolfini

16 Narrow Quay, Bristol, BS1 4QA
0117 917 2300
www.arnolfini.org.uk
Galleries, box office, bookshop - Tues-Sun.
Galleries & box office: 10am-6pm, bookshop: 10am-6pm (8pm Thur-Sun). Cafebar open daily from 10am
Entry to galleries, bookshop and exhibitions are free

This is Bristol's centre for the contemporary arts. It is very pushchair friendly. An ever-changing programme provides lots to see including exhibitions, live art and performance, dance and cinema. There are regular family-friendly events, activities and workshops on offer.

## At-Bristol

Anchor Rd, Harbourside, Bristol, BS1 5DB
0845 345 1235
www.at-bristol.org.uk
10am-5pm weekdays, term-time
10am-6pm weekends, b/hs & sch hols
£11.90 adults, £7.70 child, free U3's, £34 family
Two mins from city centre (any bus). Close to the National Cycle Network. Ferry stop at the City Centre and Millennium Square. Underground car park.

Experience the everyday and the extraordinary in this interactive science and discovery centre. You can make a programme in a TV studio, experience a walk-in tornado or make person-sized bubbles! There are a series of exhibitions that are particularly suited to U8's, such as In the Jungle and Jet, set, go. Anyone expecting a new addition to their family will also particularly enjoy the model babies from 1-9 month gestation, and feeling a baby moving in its mummy's tummy. Star gazers should not miss the Planetarium show.

## Tip

Don't miss the Toddler afternoons on a Monday. For more information see **Parent & Baby/Toddler Groups**.

Also see **Advert** and editorial over the page.

## Blaise Castle House Museum

Blaise Castle Estate, Henbury Rd, BS10 7QS
0117 903 9818
Sat-Wed 10am-5pm. Admission FREE

18th Century mansion house, showing how people lived in Victorian times. There are social history collections, domestic furnishings, costumes, textiles and toys. The Museum is set in the extensive Blaise parkland, with its cafe, adventure playground, and castle. There are stairs and no lift, and buggies must be left in the entrance. No toilets.

## Bristol City Museum & Art Gallery

Queens Rd, Clifton, BS8 1RL
0117 922 3571
www.bristol-city.gov.uk/museums
Daily 10am-5pm. Admission FREE

Many interesting and varied exhibits appealing to children, including stuffed animals, a bi-plane suspended from the ceiling in the entrance hall, a Romany caravan, and Small World, a 0-5 play area (children can touch real museum objects, dress up, and much more - excellent for crawlers). September will also see the launch of Curiosity, a mini-museum for Under 7s at Bristol Museum, where children can tell stories in the crystal cave, act out a performance on stage, or try the animuddle game. Older children and adults can request a gallery trail. Toys, colouring materials, and play-things are provided at some exhibitions. Ask staff for toddler steps if required. There is also a café with good food deals for children (see **Eating Out**).

### Family Fun Events

These are drop-in workshops and give children a chance to do hands-on activities on themes linked to current displays in museum.

# Explore  @ Bristol

## Mini Adventures...
### for tiny explorers

Storytelling    Games and    Dressing up
            activities

0845 345 1235         www.at-bristol.org.uk

Registered charity no. 1049954

# Explore more!

Explore-At-Bristol is one of the UK's most exciting hands-on science centres! With two floors packed full of over 300 interactive exhibits and fascinating special exhibitions, it brings a wealth of scientific knowledge to life in the most captivating ways.

Take a trip around the universe in the silver sphere Planetarium, join the Live Science team for fun experiments and activities, be a TV presenter, freeze your shadow, walk through a tornado, or even take a tour around the human brain – there's no end to the fun, scientific discoveries that await.

Animate It! opens on the 18th July which will be a major new interactive exhibition in association with Aardman, the creators of Wallace and Gromit. Make your own animated mini-film, or even animate yourself in our Pixellation set! From making Morph do cartwheels in front of your eyes to actually lighting a street scene from Aardman's latest Wallace & Gromit film, 'A Matter of Loaf and Death', there's so much to our cracking new exhibition.

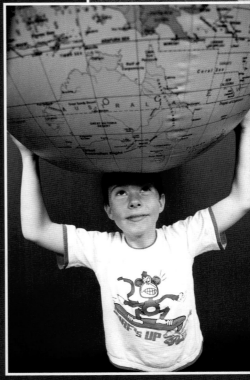

Located in Bristol's Harbourside and easily accessible by public transport or your own car, Explore has so much to offer for a fun-filled day out – plus it has a café to renew energy supplies and a shop to continue the learning at home with exciting experiments and gadgets to wow family and friends.

Explore-At-Bristol is a registered charity that aims to make science accessible to everyone. Since opening in 2000, it has hosted approaching four million visits and continually strives to make informal science learning available to the widest possible audience.

## CREATE Environment Centre

Smeaton Rd, Spike Island, Bristol, BS1 6XN
0117 925 0505
Mon-Fri 9am-5pm, ecohome 12-3pm,
cafe 8.30-11am, 12-2pm. FREE

CREATE is a riverside centre focusing on ecology and the environment, in particular recycling. It often has interesting exhibitions. The centre also has a demonstration eco-home, made of salvaged, recycled and natural materials and using energy saving systems. The centre encourages the use of public transport, the no. 500 bus or a ferry ride. There is limited parking.

## Georgian House

7 Great George Street, Bristol, BS1 5RR
0117 921 1362
Sat-Wed 10am-5pm. Admission FREE

The lovely Georgian House was built in 1790 and is furnished in period style. No buggies in the house but they can be stored. Stairs, no lift, no toilets.

## Kings Weston Roman Villa

Long Cross, Lawrence Weston, Bristol BS11 0LP
0117 903 9818
Daily. Admission FREE (you need a key collect from Blaise Castle House Museum or City Museum & Art Gallery. £5 refundable deposit required for the key)
Leave the M5 at Junction 17. On-street parking

Explore where Roman's used to live, viewing the only Roman bath suite in Bristol, mosaic floors and Roman central heating. No toilets and access is via uneven ground.

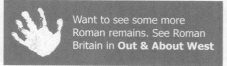

Want to see some more Roman remains. See Roman Britain in **Out & About West**

## Knowle West Media Centre

Leinster Avenue, Knowle West, Bristol , BS4 1NL
0117 9030444
www.kwmc.org.uk

This fantastic refurbishment of derelict buildings is the focal point of an artistic revolution in South Bristol. A particular strength in film and computer based art.

## Red Lodge

Park Row, Bristol, BS1 5LJ
0117 921 1360
www.bristol.gov.uk
Sat-Wed 10am-5pm
Admission FREE

Beautiful Elizabethan house with panelled rooms and a Tudor knot garden. Access can be difficult as there are stairs and no lift. Buggies are also not allowed in the house but they can be stored. No toilets.

## Royal West of England Academy

Queens Rd, Bristol, BS8 1PX
0117 973 5129
www.rwa.org.uk
Mon-Sat: 10am-5.30pm, Sun 2pm-5pm
£4 adults, children FREE

The RWA welcomes parents with young children and prams, although many of the exhibitions are of more interest to the older child (such as gallery tours and educational worksheets for 9+yrs). Keep an eye on their website for an exhibition that appeals to you.

# Out & About West

## Contents

### Summer Events

Many of the venues listed in this section hold Summer Events. For more information see: www.titchhikers.co.uk .

Caves, castles, cavernous stately homes and...garden centres?! Local folk will journey beyond city limits with many destinations in mind. This chapter contains the best family days out in the south west region immediately beyond Bristol.

(Prices in this chapter are given as an indication only).

### See a basic map of the West at the back of the book.

Why not take the train?
See Travelling Around
Bristol & The West

# CASTLES

## Berkeley Castle & Butterfly Farm

Berkeley, Gloucestershire, GL13 9BQ
01453 810332, www.berkeley-castle.com
Open April - Oct
April & May: All Sundays & B/H's 11am-5.30pm,
June & July: Sun to Thur 11am-5.30pm,
August: Sun -Thur, plus b/h wkend 11am-5:30pm.
September & October: Sundays only.
(Butterfly house open June to August).
£7.50 adult, £4.50 child, FREE U5's, £21 family (2+2)
Garden only £4 adult, £2 child
Butterfly House only £2 adult, £1 child
On A38 between Bristol and Gloucester

Twenty four generations of the Berkeley family have lived here since 1153 in what is England's oldest inhabited castle. It has been transformed over the years from a Norman fortress to a stately home full of paintings, tapestries and treasures. Lawns and terraced gardens surround the castle. Many steps mean pushchairs can't be used in the castle and baby backpacks are preferable outside. Tea rooms and plant centre.

## Caerphilly Castle

Castle Street, Caerphilly, CF83 1JD
029 2088 3143, www.cadw.wales.gov.uk
Mon-Sun 9am-5pm, seasonal variations (see website or contact for latest details).
£3.60 adult, £3.20 child, £10.40 family, FREE U5's
M4 J28 direction 'Risca' then A468 to Caerphilly.

This huge castle built in the 13th century is the second biggest in Britain after Windsor. It's a classic castle with high towers, moats, banqueting hall, working replica siege-engines and a leaning tower to make the people of Pisa green with envy! Pushchair accessible apart from the two exhibition towers.

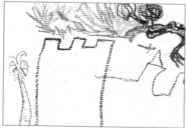

## CALDICOT CASTLE AND COUNTRY PARK

Church Road, Caldicot, Monmouthshire, NP 26 4HU
01291 420241, www.caldicotcastle.co.uk
Apr-Oct: daily 11am-5pm
Castle: £3.75 adult, £2.50 child, £12 family (2+3)
Admissions to Country Park: FREE
M4 to M48 J2 for Chepstow then A48 twd Newport then B4245, follow signs.

Caldicot is set in 50 acres of gardens and wooded country park. Although founded during Norman times, the castle was restored in the Victorian period and inhabited until the 1960s. Some furnished rooms remain in the towers. There is a lot for children including giant games (using giant playing pieces) in the gardens, buggy-friendly trails, and a wildlife pond with dipping platform. The castle also hosts a wide variety of events and re-enactments.

## Cardiff Castle

Castle Street, Cardiff, CF10 3RB
029 2087 8100, www.cardiffcastle.com
Mar-Oct: daily 9am-6pm, Nov-Feb: daily 9am-5pm
£8.95 adult, £6.35 child, FREE U5's.

Situated in the town centre, Cardiff Castle spans a 2000 year history from its Roman remains, to the Norman keep and its opulent Victorian interior. Large green for picnicking, as peacocks and ducks wander freely.

## Castell Coch

Tongwynlais, Cardiff, CF15 7JS
029 2081 0101, www.cadw.wales.gov.uk
Nov-Mar: Mon-Sat 9:30am-4pm, Sun 11am-4pm.
Apr-Oct: Mon-Sun 9am-5pm.
£3.60 adult, £3.20 child, £10.40 family, U5's FREE
M4 J32, take A470 north, follow signs

Hidden in woodland, this fairytale castle, complete with conical roofed towers, working portcullis and drawbridge, looks convincingly medieval. It was, however, built in the late 19th century for the Marquis of Bute. The inside remains faithful to the Victorian era being richly furnished and decorated. Worksheet for children in shop and audio guide available (for 8+yrs). Please note: woodland trail around castle not suitable for buggies. Coffee shop open Apr-Sep.

## Chepstow Castle

Bridge St, Chepstow, Monmouthshire, NP16 5EY
01291 624065, www.cadw.wales.gov.uk
Nov-March: Mon-Sat 9:30am-4pm, Sun 11am-4pm.
Apr-Oct: Daily 9am-5pm.
£3.60 adult, £3.20 child, £10.40 family (2+3), FREE
U5's
M4 J21 to M48 J2, then A466 and follow signs.

One of Britain's first stone-built strongholds.
Building started not long after the Battle
of Hastings in 1066 and the castle was
significantly extended over the following
centuries. Today the well-preserved ruins
perch above the River Wye offering an insight
into life in a Norman castle and plenty of
scope for exploring. Steep slope from car park
(toilets) to castle entrance.

## Farleigh Hungerford Castle

Farleigh Hungerford, Nr. Bath, BA2 7RS
01225 754 026
www.english-heritage.org.uk/farleighhungerford
Apr-Sep: daily 10am-5pm, July/Aug: 10am-6pm,
Oct: Daily 10am-4pm, Nov-March: Sat & Sun only
10am-4pm.
£3.40 adult, £1.80 child, FREE U5's
3½ miles west of Trowbridge on A366
Bus access: Bodmans 96 from Trowbridge (passes
close to Trowbridge railway station) then 1 1/2 mile.
Train access: Avoncliff 2 miles. Trowbridge 3 1/2
miles.

Ruins of a 14th century castle and chapel
with museum. Audio guide and programme
of events for children, including exhibitions,
medieval pageants. Pushchairs can be used
but backpacks are preferable. Refreshments &
snacks available. Picnics welcome in grounds.

## Sudeley Castle

Winchcombe, Cheltenham, GL54 5JD
01242 602308, www.sudeleycastle.co.uk
30th March-1st Nov: daily 10.30am-5pm
Castle & Gardens: £7.20 adult, £4.20 child
£20.80 family (2+2), free U5's, seasonal variations
M5 J9 take A46 then B4077 signs to Winchcombe.

The castle can boast many royal visitors,
including Anne Boleyn, Queen Elizabeth I and
Henry VIII. Much of the impressive collection
of furniture and paintings is from the Tudor
and Victorian periods and school-children will
enjoy the Six Wives at Sudeley exhibition.
Attractive gardens surround the castle. Coffee
shop and picnic area.

# CAVES

Going down into a mine or through caves can
leave a lasting impression on a child, entering
a fantasy world in the semi-darkness.

## Big Pit National Mining Museum

Blaenafon, Torfaen, Nr. Newport, NP4 9XP
01495 790311
www.nmgw.ac.uk/bigpit
Mid Feb-Nov: daily 9.30am-5pm, (open Dec-Jan,
phone for opening times), underground tours from
10am-3.30pm
FREE admission
J 25a M4 follow brown signs.

Blaenafon has World Heritage status. Walk
around this coal mine and find out how men,
women and children worked here for over
200 years. Children over 1 metre tall can
go underground and wear hard hats! New
museum exhibitions in the original pithead
baths, and multi-media displays of modern
mining will help to answer all their questions!
Allow four hours for visit. Coffee shop open
during peak season.

## Cheddar Caves & Gorge

Cheddar, Somerset, BS27 3QF
01934 742 343, www.cheddarcaves.com
July-Aug: 10am-5:30pm & Sep-June 10:30am-5pm.
£16.00 adult, £10.00 child, £42.00 family (2+up to 3
children). Prices include entry to all attractions.
FREE U5's
SW of Bristol on the A371, between A38 & A37

Impressive caves located in spectacular gorge.
The two main caves to explore are Gough's
with its cathedral-like caverns and Cox's with
its stunning formations and colours. Excellent
explorer audio guide of Gough's cave (5+yrs).
Buggies can be taken into the caves, although
they will have to be left in certain places and
picked up later. Baby back packs are fine,
watch the head room. Also: The Cheddar Man
museum which looks at Stone Age man and
cannibalism, The Crystal Quest — discover
dimly-lit caves inhabited by wizards, goblins,
fairy princesses and dragons; an open top
bus tour of the Gorge during summer; Jacobs
Ladder — a 274 step climb to the top of the
gorge with fantastic views of the Mendips

from the lookout tower. From here there is a 3-mile waymarked circular walk around the Gorge. The caves also offer caving, climbing and abseiling for 11+yrs, see website for details. Further down the Gorge you can watch the famous cheese being made. An open top bus tour runs during summer.

## Clearwell Caves

Near Coleford, Royal Forest of Dean, GL16 8JR
01594 832535
www.clearwellcaves.com
info@clearwellcaves.com
Feb-Oct & Dec: daily 10am-5pm
£5.80 adult, £3.80 child, £17.30 family (2+2),
U5's From Coleford take B4228 south for 1 mile,
turn right for Clearwell village (immediately after
Lambsquay Hotel).

These natural caves have had iron ore mined from them for thousands of years (by children as young as 6yrs). Nine caverns are open to the public and miners' tools and equipment are displayed. There are no steps and single buggies can be taken into the caves. Stout footwear recommended. Cafe, picnic areas and gift shop. See website for special events.

## Wookey Hole

Wookey Hole, Wells, Somerset, BA5 1BB
01749 672 243
www.wookey.co.uk
witch@wookey.co.uk
Apr-Oct, daily 10am-5pm. Nov-March, daily 10am-4pm.
£15 adult, £10 child (3-14 years), (additional children £9.50), £45 family, FREE U3's
2 miles north west of Wells, follow brown signs.

A guided tour (approx 40 mins) takes you through this impressive series of caves carved out by the River Axe. The route is not suitable for pushchairs but there is enough headroom for child back packs. For those that cannot access the caves there is now a virtual reality tour of the caves and valley. There is also the Valley of the Dinosaurs where you can stroll among full-sized dinosaurs. Other attractions include a museum, an interactive Victorian paper mill, a mirror maze, magic shows in the Wizard's Theatre, a collection of playable Edwardian Penny Arcade machines and two play barns for U10's.

# OUTDOOR FUN

## Barton Farm Country Park and The Tithe Barn

01225-713489, www.wiltshire.gov.uk
The Country Park is always open.
B3109 just out of town centre, past station

This 36 acre park, created on land belonging to the ancient Manor Farm, is set in the wooded valley off the River Avon, stretching 1.5 miles between Bradford and the hamlet of Avoncliff. A great place for walking, rowing, fishing, picnics.

### 14th Century Tithe Barn, Bradford-On-Avon

English Heritage, www.english-heritage.org.uk
Open all year, 10.30am-4pm. Admission FREE
Located 1/2 mile south of town centre off B3109.
Bus access: First/Wilts & Dorset X4/5 Bath-Salisbury.

On the edge of the park is this impressive barn, once used to store the Abbey's tithes. The granary and old cow byres have been restored as craftshops and galleries. There are also tea gardens and a childrens play area.

## Cotswold Water Park

Spratsgate Lane, Shorncote, Cirencester, GL7 6DF
01793-752413, www.waterpark.org, info@waterpark.org
Keynes Country Park open daily 9am-5pm

Britain's largest water park with over 130 lakes. Water sports, walking, nature spotting or just relaxing on the beach.

### Gateway Information Centre (and café)

Spine Road, South Cerney, GL7 5TL
01285 861459
At the A419 entrance to the park
Open daily 9am-5pm.
For accommodation, family activities and eating out information.

### Keynes Country Park

01285 868096, www.keynescountrypark.com, info@keynescountrypark.com
Oct-March daily 9am-5pm, April 9am-6pm, May & Aug 9am-9pm daily & Sep 9am-6pm.
Entry fees apply (vary according to time of year - see website for latest details).

The larger of the two country parks. Here you will find: the millennium visitor centre and a bathing beach; two large play areas; lake side walks and cycling; a boardwalk café and picnic/barbecue areas. Boats (pedalos to glass bottom boats - www.go-by-cycle.co.uk) and bicycles (phone 07970 419208 - includes adult and children's bikes, and child trailers).

### Adventure Zone
01285 861202 or email: advzone@waterpark.org
Based at Keynes, the Adventure Zone offers a range of activities for 8-16yrs including waterskiing, windsurfing, kayaking, sailing and horseriding. Pre-booking essential.

### Waterland
01285 861202
www.ukwatersports.co.uk
An outdoor pursuit centre offering sailing, windsurfing, canoeing and kayaking, archery and raft building.

### Neigh Bridge Country Park
01285 861459
Smaller park with picnic site, play area and lakeside walk.

## Royal Victoria Park
Upper Bristol Rd, Bath
01225 477010
Take A4 into Bath, about a mile before city centre.

Families tend to visit this park for its massive well-equipped playground for all ages, including skateboarders. There are also beautiful botanical gardens and a duck pond.

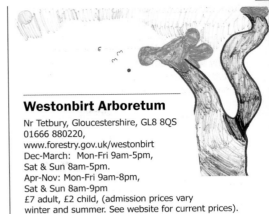

## Westonbirt Arboretum
Nr Tetbury, Gloucestershire, GL8 8QS
01666 880220,
www.forestry.gov.uk/westonbirt
Dec-March: Mon-Fri 9am-5pm,
Sat & Sun 8am-5pm.
Apr-Nov: Mon-Fri 9am-8pm,
Sat & Sun 8am-9pm
£7 adult, £2 child, (admission prices vary winter and summer. See website for current prices). M4 J18, take A46 towards Tetbury, follow brown tourist signs.

The Arboretum consists of miles of beautiful, well-marked tree-lined paths, most of them suitable for pushchairs. The Old Arboretum is dog free. The area is especially beautiful in the autumn and hence busier. Shop, plant centre and restaurant open daily, 10am-5pm.

Stay two nights at Calcot Manor and get your Arboretum tickets for **free**. See Calcot Manor and our special Titch Hikers' Deal on page 191.

## Have older children?

**Wye River Outdoor Pursuits**
Range of outdoor pursuits from canoeing to raft building, caving to abseiling, archery to low rope courses. For the over 8's (and adventurous parents!).

**Symonds Yat Canoe Hire**
01600 891069, www.canoehire.com

**Wye Pusuits**
01600 891199, www.wye-pursuits.co.uk

**Wyedean Canoe and Adventure Centre**
01594 833238, www.wyedean.co.uk

See also **Walks, Woods and Nature Reserves**

# GARDEN CENTRES

It may sound a little strange but children love these garden centres! Set in the great outdoors, they all have play areas, great food, fluffy animals and fish to peek at, and the icing on the cake - you can pick up a plant or two.

## Cadbury Garden Centre

Congresbury, Bristol, BS49 5AA
01934 875700, www.g-l.co.uk
info@cadbury.g-l.co.uk
Mon 9:30am-6pm, Tues, Thurs, Fri & Sat 9am-6pm, Wed 9am-8pm & Sun 10:30am-4:30pm.

Award winning garden centre. Cadbury has lots of facilities for children including a small enclosed outdoor play park, parent and baby room, bottle warming. There is also a Kids Club, including an online area where children can download projects and competitions, as well as joining in lots of fun activities in store.

## Eastwood Garden Plant Centre

Eastwood Park, Falfield, Thornbury, GL12 8DA
01454 260288, www.eastwoodgardencentre.co.uk
Mon-Sat 9am-5.30pm, Sun 9.30am-5.30pm
Tea shop 9.30am-4.30pm
About a mile from the M5 junction 14, on the A38 just south of Falfield.

Family-run, independent garden centre situated in what was the Victorian walled kitchen garden that served Eastwood Park country house. Play area with swings and climbing equipment near to tea shop. Small display gardens, pet enclosures with rabbits, guinea pigs, goats, chickens and ducks.

## Sanders Gardenworld

Bristol Rd, Brent Knoll, Somerset, TA9 4HJ
01278 761111, www.sandersgardenworld.co.uk
Mon-Sat - 9am-6pm, Sun - 10:30am-4.30pm, B/Hs 9am-6pm

The South West's largest purpose-built garden centre. Large pet and aquatic centre. The highlight for children is the full-size pirate ship. There are also monster trucks, swings, seesaw and rope slide. Snacks available from snack bar.

# CRAFT CENTRES

## Clevedon Craft Centre

Moor Lane, off Court Lane, Clevedon, BS21 6TD
01275 872 149
www.clevedoncraftcentre.co.uk
Sun 2-5pm, Tue-Sat 10am-5pm
Admission FREE
M5 J20, follow brown signs, Court Lane is off B3130 (Tickenham Rd).

Craft studios demonstrating a variety of skills. Jewellery, pottery, illustrations, hand-carved leather goods and stained glass are just some of the items made and sold here. There is a pond where children can feed the ducks and chickens. Refreshments are available in one of the studios.

## Ruskin Mill

Old Bristol Rd, Nailsworth, Gloucestershire, GL6 0LA
01453 837537 events
01453 837514 coffee shop
Gallery daily 10am-5pm (closed Thu pm)
Coffee shop 10am-4pm (Mon-Sat)
FREE admission.

Coffee shop and gallery with a programme of art and craft exhibitions, events and workshops, including, in term time, monthly storytelling for children (4+yrs). Park at Horsley Mill car park (the next turning on the left towards Horsley) and enjoy the 10-minute walk back along the pretty Nailsworth valley – suitable for single buggies. Parking at Ruskin Mill is for disabled visitors only.

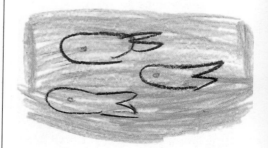

# MUSEUMS & GALLERIES

## Clevedon Heritage Centre

4 The Beach, Clevedon, BS21 7QU
01275 341 196
clevedonpier@zoom.co.uk
Mon-Fri 10am-5pm, Sat-Sun 10am-6pm
£1 adult, 75p children, U3s FREE

Photographic history of Clevedon.

## Fashion Museum

Assembly Rooms, Bennett Street, Bath, BA1 2QH
01225 477173
www.museumofcostume.co.uk
Daily 10.30am-5pm (exit 6pm)
£7 adult, £5 child, £20 family (2+4), U5's free
Combined tickets to museum and Roman Baths
(£14.50 adult, £8.70 child, £40 family (2+4).

Clothing from the late 16th century to today,
with interactive exhibitions, audio guide
and activity trolley. Child carriers for babies/
toddlers available. Children's activities during
the school holidays.

## North Somerset Museum

Burlington St, Weston-super-Mare BS23 1PR
01934 621 028
www.n-somerset.gov.uk/museum
Mon-Sat 10am-4.30pm
£4.10 adult, accompanied children FREE

Child-friendly displays, Victorian dressing up
clothes, interactive computers, passport trail,
U5's activity corner, cafe, and FREE holiday
events.

## The Shoe Museum

40 High Street, Street, BA16 0YA
01458 842169
Mon-Fri 10am-4.45pm, Sat-Sun closed
Admission FREE

Traces the history of shoes and shoe making
from Roman times to today. Many exhibits are
on the first floor.

## Victoria Art Gallery

Bridge Street, Bath, BA2 4AT
01225 477233, www.victoriagal.org.uk
Tue-Sat 10am-5pm, Sun 1.30pm-5pm, some B/H's
FREE admission

Gallery offers wide variety of art exhibitions,
which change every couple of months. Various
activities for children (3-11) during the
holidays. Call or see website for details.

## Bath Postal Museum

27 Northgate Street, Bath, BA1 1AJ
01225 460333, www.bathpostalmuseum.org
info@bathpostalmuseum.org
Mon-Sat 11am-5pm, winter 4.30pm
£3.50 adult, £1.50 child, free U6's

The only museum in the country telling the
story of the Postal Service. Children can
have fun in a reconstructed 1930s post office
weighing items, stamping forms and sorting
letters. Educational videos, discovery trails,
jigsaws, typewriters and computer games.

## Museum of East Asian Art

12 Bennett Street, Bath, BA1 2QJ
01225 464640, www.meaa.org.uk
Tue-Sat 10am-5pm, Sun & B/H's 12pm-5pm
£5 adult, £2 child U12's, free U6's, £12 family (2+2)
Opposite the Assembly Rooms.

This museum is situated in a restored
Georgian house and houses a fine collection
of ceramics, jades, bronzes and other artifacts
from China, Japan, Korea and Southeast
Asia. They welcome young visitors of all
ages. For the very young there are movable
footstools, magnifying glasses and dressing
up boxes. There is a family learning area and
an activity trolley with Origami, word searches
and colouring sheets. The Museum offers an
education and handling service to schools as
well as private children's parties.

## American Museum

Claverton Manor, Bath, BA2 7BD
01225 460 503
www.americanmuseum.org
info@americanmuseum.org
Museum: Mar-Oct Tue-Sun, Aug daily 12pm-5pm
(last entry 4pm), some B/H's. Gardens & exhibitions
12pm-5pm
£8 adult, £4.50 child (5-16yrs), (all areas)
£4 adult, £2.50 child (grounds & exhibition)
Take A36 Warminster road out of Bath, follow signs

Displays of American decorative art spanning
17th to 19th Century. Authentically furnished
rooms showing the American way of life from
colonial times to the eve of the Civil War. No
prams or baby rucksacks in the house, but
baby carriers can be borrowed. Beautiful
terraced gardens, lovely for children to run
around in but not very suitable for buggies.
Drop-in activities for children during school
holidays.

## Museums of the Bath Preservation Trust

www.bath-preservation-trust.org.uk

The Trust works to save listed buildings from
demolition and to preserve the historic beauty
of Bath. It runs four museums which, due to
restrictive planning, do not allow for disabled
facilities (and are difficult for prams). Three of
the museums have fully illustrated trails.

### Beckford's Tower

Lansdown Road, Bath, BA1 9BH
01225 460 705
Easter-Oct: Sat/Sun/B/H's 10.30am-5pm
£3 adult, £1.50 child, U6's FREE, £8 family

This 120ft tower, 2 miles north of Bath, has
great views of the countryside.

### Building of Bath Museum

The Countess of Huntingdon's Chapel,
The Vineyards, The Paragon, Bath, BA1 5NA
01225 333 895
Apr-Oct, Daily 10.30am-5pm
£4 adult, £2 child, £10 family (2+2), free U5's

This museum describes how the city of Bath
was designed and built. Join Mr Macheath, an
illustrated rat, for a drawing trail and hands-
on activities. Interactive play house (U5's),
dressing up clothes and handling boxes.
Buggies possible, back carriers preferable.

### Number 1 Royal Crescent

1 Royal Crescent, Bath, BA1 2LR
01225 428 126
Tue-Sun & B/H's 10.30am-5pm, winter 4pm
Dec-Feb closed
Open B/H's & Mondays of Bath Festival
£5 adult, £2.50 child, £12 family (2+2), U5's free

First house built on the Royal Crescent in
1767. Restored as a grand town-house of
the period. Join Lily the cat on an illustrated
family trail to find out how people lived in
the house over 200 years ago. Drawing trail,
handling boxes and dressing up clothes.

### The Herschel Museum of Astronomy

19 New King Street, Bath, BA1 2BL
01225 446865, www.bath-preservation-trust.org.uk
Feb- Mid Dec: Week Days: 1pm-5pm, (closed on
Wednesdays), Sat-Sun 11am-5pm
£4 adult, £2.50 child, £10 family (2+2), free U5's

For budding young astronomers. It was the
home of William Herschel, who discovered the
planet Uranus in 1781. An auditorium shows
programmes on space travel and astromany.
Follow the family trail with Sirius the dog star,
or an audio guide. Part of Spaced Out UK, a
large scale model of the solar system built
across the UK with fantastic sculptures.

## Museum in the Park

Stratford Park, Stratford Road, G loucestershire, GL5
4AF
01453 763394, www.museuminthepark.org.uk
Apr-Sep: Tues - Fri 10am-5pm, Sat &Sun 11am-5pm,
B/H's 11am-5pm. Closed Good Friday. Open every
day in Aug.
Oct-Mar: Tues - Fri 10am-4pm, Sat & Sun 11am-
4pm.
Admission FREE
M5 J13, A419 follow signs to Stratford Park.

Set in beautiful parkland, this family-oriented
museum has plenty for all ages with colourful
interactive displays. Displays include local
history and a room devoted to childhood over
the years. There are quiz trails for children.
Free car parking at Stratford Park Leisure
Centre (café, indoor and outdoor pools). See
website for the many Holiday Events.

## Gloucester Folk Museum

99-103 Westgate Street, Gloucester, GL1 2PG
01452 396 868
www.gloucester.gov.uk
Tue-Sat 10am-5pm
Admission FREE

Child-friendly museum of social history, with
a wide variety of holiday activities. In the
Toy Gallery there is a wendy house, a puppet
theatre and toy cupboard. The portal ICT
gallery has quizzes for all ages. There are toys
in the garden which has farm animals in the
summer. Free half-term and holiday activities,
and free kids club Sat 11-3pm.

## National Waterways Museum

Llanthony Warehouse, Gloucester Docks, GL1 2EH
01452 318200
www.nwm.org.uk/gloucester/
Apr - Oct: 10am-5pm daily. Nov - Mar: 11am-4pm
Sat & Sun only.
£3.95 adult, £2.75 child, £12 family, U5's free
M5 J12 follow brown tourist signs to Historic Docks.

This award-winning museum is housed in a
listed Victorian warehouse within the historic
Gloucester Docks. Newly reopened in May
2008 it features a new exhibition - Water
Lives. Exhibits range from touch-screen
computers to interactive pulleys, to portray
the history of canals and rivers in a hands-on
way. Outside, you can watch a blacksmith at
work or board historic boats. Regular holiday
activities - see website or phone for futher
details.

### Queen Boadicea II

01452 318227
www.nwm.org.uk/boatside

gloucestercruises.org.uk/dailytrips.html
From Easter to Oct: 12pm-4pm
Sailings at 12 noon, 1.30pm and 2.30pm (during
peak times - weekends June-Aug & school summer
holidays).
For museum visitors: entrance fee includes boat trip.
For non museum visitors: £4.75 adult, £3.50 child,
U5's FREE, £15 family (2+2)

You can board the boat at either the museum
(combined boat and museum tickets available)
or at Merchants Quay in Gloucester Docks.
Trip lasts 45 minutes.

## Nature in Art

Wallsworth Hall, Main A38 Twigworth, GL2 9PA
01452 731422, www.nature-in-art.org.uk
Tue-Sun & B/H's 10am-5pm
£4.50 adult, £4 child, U8's FREE £13 family (2+2)
M5 J11A, take A417 and A40 to A38 north. Brown/
green sign at entrance
Bus: Bus no.71 from Gloucester bus station.

This museum is full of art inspired by nature.
Sculptures, tapestries, ceramics and paintings.
There is an activity room with jigsaws and
brass rubbings. Handling boxes in some of
the galleries. Half day activities run during
school holidays - see website. These need
to be booked in advance, U8's must be
accompanied by an adult. Coffee shop selling
hot and cold meals and snacks.

## Cheltenham Art Gallery and Museum

Clarence Street, Cheltenham, GL50 3JT
01242 237431, www.cheltenhammuseum.org.uk
Apr-Oct: daily 10am-5pm. Nov-Mar 10am-4pm,
(except 1st Thur every month opens at 11am & 3rd
Thur of each month open until 8pm). FREE

The collections relate to the Arts and Crafts
Movement with fine examples of furniture,
silver, jewellery, ceramics and textiles. Other
displays include oriental art, a history of
Cheltenham, sparkling costume accessories,
archaeology and natural history. Discovery
trails and handling tables for all ages, and
activities and colouring sheets for U5's.
Regular children's actvitiy events.

## Dean Heritage Centre

Soudley, Cinderford, Gloucestershire, GL14 2UB
01594 824024, www.deanheritagemuseum.com
Mar-Oct: 10am-5pm, Nov-Feb 10am-4pm.
£5.40 adult, £2.75 child, £15.40 family (2+4), free
U5's
B4227 between Blakeney and Cinderford.

History of the forest and its people in this
newly refurbished museum. Children can take
woodblock rubbings of forest scenes. In the
grounds there is a reconstructed Victorian
foresters cottage with Gloucester Old Spot pig
and chickens. Adventure playground with a
hurdle maze and a BBQ area. Some woodland
walks from here are accessible by pushchair
and wheelchair. A deck at the café overlooks
the millpond with working waterwheel. 61

## Hopewell Colliery Museum

Cannop Hill, Coleford, GL16 7EL
01594 810706
Mar-Oct: daily 10am-4.00, £3.50 adult, £2.50 child
On B4226 Cinderford to Coleford road, a mile west
of Beechenhurst Lodge.

Local miners will take you underground to
show you around the old mine workings
(45min trip). The descent into the mine is
steep (as is the exit) but the route through
it is level (just over ½ mile). Not suitable
for pushchairs or back-carriers, children of
walking age are welcome and will be kitted
out with safety helmets and lamps. Practical
footwear and warm clothing recommended.
There's a tea room, picnic and play area and
narrow gauge railway.

## National Museum and Gallery

Cathays Park, Cardiff, CF10 3NP
029 2039 7951, www.nmgw.ac.uk
Tues-Sun 10am-5pm & B/H's
Admission FREE
Follow signs to Cardiff city centre, nr to University.

Superb range of art (best collection of
Impressionists in Europe outside Paris),
natural history and science. Exhibitions on the
evolution of Wales, with life size dinosaurs
and Ice Age creatures. The Glanely Gallery is
an interactive area enabling children to touch
items not normally on display. Steps up to the
main entrance, sloped access at side gate.
Restaurant and coffee shop. Lots of children's
events.

## Techniquest

Stuart Street, Cardiff, CF10 5BW
029 2047 5475, www.techniquest.org
Mon-Fri 9.30am-4.30pm, Sat-Sun and B/Hols
10.30am-5pm, School Hols 9.30am-5pm.
£6.90 adult, £4.80 child, £20 family (2+3), free U4's,
Annual Family: £47. Planetarium show: £1.20 extra
per person

On the waterfront, this large Science
Discovery Centre for children has over 150
hands-on exhibits. There is an interactive
Science Theatre Show and Planetarium. For
younger children there are curiousity boxes
in the Discovery Room. Regular events for
children in holidays.

## St Fagan's Museum

St Fagans, Cardiff, CF5 6XB
029 2057 3500, www.nmgw.ac.uk
Daily 10am-5pm, Admission FREE. Car parking:
£2.50.
4 miles west of Cardiff city centre, just off A4232.
M4 J33, follow tourist signs, bus from city centre.

A village chronicling the history of Wales. A
whole day is needed to see everything. Over
40 buildings have been transported here
from all over Wales and rebuilt in attractive
parkland. They give a fascinating insight into
how people lived, worked and spent their
leisure time over the past 500 years. Children
will enjoy comparing a row of ironworker's
houses each furnished from a different
decade, sitting in a Victorian classroom and
seeing traditional crafts. Also a large indoor
museum, and a variety of places to eat. Wide
variety of regular children's events.

# STATELY HOMES

## Bowood House & Gardens

Derry Hill, Calne, Wiltshire, SN11 0L2
01249 812102, www.bowood-house.co.uk
Mar-Nov, daily:
House - 11am-5.30pm, Grounds - 11am-6pm, Coffee
Shop 11am-5:15pm, house restaurant 12:30pm-
2:30pm & rhodedendron walks 11am-6pm.
House & gardens: £8.40 adult, £6.85, child (5-15yrs)
£4.75 child (2-4yrs), FREE U2's, £26 family (2+2)
Season tickets available.
Off A4, Derry Hill village, midway between Calne and
Chippenham

Capability Brown designed the beautiful park
in which Bowood stands. The huge grounds
include a lake, waterfall, cave, Doric temple
and ample space for games and picnics. More
formal gardens can be found in front of the
stately home itself, which contains displays of
furniture, art, costumes and family heirlooms.
There is also a woodland garden of azaleas
and rhododendrons (separate entrance off
the A342) which is open for 6 wks during the
flowering season (May and June).

Bowood has a superb outdoor adventure
playground for children under 12 with a life-
size pirate ship, high level rope-walks, giant
slides, shutes, trampolines and an indoor soft
play palace for younger children.

## Owlpen Manor

Nr Uley, Gloucestershire, GL11 5BZ
01453 860261, www.owlpen.com
May-Sep, Tue/Thu & Sun, (closed B/H's).
House 2pm-5pm
Restaurant & gardens 12-5pm
£5.75 adults, £2.75 child (4-14yrs), £15.50 family
Gardens & grounds £3.75 adults, £1.75 child
1 mile east of Uley, off B4066 Dursley-Stroud road.

A romantic Tudor manor house with formal
terraced yew gardens set in a beautiful
Cotswolds valley. Contains family portraits and
collections, 17th-century wall hangings and
Cotswold Arts and Crafts furniture. Grounds
include medieval buildings, a mill pond
and early Georgian mill. The Cyder House
Restaurant offers light lunches and cream teas
(as well as formal dinners).

# NATIONAL TRUST PROPERTIES

www.nationaltrust.org.uk
01985 843600 (Wessex branch)

National Trust properties are becoming
increasingly child friendly, with many making
provision for baby changing, feeding and
transportation requirements. Often, trails, quiz
sheets and activities are on offer for older
children. The website (see above) is superb,
making planning a day out effortless.

## Clevedon Court

Tickenham Rd, Clevedon, N. Somerset, BS21 6QU
01275 872257, www.nationaltrust.org.uk
Apr-Sep: Wed/Thu/Sun & B/H mondays 2pm-5pm.
£6.30 adult, £3 child, FREE U5's (prices include gift
aid donation).
B3130 1½ mile east of Clevedon. Signposted from
M5, exit J20. Bus access: First 364 Bristol-Clevedon.

This 14th-century manor house has been
home to the Elton family since 1709.
Eltonware pots and vases and a collection
of Nailsea glass are on display. Attractive
terraced garden — not suitable for buggies
but lovely slopes for rolling down. Children's
guidebook and nursery rhyme trail available.

## Dyrham Park

Dyrham, nr. Chippenham, Gloucestershire, SN14 8ER
0117 937 2501, www.nationaltrust.org.uk
Park: 14th Mar-1st Nov: daily 11am-5.30pm
House: Mon-Tue, Fri-Sun 11-5pm
Garden: 28 Feb- 8 Mar Sat & sun 11am-5pm,.14
Mar-30 June Mon, Tue, Fri-Sun 11am-5pm. 1 Jul- 30
Aug daily 11am-5pm. 31 Aug- 1 Nov Mon, Tue, Fri-
Sun 11am-4pm. 7 Nov-20 Dec Sat & Sun 11am-4pm.
Garden and house: £10.50 adult, £5.25 child, £26.25
family (2+3)
Garden and Park: £4.20 adult, £2.10 child, £9.35
family, FREE U5's
M4 J18, take A46 towards Bath for 2 miles.
Bus access: Special link from Queens Square, Bath.

House and gardens built at the turn of
the 18th century, with most of the original
furnishings. Family activity pack and children's
guidebook available. No prams in house;
baby slings and hip-carrying infant seats
for loan. Spacious grounds and deer park.
Family activity days - see website or phone for
further details.

## Lacock Abbey, Fox Talbot Museum & Village

Lacock, Nr Chippenham, Wiltshire, SN15 2LG
01249 730459, www.nationaltrust.org.uk/lacock
Museum, cloisters and garden:
23 Feb-1 Nov 11am-5:30pm daily. 7 Nov-20 Dec
11am-4pm Sat & Sun. 2-31 Jan 11am-4pm Sat/Sun.
Grounds and cloisters:
28 Feb - 1 Nov - Daily 11am-5:30pm.
Abbey: 14 Mar-1 Nov Mon, Thurs-Sun 11am-5pm.
Abbey, museum, cloisters and garden:
£10.50 adult, £5.30 child, £26.30 family (2+3),
FREE U5's. Other ticket variations available
M4 J17, take A350, 3 miles S of Chippenham
Bus access: Faresaver 73 Melksham-Corsham- First
234 Chippenham-Frome.

The Abbey was founded in 1232 as a nunnery and transformed into a family home in the 16th century. Children's quiz and spacious grounds to explore. Front-carrying baby slings for loan. The Museum of Photography commemorates the life of William Henry Fox Talbot who made the earliest known photographic negative. The upper gallery has changing exhibitions. The medieval village with its many lime washed half-timbered houses has been used as a location for several period dramas such as Pride and Prejudice. The Abbey was also used to film parts of the Harry Potter films. There is a small children's play area opposite the museum and lots of places to eat in the village.

## Newark Park

Ozleworth, Wotton-under-Edge, GL12 7PZ
01793 817666, www.nationaltrust.org.uk
4 Mar-28 May 11am-5pm Wed & Thu. 3 Jun-1 Nov
11am-5pm Wed, thu, Sat & Sun.
£5.90 adult, £2.95 children, £15.25 family
By road: 1 1/2 ml E of Wotton-Under-Edge, 1 3/4
ml S of junctions A4135 & B4059, follow signs for
Ozleworth. House sign posted from main road.
Bus: First 309, 310 Bristol-Dursley, alight Wotton-
Under-Edge, 1 3/4 ml.

National Trust property, high on a limestone cliff, with far-reaching views. It started life as a hunting lodge in the 1550s. Disabled and buggy access only on ground floor. You can stroll in the deer park and gardens, or follow a longer circular walk through the Lower Lodge Woods, see **Walks, Woods & Nature Reserves**.

## Tyntesfield

Wraxall, North Somerset, BS48 1NT
0844 800 4966 (info line)
01275 461 900
House/chapel Mar-Nov Sat-Weds, 11am-5pm
Gardens Mar-Nov Sat-Weds, 10.30am-5.30pm
House, chapel and gardens: £9.45 adult, £4.75 child,
£23.60 family (2+3)
Gardens only: £4.75 adult, £2.35 child, £11.90 family
7 miles SW of Bristol on B3128.

Spectacular Victorian Gothic-Revival country house and 500-acre estate, recently acquired by the National Trust. Situated on a ridge overlooking the beautiful Yeo Valley, the mansion bristles with towers and turrets and contains an unrivalled collection of Victorian decorative arts. There are quiz trails for over 8's and more provision for younger children is planned. Pre-booked guided tours are available. Timed tickets in operation (no guaranteed entry on very busy days). No buggies or back packs are allowed in the house, but there is free loan of hipster carriers. There's a private chapel, formal gardens and a working walled kitchen garden. If you forget your picnic, there is a kiosk for hot drinks and sandwiches. Occasional theatre productions held in the grounds. See **Children's Theatre**.

## Woodchester Park Mansion

Nympsfield, Stroud, Gloucestershire, GL10 3TS
01452 814213 park
01453 861541 mansion
www.woodchestermansion.org.uk
Mansion: Sat-Sun & b/hs 11am-4pm (last entry).
Opening times/days vary throughout the year - see
website/phone for latest details.
£5.50 adults, children under 14 FREE
Nympsfield Rd 300m from the junction with he
B4066 Uley-Stroud. Car park is a mile from the
mansion, with regular free bus transfer on open
days.

National Trust-owned park in a secluded Cotswold valley with trails through scenic woodland, parkland and around lakes. The Mansion, a Grade 1 listed building, was built in the 19th-century in the French Gothic revival style but never finished. It is rumoured to be haunted. Rare bats use the roof spaces in summer. See them from the observatory or join a bat-watching evening. Tea rooms.

# SEVERN ADVENTURES

The Severn Estuary has the second highest tidal range in the world — it can be as much as 50 feet. This contributes to the great natural spectacle of the Severn Bore, details below. The estuary itself can be explored by steamships Waverly and Balmoral, see Beaches and Travelling Around. Flat Holm and Steep Holm, the two islands between Cardiff and Weston-super-Mare, are wildlife havens with fascinating histories and well worth visiting (over 5's only).

Although there's no pedestrian access to the new Severn Crossing you can still walk or cycle across the old bridge away from the traffic (park at Aust Services off J1 M48).

## Severn Bridges Visitor Centre

Shaft Rd, Off Green Lane, Severn Beach, BS35 4NQ
01454 633511
www.severnbridgesvisitorcentre.org.uk
M5 J17 take B4055 through Pilning. Continue straight on. At mini-r'about follow Green Lane over M49. Right at lights into Shaft Rd.

Educational exhibition showing the history of the River Severn crossing and the construction of the two road bridges. The centre is moving to Wales (see website) but car parking is still available for walks along the estuary.

## The Severn Bore

www.severn-bore.co.uk

The Severn Bore is a large surge wave in the estuary of the River Severn which makes a truly spectacular sight at its best. It occurs because of the shape of the estuary — it narrows from 5 miles wide at Avonmouth, to less than 100 yards wide by Minsterworth. As the water is funnelled into an increasingly narrow channel, a large wave is formed. This occurs at least once during most months of the year, but the Bore is largest around equinoxes. Surfing the Bore has become a competitive sport. See website for timetable and viewing points. Get there early, as the Bore can arrive up to half an hour either side of the scheduled time.

# ROMAN BRITAIN

There are several Roman sites near Bristol that are worth a visit. Take notes for that primary school project down the line.

## Chedworth Roman Villa

Yanworth, Near Cheltenham, Glos, GL54 3LJ
01242 890256, www.nationaltrust.org.uk
chedworth@nationaltrust.org.uk
Mar-Nov: Tue-Sun & B/H's 10am-5pm, (10am-4pm winter).
£6.65 adult, £3.90 child, £17.50 family (2+3), FREE U5's
M5 J11A take A417 east, A436 then right via Withington, follow signs.

Owned by the National Trust, this is one of the best examples of a Roman Villa in England. The remains of this substantial dwelling indicate that it would have been inhabited by a very wealthy family. There are two well-preserved bathhouses, hypocausts demonstrating how the Roman invention of under-floor heating worked, beautiful mosaics, a latrine, and a museum housing objects from the villa. Entertaining audio guide for children, 6+yrs. If you can, coincide your visit with one of the Living History Days where you can join in with demonstrations of day-to-day Roman life. Children's activities during the holidays. Pushchairs are admitted but there are some steps. There are good walks in Chedworth Woods and along the disused railway track.

## National Roman Legion Museum

High Street, Caerleon, Newport, NP18 1AE
01633 423134, www.nmgw.ac.uk
Museum: Mon-Sat 10am-5pm, Sun 2pm-5pm
Fortress baths: Mon-Sat 9.30am-5pm
FREE admission
Museum, Barracks and Amphitheatre: £2.90 adult, £2.50 child, £8.30 family (2+3)
M4 J24 follow signs to Caerleon and Museum.

Nearly 2000 years ago, the Romans established a fortress at Caerleon. In the museum you can discover how the Roman soldiers lived, fought, and worshipped. At weekends and during the holidays, a barrack room can be visited where you can try on replica suits of armour and take part in the daily activities of a soldier. Also the remains of the Fortress Baths, with video, sound and light displays. A short walk from the museum is Britain's best example of a Roman Amphitheatre where gladiators battled to the death. Impressive re-enactments are held here every June (ring 01633 423134) - see below.

### Caerwent
10 miles from Caerleon on the A48 or from Bristol M4 then M48 J2

Having visited the museum at Caerleon you could stop off at the wonderfully-preserved town of Caerwent where the remains of shops, a courtyard house, temple and forum can be seen. In the 4th century, when the Romans were struggling to retain power, a high wall was built around the town, most of which still stands today.

## Roman Baths and Pump Room
Pump Room, Stall Street, Bath, BA1 1LZ
01225 477 785, www.romanbaths.co.uk
Jan-Feb 9:30am-4:30pm (exit 5:30pm). Mar-June 9am-5pm (exit 6pm). July-Aug 9am-9pm, (exit 10pm). Sep-Oct 9am-5pm (exit 6pm). Nov-Dec 9:30am-4:30pm (exit 5:30pm).
From £11 adult, £7.20 child, U6's free, £30 family (2+4) Combined tickets to museum and Roman Baths are good value and valid for 7 days, approx £14.50 adult, £8.70 child, £40 family (4+4).

One of the best preserved Roman sites in Northern Europe, this spa is a fine example of ancient engineering. The spring produces over a million litres of hot water a day. Taste it for yourself! Children's audioguide available. Unsuitable for pushchairs but back packs available.

# WHEELS & WINGS
Many children go through a stage of being fascinated with transport, be it wheeled or winged. Most of the places listed below all display the life-sized article. However, if you fancy something smaller, there's Bourton Model Railway, and for the hands-on approach try Diggerland, see Just for Fun.

## Bourton Model Railway
Box Bush, High Street, Bourton-on-the-Water, GL54
01451 820686, www.bourtonmodelrailway.co.uk
Apr-Sep: daily 11am-5pm
£2.50 adult, £2 child, £7.50 family (2+2)
Oct-Mar: Sat-Sun 11am-5pm only
Limited opening in Jan

Over 500 sq ft of scenic model railway layouts. 40 British and continental trains run through realistic and detailed scenery; some are interactive. There is a well-stocked model and toy shop, with extended opening hours.

## Cotswold Motoring Museum and Toy Collection
The Old Mill, Bourton-on-the-Water, Glos, GL54 2BY
01451 821 255, www.cotswold-motor-museum.com
Feb-Oct: daily 10am-6pm
£3.80 adult, £2.60 child, £11.50 family (2+2), FREE U4's
Located off A40, on A429 between Cirencester & Stow.

Impressive car collection dating back to the 1920s, and the museum has lots of other transport memorabilia including over 800 enamel signs. Also includes a big toy collection (including children's pedal cars and dinky toys), a workshop based on a 1920s village garage, a blacksmith's and this is also where Brum the little car lives. Children's quizzes, puzzles and jigsaws.

## Haynes Motor Museum
Sparkford, Nr Yeovil, Somerset, BA22 7LH
01963 440804, www.haynesmotormuseum.co.uk
Daily 9.30am-5.30pm
£7.50 adult, £4 child, £9.50-£22 family, FREE U5's
M5 J25 then A358 & A303 to Sparkford. Or A37 south to A303.

If you've got a car fanatic in your household,

Britain's most extensive car collection on permanent display should keep them happy, although it is more look than touch. Hundreds of cars, ranging from the Chevrolet Corvette to the Sinclair C5. There is also a Hall of Motor Sport, motorbike display, a bus full of soft play equipment (open sch summer hols), an indoor children's activity centre and a themed outdoor play area.

## STEAM

Kemble Drive, Swindon, SN2 2TA
01793 466646, www.steam-museum.org.uk
Daily 10am-5pm
£6.40 adult, £4.25 child, £17(family 2+2), £20.20 (family 2+3). FREE U3's
M4 J16, follow signs to Outlet Centre.

The Museum of the Great Western Railway gives you an idea of what it was like to work on and use the GWR with lots of hands-on exhibits. Reconstructed platforms, a cab simulator, and family activities during the school holidays. Special appearances by Thomas the Tank Engine and engines in steam, help bring history to life.

## The Helicopter Museum

Locking Moor Road, Weston-super-Mare, BS24 8PP
01934 635 227, www.helicoptermuseum.co.uk
Wed-Sun, Apr-Oct 10am-5:30pm, Nov-Mar 10am-4:30pm, 18July-31 Aug 10am-5:30pm.
£5.50 adult, £3.50 child, £15.50 family (2+2), £17.50 (2+3).
M5 J21, on the A368/A371, follow signs.

The world's largest dedicated helicopter museum housing the world's oldest, fastest and ugliest helicopters! Themed play area. Special events include Helicopter Experience Flights and the annual Heliday (usually the last weekend in July), a static helicopter display on Beach Lawns, the seafront. This features civil and military helicopters and pleasure flights from the beach.

## Fleet Air Arm Museum

RNAS Yeovilton, Ilchester, Somerset, BA22 8HT
01935 840565, www.fleetairarm.com
Apr-Oct: daily 10am-5.30pm, (last entry 4pm).
Nov-Mar: Wed-Sun, 10am-4:30pm, (last entry 3pm).
£11 adult, £8 child (5-16), £35 family (2+3), FREE U5's
Take the A37 south of Bristol (50mins). Located on the B3151 just off A303 & A37.

Displaying the largest collection of Naval aircraft in Europe, this museum will appeal to children, especially if they are aircraft-enthusiast toddlers. Follow the development of British aircraft from wooden bi-planes through to Concorde. You can sit in the cockpit of a jet fighter, or even experience life aboard an aircraft carrier, arriving on the flight deck via a simulated helicopter ride. Being next to the air base, there's a good chance of seeing Sea Harriers and helicopters going through their manoeuvres outside. There is also a children's adventure playground, restaurant and shop.

## RNAS Yeovilton Airday

www.yeoviltonairday.co.uk

Entertainment on the ground as well as flying displays at this annual event.

## Royal International Air Tattoo

RAF Fairford, Gloucestershire, GL7 4NA
01285 713 456
www.airtattoo.com
M4 J15, follow signs

This fascinating, huge aircraft fest takes place annually at RAF Fairford in mid July.

# JUST FOR FUN

## Boomerang

The Outback, Merlin Way, Bowerhill, Melksham,
Wiltshire, SN12 6TJ
01225 702000, www.boomeranguk.co.uk
Daily: Mon-Fri 9am-6pm, Sat & Sun 10am-6pm.
Unlimited play time (1.5hr restriction when full)
Prices from 75p-£4.20, call for peak times & pricing
M4 J17, A350 to Melksham then follow signs for
Bowerhill & Sports Centre.

Huge area of softplay equipment for U11's
or 1.5m offering unlimited playtime when
not full. Separate room for U1's with activity
centres, play mats, bottle warmers etc.

## Diggerland

Verbeer Manor, Cullompton, Devon, EX15 2PE
08700 344437, www.diggerland.com
Opening times vary throughout year (phone or see
website for latest details).
£15 pp (3yrs-65), FREE U3's. Online booking.
Buy credits for riding/driving motorised diggers
M5 J27 take A38 east, follow signs for 3 miles

Large adventure park. Children and adults
can ride in and drive different types of
construction machinery including dumper
trucks and diggers, all under strict
supervision. Age limits apply. Other attractions
include pedal power diggers, digger sandpit,
bouncy castle and play area.

## Fundays Playbarn

Unit 8, Willow Court, Bourton-on-the-Water
Industrial Park, Gloucestershire, GL54 2HQ
01451 822999, www.fundaysplaybarn.com
Daily 10am-6pm, B/H's 10.30am-5pm
Hols & w/e's £1 adult, from £3.50 child (1-3yrs) £4
child (4-12yrs) £1.25 (U1's)
A429 north of Bourton, sign on right after Coach &
Horses pub.

Large indoor playbarn for under 12's.
Separate toddler zone. Outdoor area open in
the summer with go-carts and giant chess.

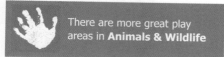
There are more great play
areas in **Animals & Wildlife**

## Magicland

Meadow Rd, Circencester, Glos, GL7 1YA
01285 885570, www.magicland.co.uk
Daily 10am-6pm
Peak/off-peak: £1/50p adults, £4.75/£2.50 child
5-12yrs, £3.75/£2 child 1-4yrs, FREE U1's

Magicland offers a 13,000sq foot arena
containing soft play structures, slides, a
70ft astra slide and cannon arena. This area
contains four pneumatically powered cannons
that allow you to shoot foam balls at various
targets including other visitors! There are safe
toddler areas, a five-a-side football pitch and
café overlooking the play area.

## Puxton Park

Cowslip Lane, Hewish, W-S-M, BS24 6AH
01934 523500, www.puxton.co.uk
Daily 9am-5:30pm summer (varies during winter).
£7.50 adult, £6.50 4-16 years, U3's FREE, Family
(2+2) £25. (Annual membership available).
Puxton Park has fast established itself as
one of the West's big attractions. Both
functional and fun, Puxton combines a large
well supervised indoor play area with the
chance to purchase locally produced food
from its Farm Shop. It has two restaurants;
the informal 'Cow Shed Cafe', which serves
snacks, cakes and drinks, and the 'Meadows
Restaurant' , a more formal affair. Both make
use of the produce available in the farm shop.

# Travelling Around Bristol & The West

## Contents

Remember to cross reference with the other chapters if you are planning a big day out.

## Summer Events

Many of the places listed in this Section have Summer (and Winter) Events. We have mentioned some of these, but check out: www.titchhikers.co.uk for times & dates

'Getting there' can be part of the fun and with this in mind we include in this chapter bus, rail and cycle details. One feature of the local travel scene reflected in the chapter is the increasing emphasis being placed on cycling. Bristol became the first Cycling City in 2008, and there are many good reasons, to do with health, environment, enjoyment and choice, why parents and carers may decide to join the growing number of regular cyclists.

## Useful Websites & Contacts

**www.travelbristol.org, 0117 903 6701**
An excellent site with all you need to know about travelling around Bristol.

**www.visitbristol.co.uk**

**www.bristol.gov.uk, 0117 903 6701**

**www.transportdirect.info**

**www.traveline.org.uk, 0871 2002233**
(Public transport information)

# Railways for Pleasure

## Ashton Court Estate Minature Steam Railway

Nr Clifton Lodge, BS8 3PX
0117 946 7110
www.bristolmodelengineers.co.uk
Enter through Clifton Lodge on A369, turn right, then right again
Apr-mid Oct: Suns & some Mons 12-17.15
Phone for passenger services prior to visiting
60p 1 circuit, 10 circuits for £5

Sit astride trains on track ½ mile long. Ramps and footbridges for pushchairs are by the ticket office. Toilets at the golf café.

## Avon Valley Railway

Bitton Station, Willsbridge, BS30 6HD
0117 932 7296 talking timetable
0117 932 5538 general enquiries
www.avonvalleyrailway.co.uk
Varying timetable throughout year with many special events. See website or phone for more details
From £6 adult, £4.50 child (U3's free), £15 family (2+2)

Fare allows unlimited travel on day of issue (except special events). This line runs along the former Mangotsfield to Bath Green Park branch of the old Midland Railway. There are links to boat trips; see 'Boats, Ferries and Canoes' later in this chapter. Many special days throughout the year including Thomas Days (May and Oct), Teddy Bears Picnics, and Santa Specials. Also see **Walks, Woods & Nature Reserves** for information about walks accessible from the Avon Valley Railway.

## Bristol Harbour Railway

Princes Wharf, Wapping Rd, Bristol, BS1 4RN
0117 922 3571
www.bristol.gov.uk
Mar-Nov selected w/e's & B/H's every 40 mins between 11am-5pm
£3 rtn, £2 single, U6's FREE

This train steams along the dockside from the ss Great Britain. Locally built engines (Henbury or Portbury) pull the wagons which once ran at the Avonmouth Docks.

Check out YouTube where there are lots of films of Bristol Harbour Railway!

## Bristol Severn Beach Line

www.firstgreatwestern.co.uk, 08457 000 125
Day returns from about £3 (under 5's free)

The Bristol to Severn Beach railway line runs from Temple Meads to the Avonmouth and Severn Beach, via 9 local stations and passing through the Avon Gorge and the mile-long tunnel under Clifton Down. It has been described as one of the most scenic lines in Europe.

The line is divided into three ticket zones comprising of:

Inner Zone: Bristol Temple Meads - Clifton Down

Outer Zone: Clifton Down - Severn Beach

Line Zone: all stations from Bristol Temple Meads to Severn Beach

Each zone carries a different flat rate train fare, and you only pay for the zone you're travelling in.

SUPPORT THE
severn beach li

## Dean Forest Railway

Norchard Railway Centre, Lydney, Gloucestershire
01594 843423 information line
01594 845840 enquiries
www.deanforestrailway.co.uk
M4, M48 Chepstow, Norchard is on B4234 just north of Lydney (Accessible by train and bus)
Varying timetable throughout the year with many special events. See website or phone for more details
From £10 adult, £5 child, £28 family (2+2), U5's free

This line runs from Norchard to Lydney Junction, then on to Parkend. Special timetabled events throughout the year including Thomas and Santa Specials. Booking essential. Other attractions include riverside walks, boating lake, park, Railway Museum, café in classic restaurant coach open on Steam Days. Pushchairs can be taken on the trains (preferable to have folding pushchair as needs to be stored in guard's compartment if open) or stored in the station building. Visitors with wheelchairs can be catered for but call enquiry line above if there are any particular concerns. There are no toilets on the trains. Baby changing at Norchard Station.

## East Somerset Railway

Cranmore Railway Station, Shepton Mallet, BA4 4QP
01749 880417, www.eastsomersetrailway.com
Signposted off A361 between Shepton Mallet & Frome.
Ticket Office & shop: 10am-5pm on operating
days. Apr-Sep: w/e's & some weekdays. Oct-Mar:
occasional service. Call or see website for timetable.
Returns from: £7.50 adult, £5.50 child (U3's free),
£22 family (2+2)

Just over 20 miles from Bristol. A round trip
of 35 minutes between Cranmore Station and
Mendip Vale Station. Cafe can be found in
the ground level of the main station building
at Cranmore, and serves a wide range of
hot and cold refreshments and meals on all
operating days. Children's playground, picnic
area and toilets are also found at Cranmore.
Special events include Thomas, Easter event,
and Santa Special - booking recommended.
The station is pushchair friendly with storage
space on the trains.

## Gloucestershire and Warwickshire Railway

The Railway Station, Toddington, Glos, GL54 5DT
01242 621405, www.gwsr.com
M5 Jct 9, A46, B4077 junction with B4632
Open most w/e's Apr-Dec plus select other openings.
Phone or see website for full timetable. £11 adult,
£6.50 child, U5's free, £30 family (2+3)

Fare allows unlimited travel on day of issue.
The railway operates a round trip of 20 miles
from Toddington to Cheltenham Race Course
station with a brief stop along the way at
Winchcombe. The line passses through the
beautiful Cotswold hills and you will have views
over the Vale of Evesham to the Malvern Hills
beyond. Special events throughout the year
such as visits from Postman Pat, Fireman Sam,
and Santa Specials.

## Perrygrove Railway

Coleford, Forest of Dean, Glos, GL16 8QB
01594 834991, www.perrygrove.co.uk
April-Dec, w/e's, every day in school Summer Holiday
From £4.95 adults, £3.95 child, Free U3's, £16.80 family
(2 + 2) (no credit cards). Unlimited travel on day of issue.
½ mile south of Coleford on B4228, nearest mainline
railway station Lydney

Narrow gauge railway runs through farm and
woodland for a 1½ mile return trip. Visitors
also able to walk through the woods (with
pushchairs), explore the indoor village and
secret passages, and take part in an optional
treasure hunt (£1.80). Birthday parties
welcome. Café available, picnics encouraged.

## West Somerset Railway

The Railway Station, Minehead, Somerset, TA24 5BG
01643 707650 talking timetable
01643 704996 general enquiries
www.west-somerset-railway.co.uk
Trains run all year but variable timetable.
Wide range of fares depending on journey length.
Free U5's. Phone for full timetable & fares. Tesco
Clubcard tokens can be used to buy tickets
M5 Jct 25, brown tourist signs to Bishops Lydeard

The train line runs for 20 miles between
Bishop's Lydeard and Minehead along the
coast and Quantock Hills. Ten restored
stations along the line have a variety of
signal boxes, museums, displays and steam
and diesel engines to visit. Buffet and toilets
on all regular, timetabled trains. Access for
wheelchairs. Special events include Thomas,
and Steam Gala Days, booking is essential.

## First Great Western

Customer service 0845 7000 125
Train Tracker (live timetables) 0871 200 4950

### Bristol Parkway (BS34)

Ticket office Mon-Fi 5.40am-8pm, Sat 6.50am-6pm,
Sun 8.30am-7pm. Parking 24hrs

Facilities: lifts, disabled access, cycle storage,
self-service ticket machines, shop, café, regular bus
service into Bristol city centre. Ticket office open
Mon-Sat 5am-7pm, Sundays 8am-7pm. Ticket office,
toilets and baby changing located near entrance.

### Temple Meads (BS1)

Booking office Mon-Sat 5.30am-9.30pm, Sun 6.45am-
9.30pm. Short-term parking on station forecourt (20
mins free) longer-term parking (some undercover).

Lifts, baby changing off Ladies', refreshment
outlets platforms 3 & 10, & subway, cycle storage.
WHSmith in main entrance. Shuttle bus operates to
the airport. Regular bus services into around Bristol.

### Tips for families:

FGW often have family carriages and free
activity packs for children (from the buffet
on high speed trains).

If you reserved your tickets online, make sure
you take your reference number for when you
collect them.

# Safe Cycling

## CYCLE ROUTES

### Ashton Court

Long Ashton, BS41 9JN

After passing through the entrance to Ashton Court by the suspension bridge, take the second track on the right (after the road for the golf course). There are numerous trails through the woods but it is very hilly and quite rough.

### Ashton to Pill Cycle Way

Starts from the Create Centre (BS1 6XN) on Cumberland Road, or from Leigh Woods if you take the first right after the Clifton suspension bridge and follow the road for ¾ mile; it is signposted from there. Refreshments can be bought in Pill.

### Bristol and Bath Cycle Way

www.bristolbathrailwaypath.org.uk

A 13-mile route which you can start either from Bristol Bridge or from St Phillips Road, Old Market. Bitton is an interesting place to stop, where there is a steam railway (or start your ride from here, as the route crosses the road **see feature on page 74**). Family friendly pubs along the way include the Bird in Hand and Jolly Sailor on the river at Saltford.

### Forest of Dean Cycle Trail

This is a beautiful area for cycling. There is a popular circular 12-mile family cycle route, with several access points (one being Pedalabikeaway).

### Kennet and Avon Canal Towpath

This goes east out of Bath, starting behind Bath Spa railway station. Three easy access points are: Bradford-on-Avon (station car park); Hilperton Marina (car parking and toilets); and the visitor centre at Devizes Wharf (pay and display). A cycle route with plenty to look at on the canal and several places to stop for food and drink. Besides the aquaducts at Avoncliff and Dundas, the other amazing feat of engineering is the flight locks at Caen, West of Devizes. Canal cycle tracks can be narrow in places, so not suitable for inexperienced cyclists, however they are flat.

## SUSTRANS

2 Cathedral Square, College Green, BS1 5DD, www.sustrans.org.uk, 0845 113 0065

This sustainable transport charity works on practical projects to encourage people to walk, cycle and use public transport in order to reduce motor traffic and its adverse effects. Their main project is the National Cycle Network which currently provides more than 10,000 miles of cycling and walking routes throughout the UK. Maps and free leaflets also available.

**Free cycle maps for Bristol & Somerset** (can be downloaded from www.bristol.gov.uk):

Bristol - 0117 9290440, North Somerset - 01934 888 888, Bath & N.E Somerset - 01225 477000, South Glos - 01454 868686, Whitchurch Railway Path - 0845 1130065

**Other free maps:**

Family Explorer North Somerset - Weston TIC 01934 888800

Avon Cycle Way - www.bristol.gov.uk, 0117 903 6822

## CYCLE HIRE COMPANIES

### Blackboy Hill Cycles

180 Whiteladies Road, Clifton, BS8 2XU
0117 973 1420, www.blackboycycles.co.uk
Mon-Sat 9am-5.30pm, Sun 11am-4pm.

For all things bike; a Bristol institution.

### Bristol Bicycle Hire

Smeaton Rd, adj to Bonded Warehouse,
Cycle Route 41, Hotwells
0117 965 5192, 0780 3651945 (mobile)

Pre-booked bike hire. Children's trailers/seats.

### Ferry Station Bristol

Narrow Quay, BS1 4QA
0117 3763942/0750 0453768
www.ferrystation.co.uk
Mon/Tue 8am-4pm, Wed/Thur 8am-6pm, Fri 8am-11pm, Sat 10am-11pm, Sun 10am-6pm

Infant seats and child bikes available.

### Forest of Dean Cycle Hire

Pedalabikeaway Cycle Centre, Colliery Offices,
Cannop Valley, near Coleford, GL16 7EH
01594 860065, www.pedalabikeaway.com
Jan-Dec every day except Mon, and Jul, Aug, school
hols when open every day. Apr-Oct 9am-6pm,
Nov-Mar 9am-5pm. Hourly, daily & family rates.
Bikes & facilities for disabled.

This friendly shop is situated on the 12-mile circular family cycle trail, hiring out bikes, buggy and bike trailers. Helmets are free. Their motto is "bikes for everyone", particularly those with special needs. Routes, maps, information, books, parts, accessories and repairs available. Café for hot & cold refreshments.

### Lock Inn Cottage

48 Frome Road, Bradford-on-Avon, Wiltshire, BA15
01225 867187, www.thelockinn.co.uk
Daily 9am-6pm (bikes must be back by 5.30pm)

3hr, day and weekly rates

Here you will find an extensive bike/hire shop and canal-side café, ideally situated on the

Kennet and Avon canal towpath. You can hire (or buy!) all family biking equipment, helmets, seats, trailers etc. Canoes and boats also for hire, see **Boats, Ferries & Canoes**.

### The Bath and Dundas Canal Co.

Brass Knocker Basin, Monkton Combe, Bath, BA2 7JD
01225 722292, www.bathcanal.com
Open daily, 10.30am-5.30pm
Hourly, daily & weekly rates, pre-booking recommended

Situated at the end of the Somerset Coal Canal stretch with easy access to Kennet and Avon. Offers a range of family bikes and accessories to hire. Canoes and boats for hire, see below.

## USEFUL CONTACTS

### Bristol Cycling Campaign

Box No. 60, Booty, 82 Colston St, BS1 5BB
www.bristolcyclingcampaign.org.uk

Cycling information (maps, bike rides etc.), campaigns, and lots more.

### Cycle West

www.cyclewest.co.uk
Information on how to start cycling, cycle training, where to ride, events, and lots more.

### Life Cycle UK

86 Colston Street, Bristol, BS1 5BB
0117 929 0440, www.lifecycleuk.org.uk

Provides information and advice on cycling with your children. Also runs cycle training courses for 8 + years.

# Bristol & Bath Railway Path

www.bristolbathrailwaypath.org.uk

## What is it?

The Bristol & Bath Railway Path is a 13 mile mainly off road route, winding through the changing scenery between the cities of Bristol and Bath. Although the path is particularly popular with cyclists who use it for both cummuting and leisure, it is also open to walkers.

## How suitable is it for small children?

The whole route is suitable for children but you should keep in mind that there are one or two roads to cross depending on where you access the route (these are signal controlled). A particularly nice section for children is the rural stretch between Bitton Station and Saltford, or if you fancy a slightly longer cycle, access it at Warmley. If you want a more urban cycle, start nearer Bristol Centre. There are a few play areas on the way at St Philips and Kilburn Rd, but there is also a longish tunnel.

## Where can you get refreshments?

Warmley is the first cafe as you travel from Bristol. This serves rolls and chips. Bitton Station has a nice cafe, or you can try one of the pubs in Saltford (you need to leave the track for these).

## How can I find out more?

The website includes excellent maps to download, which list everything that you could need to know en route. You can also ask for a copy of the Railway Path Access Guide which gives detailed information and maps about access points, gradients, steps and more - for people using pushchairs, wheelchairs, mobility scooters or those with other access requirements.

Please note: this booklet is available in hard copy format only.

See also **Eating Out & Travelling Around**

**For further advice on access to the Path for disabled people:**
   * **Bristol City Council: Access Hotline: (0117) 903 6840**
   * **South Gloucestershire Council: (01454) 863640**
   * **Bath and North East Somerset Council, Access Officer: (01225) 477670**

# Tips

- Make sure you take a drink and a snack.
- There's often lots going on at Bitton Station in the Summer so check before you leave.
- If you are travelling with children who are independent cyclists, it's worth explaining about the keeping left on the path rule before you begin (this can be more confusing than you might think but will be appreciated!)

# Boats, ferries, & canoes

## BOAT OR CANOE HIRE

### Bath Boating Station

Forester Rd, Bathwick, Bath, BA2 6QE
01225 312 900
www.bathboating.co.uk
Apr-Oct: daily 10am-6pm
£7 adult/£3.50 child 1st hr, free U5's
Follow A36 through Bath. Just after big roundabout at
Sydney Gardens, Forester Rd is 1st on left

A couple of miles NE of the centre you'll find this Victorian boating station with rowing boats, punts and canoes for hire. Also operate boat trips to Bathampton taking about 1 hour (£8 adult/£4 child, free U5's).

### Canal Narrow Boat Hire

Ever fancied taking a canal boat out yourself for a day or more?

#### Bath Narrow Boats
Bathwick Hill, Bath, BA2 4EL
01225 447276
www.bath-narrowboats.co.uk
Mainly day hire.

#### Sally Boats

01225 864923, www.sallyboats.ltd.uk
Operates out of Bradford-on-Avon.

#### Anglo-Welsh Waterway Holidays
0117 304 1122, www.anglo-welsh.co.uk
Have local bases in Bath & Monkton Combe.

#### Wessex Narrow Boats

www.wessexboats.co.uk
Day hire: 01225 765243. Week hire: 0845 1264098
Open: 9am-5pm. £105-£130 per day.
Located on the Kennet & Avon Canal.

## The Bath & Dundas Canal Co.

Brass Knocker Basin, Monkton Combe, Bath
01225 722292, www.bathcanal.com
Daily 8am-dusk, some seasonal variations
Electric boats from £45 1/2 day, Canadian canoes from
£21 for 1/2 day
Take A36 south of Bath, at Monkton Combe turn left at
lights on to B3108

Hire electric boats (sit 4-12) or canoes (sit 2-4). Need a bicycle as well? See **Cycle Hire**.

## The Lock Inn

48 Frome Rd, Bradford-on-Avon, Wiltshire, BA15 1LE
01225 867187, www.thelockinn.co.uk

Daily 9am-6pm. Canoe Hire: £20 (3 hrs), £30 (9 hrs)

Hire canoes to paddle along the canal from this pleasant spot. The canoes are very safe and easy to use; life jackets are inclusive. Canoes can accommodate two adults and two children. It's easiest to go towards Bath as there are no locks to negotiate (canoes must be caried round) and there are plenty of pubs and tearooms along the way. Pre-booking is advisable as it gets very busy in the summer. Credit/debit card necessary for deposit. Also see **Cycle Hire**.

*There are no locks on the canal between Bradford-on-Avon and Bath.*

Like boats? Why not make then set sail your own at Brunel's ss Great Britain's annual Dream Boat Event. See page 48.

Dream Boats courtesy of Brunel's ss Great Britain

# BOAT RIDES

## FERRIES

### The Bristol Ferry Boat Company

MB Tempora, Welsh Back, Bristol, BS1 4SP
0117 927 3416, www.bristolferry.com
Daily 10.30am-6.25pm (weekdays start earlier) It is
strongly advised to contact for a timetable.

This friendly company operates a waterbus
service from Hotwells to the City Centre
and from the City Centre to Temple Meads
Station. There are many stops allowing
access to tourist attractions along with cafes,
restaurants and pubs. Chartered trips which
go beyond the harbour to the river and gorge
run Apr-Oct. Discount for ticket holders in
the Ferry Station Cafe (see **Eating Out** and
**Bristol Visitor Attractions**).

### The Hotwells Ferry

Daily 10.30am-6.25pm (weekdays start earlier)
Single from £1.60 adult, £1.30 child,
Return from £2.70 adult, £2.10 child
Round Trip £4.90 adult, £3.30 child, £14 family
(2+2). Other fares available

The Hotwells Ferry is in operation between
Hotwells and the City Centre. The 40 minute
round trip includes the ss Great Britain.

### The Temple Meads Ferry

Daily 10.10am-6.10pm (weekdays start earlier)
Single from £1.60 adult, £1.30 child
Return from £2.70 adult, £2.10 child
Round Trip £4.90 adult, £3.30 child, £14 family
(2+2). Other fares available

Operates between Temple Meads and the City
Centre. This is a 60-minute round trip that
includes the ss Great Britain and Castle Park.

### River Avon Scenic Boat Trips

0117 932 5538, www.avonvalleyrailway.co.uk
Apr-Sep, most Sun, B/H's, & many days throughout
school holidays
From £4.50 adult, £3 child, FREE U5's

Sailings on 'River Princess' to parts
unreachable by other forms of transport.
Toilet facilities and disabled access.

### The Kennet & Avon Canal Trust

www.katrust.org

#### Bath

The Canal Centre, Brassknocker Basin, Limpley
Stoke, Bath
0800 121 4682
End Apr-Oct Sun & B/H's 12pm or 2.30pm
From £6 adult, £3 child, FREE U5's
Off A36 turn at Viaduct Inn traffic lights towards
Limpley Stoke on B3108. After 50 metres turn left
into Visitor Centre car park

Two trips offered. The first (12pm - 2hrs) to
Claverton, Pretty Conkwell Woods and return.
The second (2.30pm - 3hrs15) to Avoncliff
and return. Licenced bar and toilets.

#### Bradford-on-Avon

Bradford-on-Avon, BA15 1LE
01225 868683
End Apr-Oct: w/e's & B/H's & Wed pm
From £5 adult, £4 child, £14 family, free U5's

A relaxing way to see the canal is on this
comfortable narrowboat. Two trips are
offered: past the Tithe Barn to Meadows
Bridge, 1hr (11.30am-12.30pm); to Avoncliff
Aquaduct, 2hrs (2.30pm-4.30pm). Advance
bookings can be made at the Cottage Shop.
Boat leaves from the cottage on Canal Wharf
less than half a mile south of town centre.
Wheelchair lift and toilet on board. See
website for details of many special trips.

### Waverley & Balmoral

0845 130 4647, www.waverleyexcursions.co.uk
May-Sep, range of fares from £14 adult, child half price,
free U5's

Sailings from Clevedon Pier, Bristol and
Weston-super-Mare (also from Minehead,
Ilfracombe, Watchet, Sharpness and
Bridgwater). Cruise in "Big Ship" style aboard
the Waverley, the last sea-going paddle
steamer in the world and the Balmoral,
a traditional pleasure cruise ship. Cruises
around Holm Islands and the coast of Wales.
For full details and timetable contact Waverley
Excursions Ltd directly. Facilities include a self-
service restaurant, fully licensed bar, heated
observation lounges, souvenir shops. One or
two children's cruises every year such as the
Teddy Bears Picnic Cruise.

# ROUTINE DIRECTORY

## First Buses

www.firstgroup.com
(Traveline bus timetable enquiries: 0871 200 2233)

### Bristol Bus Station

Marlborough Street, BS1 3NU
0845 606 4446 (Mon-Sat 8am-5.30pm)
Operating many services throughout the
Bristol area, with ticket offers for all day use:

- FirstDay South West - gives you unlimited travel all day on FirstGroup services in the South West of England (some restrictions apply). £7.50 peak, £6.70 off-peak, £5.50 child, £16 Family (2+3).

- FirstAttraction tickets - combine your fare with your attraction ticket, and get a discount. (15% off Bristol Zoo Gardens).

- Freedom Travelpass - for unlimited travel on bus and rail services in Bristol, Bath, North Somerset, North East Somerset, and South Glos. Buy your Freedom Travelpass from the bus driver on First services, the ticket office at your local staffed train station, or the conductor on board the train if the station is unstaffed. 1 day, 1 week or 1 calendar month-long Freedom Travelpass. A photocard is required for the monthly Freedom Travelpass (08457 000 125).

Purchase tickets at the Travel Bristol Centre (Colston Street), Bristol Bus Station Booking Office or from the driver.

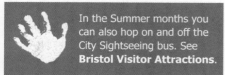

In the Summer months you can also hop on and off the City Sightseeing bus. See **Bristol Visitor Attractions**.

## Airport

### Bristol International Airport

Bristol, BS148 3DY
www.bristolairport.co.uk
0871 334 4444 (general enquiries)
0871 334 4344 (arrivals/departures)

Small, easy to navigate airport.

## National Express

Enquiries & reservations 0871 818181
www.nationalexpress.com, 8am-10pm
Coaches - children under 3 travel free
Trains - children under 5 travel free

Book coaches online. Now possible to also book trains through their website.

## Park & Ride

www.parkandride.net, 0117 922 2910 (office hours)
Leaflet to download from website.

## National Rail

08457 48 49 50, www.nationalrail.co.uk

Also see information under Railways for Pleasure in this chapter.

## Sea Travel

### Brittany Ferries

0871 244 0439, www.brittany-ferries.co.uk
Plymouth to Roscoff and Santander, Poole and Portsmouth to Cherbourg (other routes available)

### Condor Ferries

01202 207216, www.condorferries.co.uk
(Weymouth, Poole, Portsmouth to Guernsey, Jersey, Cherbourg, St Malo - contact for actual routes)

### Irish Ferries

08717 300 400, www.irishferries.co.uk
Pembroke to Rosslare

### Stena Line

08705 70 70 70, www.stenaline.co.uk
Fishguard to Rosslare

Got the urge to have a family time away in the South West? See Family Holidays and Weekends Away

# Animals & Wildlife

## Contents

For a city heavily populated by humans, Bristol has some impressive opportunities to get close to the animal kingdom. Much investment has gone into big regional attractions, like Bristol Zoo and Noah's Ark, and they are superb places to visit time and time again with young children. As are the city farms which aim to meet the needs of local people through their wide range of social, environmental, and educational activities.

### Useful Information:

**Avon Wildlife Trust**

32 Jacobs Well Rd, Bristol, BS8 1DR
0117 917 7270, www.avonwildlifetrust.org.uk

Website includes local events and wildlife walks.

**Royal Society for the Protection of Birds**

The Puffins, New Road, Parkend, Lydney, GL15 4JA
01767 680551, www.rspb.org.uk

Excellent website including kids section.

Summer Events
Winter Events
Look out for all the great Summer and Winter events that take place in the venues listed in this section. Check their websites or www.titchhikers.co.uk

## ZOO

### Bristol Zoo Gardens

Clifton, Bristol, BS8 3HA
0117 974 7399, www.bristolzoo.org.uk
Daily 9am-5.30pm, 5pm off-peak
£12 adult, £7.50 child 3-14yrs, £35 family (2+2),
FREE U3's. (These are Gift Aid Visitor prices which
include a voluntary contribution of approx 10%
above normal admission prices). Good annual
membership deals and benefits. Baby changing and
feeding facilities. Cafe.
Follow the brown tourist signs from the M5 J17 or
from Bristol city centre

A haven for families with young children,
Bristol Zoo has lots to see and do, from the
animals to the playground, and many summer
and winter events.

Monkey Jungle, featuring "meet the lemurs",
offers a forest-like experience where monkeys
mingle with gorillas and visitors enjoy close-
up, walk through, encounters with lemurs.

There is also the award winning Seal &
Penguin Coasts where you come face to face
with seals and penguins through transparent
underwater walkways. Other favourites
include Gorilla Island, Twilight World, Bug
World and the Reptile House. From the
smallest and rarest tortoise in the world, to
the largest ape, there are over 400 exotic and
endangered species to experience.

Call the Zoo (0117 9747385) or check their
website to find out about other regular events
such as storytime and music events.

### Feeding and Talk Times:

11.00am Lion talk

12.30pm Gorilla feeding & talk

1.30pm Butterfly Forest  2.00pm Meerkat talk

2.30pm Lemur talk  3.00pm Prairie dog talk

3.00pm Penguin talk & feed  3.30pm Seal talk & feed

### Animal Encounters

Meet some smaller animals close-up.

1pm, 3pm and 4pm at peak season

12pm, 2pm and 3pm off peak season

For **Parent & Toddler Coffee Mornings** see
**Parent & Baby-Toddler** section.

### New at the Zoo

Coral Cafe - Freshly prepared, often local, fair
trade, rainforest alliance and organic products.

Explorers' Creek - The new attraction features
three areas: a water play area, a tropical bird
house and a walk-through parrot feeding area.

ZooRopia - For the older children, Europe's
first aerial ropes course set within a zoo and
designed for ages five and upwards. There's a
net ramp, a plank bridge, looped vines, hanging
logs, and a zip wire (additional charge for this
attraction. Parents/carers can walk under their
children, take part, or children can complete the
course alone).

### Summer Activities

Puppet shows, ecology weekends, meet insects
and animals, evening entertainment such as
Boogie for Brizzle.

### Winter Activities

Expect such delights as Nosieless Fireworks on
Bonfire Night, then Santa's Grotto, Christmas
Train, Carol Singing Evenings, meeting and
feeding of Santa's reindeer and much more for
the Festive season.

## LOCAL FARMS & PARKS

### Avon Valley Country Park

Pixash Lane, Bath Rd, Keynsham, BS31 1TP
0117 986 4929
www.avonvalleycountrypark.co.uk
Open every day 10am-6pm, closed Nov-April
£7 adult, £6.50 child, FREE U2's, season tickets
available
A4 towards Bath, follow brown signs

Farm trail leads through several fields of farm
animals and rare breeds. Other attractions
include a land train, a miniature ride-on
railway, large adventure playground, a barn
accommodating soft play and impressive slides,
quad bikes for any age (additional cost, over 4's)
and a duck pond with boats for hire. Lovely walk
along the river with assault course for children.

## Hartcliffe Community Farm

Lampton Ave, Hartcliffe, Bristol, BS13 0QH
0117 978 2014
Daily 9am-4pm
Admission FREE (donations welcome)
Signposts from Bishport Ave

The main site is 35 acres of pasture with a collection of farm animals. Kiddies Corner contains goats, rabbits and ducks. There are pigs and sheep. The farm now has its own aviary with budgies, canaries, cockatiels and peacocks.

## HorseWorld

Staunton Lane, Whitchurch, Bristol, BS14 0QJ
01275 540173
www.horseworld.org.uk
Winter (Nov-end March) - Weds-Sun, 10am-4pm. Every day sch hol. Summer (Apr-end Oct) - daily 10am-5pm
£6.75 adult, £4.75 child (U3's FREE), £20 family ticket (2+2)
Access: Just off the A37

Horseworld is an equine welfare charity. Learn about the rescue, rehabilitation and re-homing work undertaken. Great opportunity for children to meet horses, donkeys and ponies. Museum with audio-visual presentation, nature trails, tractor rides and pony and pet handling, plus indoor and outdoor play, and cafe, make for a good family day out. Some family events during the year. Keep an eye on their website or look at www.titchhikers.co.uk

## Lawrence Weston Community Farm

Saltmarsh Drive, Lawrence Weston, BS11 0NJ
0117 938 1128, www.lwfarm.org.uk
Tue-Sun 9.30am-4.30pm (summer) 3.30pm (winter)
Admission FREE (donations welcome)

A city farm set in 6 acres of land, sheep, goats, pigs, chickens and rabbits. Some rare breeds. There is also an outdoor play area, bee-keeping club, educational projects and a volunteer programme. Refreshments available.

## Noah's Ark Zoo Farm

Failand Rd, Wraxall, Bristol, BS48 1PG
01275 852606, www.noahsarkzoofarm.co.uk
Feb-Oct: Mon-Sun, B/H's 10.30am-5pm
Open on Mon sch hols
£10.50 adult, £8.50 child, £35 family (2+2) or £33 (1+3), U2's FREE
Annual: £42 adult, £34 child, £140 family (2+2), £132 (1+3)
Bristol to Clevedon road via Failand ( B3128 ). Or M5 J 20. Follow brown tourist signs.

This farm creatively combines religious and agricultural themes. A full day's activity with 85 different kinds of animal from chicks to rhinos. There are daily animal shows, reptile and rhino encounters, tractor and trailer rides, a huge variety of indoor and outdoor play equipment (large, open and airy), a straw den with rope swings and several adventure trails. If that isn't enough, there is also a lookout tower offering stunning views across the Severn Estuary to Wales, and Noah's Ark has the longest hedge maze in the world! The theme of this farm (Noah's Ark and the creationist view of evolution) is explored in exhibitions, during the tractor ride and whilst feeding and handling the animals in the barn.

New

Tigers, Tapir, Welly Splash Pool and Bird Waterworld.

## St Werburgh's City Farm

Watercress Rd, St Werburgh's, Bristol, BS2 9YJ
0117 942 8241
Daily 9am-5pm (summer) 4pm (winter)
Admission FREE (donations welcome)

A small community farm set among allotments. Animals include pigs, goats, rabbits, guinea pigs, ducks, geese, sheep and chickens, and sometimes lambs and kids. The site includes a large pond and farm shop selling plants and organic produce. Teens (13-19yrs) can learn community farm skills by joining their environmental youth work programme. Other attractions are the adventure playground for U8's, café (closed Tues) and a children's homeopathic clinic. A community building next to the café can be hired out for kids birthday parties. See also **Eating Out.**

## Windmill Hill City Farm

Philip Street, Bedminster, Bristol, BS3 4EA
0117 963 3252, www.windmillhillcityfarm.org.uk
Tue-Sun: 9am-5pm
Admission free (donations welcome)

Well laid out paved farmyard with animal enclosures. Wide paths lead to paddocks, a small nature reserve, gardens and allotments. The Play Centre is for 1-5's, with indoor and outdoor areas. Adventure playground for 5-11's. U8's must be accompanied by an adult. Holiday activities and events. Educational group visits to the farm can be arranged.

See also **Eating Out, Childcare, Pre-schools.**

## SOIL ASSOCIATION ORGANIC FARMS

Enjoy the great outdoors, while learning a little more about organic farming and meeting the animals. Organic farms with open access to the public are available at:

### Barley Wood Walled Garden, Bristol

Long Lane, Wrington, Nr Bristol, BS40 5SA
Open to the public 9.30am-4.30pm daily. Entry April-October £2.50, Nov-Mar £1, children under 16 free

### Hindon Farm

Bratton, near Minehead, Somerset, TA24 8SH
01643 705244, www.hindonfarm.co.uk
Contact the farm for shop opening times. Whether you wish to visit the farm shop, stay in the holiday cottage or picnic along the farm trail.

### St Augustines Farm

Arlingham, Gloucestershire, GL2 7JN
01452 740277, www.staugustinesfarm.co.uk
Opening times: Open end March to October, from 11am-5pm. Open every day except term time Mondays. Adults £5.50, Children (aged 2 to 16yrs) £4.50, Concessions £5.00, Babies (aged under 2yrs) Free. Season tickets available

Gift shop, cafe selling hot and cold drinks, snacks and ice cream

St Augustines Farm is a real, working farm, where Robert and Elaine Jewell's family have farmed for 6 generations. In 1988 Robert and Elaine were one of the first farms to let families and school children in to see what farms and farming are really all about. By 1996 they had started converting the farm to Organic production and by 1998 St Augustines Farm was accepted for registration by the Soil Association. Today, the farm has an impressive array of activities available to complement your farm visit including a play barn and adventure play area, tractor and trailor rides at peak times, cafe and gift shop.

For more information on all these farms, as well as information about more organic farms, see:

www.soilassociation.org - 'organic farm visit'

## Tips

- When visiting farms, zoos and wildlife centres, it's wise to take precautions to avoid "zoonoses" — diseases spread to humans via animal carriers. The risk is easily controlled by making sure your children wash their hands after contact with animals. If you are pregnant, or think you may be pregnant, avoid contact with pregnant ewes and newborn lambs.

- Season tickets are often a bit of a chunk of cash to hand over, but well worth it in the long run for the ability to enjoy out of hours fun.

# FURTHER AFIELD

## Animal Farm Country Park

Red Road, Berrow, Nr Burnham-on-Sea, TA8 2RW
01278 751 628, www.animal-farm.co.uk
Daily 10am-5.30pm, closes 5pm in winter
£7 adults, £6.50 child, £26-38 family ticket (2+2, 2+3, 2+4), FREE U2's

Large variety of animals, including rare breeds, set in 25 acres of countryside. Opportunities to cuddle and feed the animals. Huge indoor and outdoor play areas with toddler zones. Many summer events which are free with entry.

## Apex Leisure and Wildlife Park

Marine Drive, Burnham-on-Sea, TA9 3YY
Sedgemoor Parks Dept: 01278 435435
42-acre park, walks, ducks, skate park, BMX biking (members only) and a play area.

## Birdland Park and Gardens

Rissington Road, Bourton-on-the-Water, GL54 2BN
01451 820480, www.birdland.co.uk
Apr-Oct: 10am-6pm, Nov-Mar:10am-4pm
Penguin Feed: 2.30pm
£5.50 adult, £3.30 child, £16 family (2+2), FREE U4's
Season tickets available

Over 500 birds can be seen in a natural setting of woodland and gardens. The River Windrush runs through the park forming a natural habitat for flamingos, pelicans, storks and waterfowl. The colony of penguins is fun to watch at feeding time (2.30pm). Over 50 aviaries contain exotic birds. Nice picnic spots, play area and café.

*Summer Activities*

Bird of prey encounter days, meet a keeper, and various other events are regular features throughout the summer months. See website or www.titchhikers.co.uk for more details.

## Brean Down Tropical Bird Garden

Brean Down, Brean, Somerset, TA8 2RS
01278 751 209
www.burnham-on-sea.co.uk/brean_bird_garden
Apr-Oct: daily 10am-Dusk
£2.95 adult, £1.95 child

Located at the foot of Brean Down. Largest selection of tropical parrots in the West!

## Butts Farm

Nr South Cerney, Cirencester, GL7 5QE
01285 869414
Feb half term - Oct half term: Tue-Sun 10.30am-5pm, closed Mon except b/hs
£5 adult, £4 child, U3's FREE, £16 family (2+2)
3 miles east of Cirencester on the old A419 towards Swindon, follow brown tourist signs

Near Cotswold Water Park, this is a very hands-on farm, which specialises in rare breeds. Children can bottle-feed young animals, feed the pigs, ride ponies (Thurs & Sun at 2pm), cuddle the smaller animals and go on a tractor-trailer safari. Excellent farm shop selling local produce.

## Cattle Country Adventure Park

Berkeley Heath Farm, Berkeley, GL13 9EW
01453 810 510, www.cattlecountry.co.uk
Feb half term: daily, 10am-4pm. Feb-Easter: Sun only. Easter-Sep: Sat-Sun 10am-5pm, daily sch hols
£6.50 adult/child, FREE U3's, prices seasonal
M5 J14 take A38 and follow brown tourist signs.

This is a great family day out with lots of indoor and outdoor activities that parents can join in with. Two dedicated play areas for U7's (one indoor, one outdoor), two play barns with slides, ball pools and much more. There is also a digger ride, ride-on tractors, mini golf, a boating lake, a jumping pillow, climbing net, and a miniature railway offering rides through the park. In the summer of 2008, a children's castle with towers, bridges and a zip slide joined the park with excellent reviews. Not forgetting the animals, there is a farm trail that passes a willow maze, wallabies, a herd of American bison, and a place for children to meet and feed the animals.

*Summer Activities*

There is a splash pool for the summer months.

Penings

## Cotswold Farm Park

Guiting Power, Nr Stow-on-the-Wold, GL54 5UG
01451 850307, www.cotswoldfarmpark.co.uk
Mar-Sep: daily 10.30am-5pm
£6.75 adult, £5.50 chlid, £22 family (2+2), U3's FREE
Follow brown signs from Bourton-on-the-Water.

Rare British breeds, informative animal audio guide, seasonal demonstrations of lambing, shearing and milking. Children may cuddle and feed animals in the touch barn. Battery-powered Tractor Driving School (3-12yrs), pedal tractors for toddlers. Tractor trailer rides, woodland walks (download map from their excellent website), nature trails, adventure playground and indoor play area. Regular fun horserides are also held (need to bring own horse - call or see website for more details). The campsite gives reduced rates to the park.

*Summer Activities* ✸

Milking and shearing. Call for more details.

## Cotswold Wildlife Park

Burford, Oxfordshire, OX18 4JP
01993 823 006, www.cotswoldwildlifepark.co.uk
Daily 10am-6pm (summer - last admission 4.30pm),
10am-5pm (winter - last admission 3.30pm)
£10 adult, £7.50 child, U3's FREE
Annual: £45 adult, £32.50 child
Jct 15 M4, A419, A361, from Lechlade follow brown tourist signs.

Spacious enclosures with rhinos, zebras, leopards, emus, wallabies, lions and more. Other attractions include children's farmyard, adventure playground, miniature railway, reptile house and animal encounters — feed the penguins, ducks and big cat. New to the park is a Madagascar, multi species, walk through exhibit.

*Summer Activities* ✸

Retile awareness days, birds of prey demonstrations, and brass rubbing.

*Winter Activities*

Santa stops by in December.

## Court Farm Country Park

Wolvershill Rd, Banwell, Weston-super-Mare, BS29 6DL
01934 822 383, www.courtfarmcountrypark.co.uk
Mar-end Oct: daily 10am-5.30pm
Winter: Tue-Sun 10am-4.30pm
£6.25 adult, £4.75 child, £20 family (2+2), FREE
Season ticket: £24 adult, £18 child
Reduced rates winter
M5 J21 the follow brown tourist signs

A working farm with massive undercover fun area and an outdoor Adventure Land play area with aerial skyway and trampolines. Also tractor rides, pony rides (2.15pm, 3 years upwards), safari jeeps, ride on tractors, and handling the pets! Maize maze from mid July to end Sept. New Robin Hood Maze opens this summer. Lots of activities always going on for children including milking, twice daily in the Animal Barn - 11am & 4.30pm, and animal feeding (late afternoon).

*Summer Activities* ✸

Bottle feeding takes place in the Animal Barn at 12am and 3pm daily from Mid February to early September.

## Dick Whittington Farm Park

Little London, Longhope, Gloucestershire, GL17 0PH
01452 831000, www.dickwhittington.info
Daily 10am-5pm
£4.50 adult & 10+yrs, £5 child, £4 U3's, Free U1's
A40 from Gloucester towards Ross-On-Wye, take a
left turn in Huntley and follow brown tourist signs

Farm park set in secluded valley. Adventure
barn with five different soft play units suitable
from toddlers to age 10 yrs. Outside a
big sandpit, play area, pets corner, tractor
rides, nature trail and picnic area. You can
see pigs and goats in the paddocks, or visit
the Aquarium Room which also houses an
Ant Colony. See website for special events
including lots of Easter events.

## Greenmeadow Community Farm

Greenforge Way, Cwmbran, Gwent, NP44 5AJ
01633 647662
www.greenmeadowcommunityfarm.org.uk
Daily 10am-6pm, winter 10am-4.30pm, closed Jan
£4.50 adult, £3.50 child, £16 family (2+3), FREE U2's
M4 J26, go north to Cwmbran following brown signs

Farm animals in paddocks and barns. Tractor
and trailer rides, machine milking viewed from
glassed in area, adventure playground for
ages 7+yrs and a large sandpit and tractor
play area for U5's. Paddling pool with water-
spurting dragon in summer.

## Longleat

Nr Warminster, Wiltshire, BA12 7NW
01985 844 400, www.longleat.co.uk
Safari Park: Feb half term, 10am-2.30pm, end Feb-end
Mar w/e's only, 10am-3pm, Apr-Nov daily 10am-4pm,
w/e's, B/H's & summer hols 10am-5pm (attractions
payable on individual basis or purchase a passport
ticket: £23 adult, £15 child, FREE U3's (available for
one season, online booking available)
House: Open daily. For a detailed breakdown see
website or call, £10 adult, £6 child
A37 (Wells Road) south to Farrington Gurney,
left onto A362, through Frome and follow brown signs

Longleat comprises a stately home, safari
park, and other attractions. Drive through
the safari park (soft top cars not permitted)
and see giraffes, zebras, tigers and lions
in their enclosures. The monkey jungle is
optional as they will clamber on your car, so
not recommended for the car proud (there
is a safari bus available!) but children will
love it. The other attractions include Postman
Pat's Village, Butterfly Garden, King Arthur's
Mirror Maze, Blue Peter maze, miniature
steam railway, pets corner, a large adventure
playground, a safari boat trip where you
can see hippos and sea lions. Not all areas
are buggy friendly and pushchairs are not
permitted in the house (a small number of
hipseats are available to borrow).

### Summer Events

Summer family show with challenges, prizes
and special guests.

### Winter Events

Santa train and Christmas carol workshop.

## Puxton Park

Cowslip Lane, Hewish, Weston Super Mare, BS24 6AH
01934 523500, www.puxton.co.uk
Daily 10am-5pm
£4 adult, £5 child, , £15 family (2+2), U3's FREE
Aprox 1/2 mile from J21 M5 follow A370 signposted
Congresbury/Bristol. Bus stop at entrance

One of the West's newest attractions, Puxton
Park really does have something for everyone.
There are indoor and outdoor play areas
(including a toddler sand pit), indoor and
outdoor animal enclosures including Pets
Village (rabbits, chipmunks, guinea pigs,
ducks, chickens and much more) and the
Paddocks where you will find ponies, pigs, and

goats. There is also a conservation area with a large pond, the Puxton Falconry Centre with owls, hawks and falcons, and the Puxton Farm Dairy. Should you get hungry, you can choose from one of two restaurants with a range of good food, including organic produce. And there is also a farm shop, so you can stock up on some goodies before heading home.

See also **Eating Out, and Parties.**

## Prinknash Bird and Deer Park

Cranham, Gloucestershire, GL4 8EX
01452 812727
www.prinknash-bird-and-deerpark.com
Daily 10am-5pm (summer), 4pm (winter)
£5 adult, £3.50 child, U3's FREE
M5 J11a, on the A46 between Cheltenham and Stroud, follow brown tourist signs

Set in the grounds of a working abbey, the bird park has aviaries housing exotic birds, and a lake. Many birds including ducks, mute swans, black swans, peacocks and cranes wander freely and will feed out of your hand, as will tame deer and pygmy goats. There is a tearoom and playground by the Abbey, and an 80 year old 2-storey Tudor style wendy house.

## The National Birds of Prey Centre

Newent, Gloucestershire, GL18 1JJ
0870 990 1992, www.nbpc.co.uk
Daily 10.30am-5.30pm (closed Dec and Jan)
£9 adult, £5.50 child, £27 family (2+2), FREE U2's
M5 J11a, A40 Ross-on-Wye, B4215 to Newent, follow brown tourist signs.

The centre houses one of the most significant collections of birds of prey in the UK. Over 60 species of birds, including eagles, falcons and buzzards with flying displays three times daily.

**Flying Times:**

11.30am, 2pm, 4.15pm (summer)

11.30am, 1.30pm, 3.30pm (winter)

## Tropiquaria

Washford Cross, Watchet, West Somerset, TA23 0QB
01984 640 688, www.tropiquaria.co.uk
End Mar-Nov: daily 10.30am-5pm (6pm end July-early Sep), Winter openings: w/e's, Weds 11am-4pm
£7.50 adult, £6.50 child, £25 family (2+2)
FREE U3's
M5 J23, take A39 twds Minehead. It's between Williton and Washford

Housed in the old BBC transmitting station, this colourful aquarium is home to frogs, snakes, lizards, birds and spiders. Outside there are lemurs, wallabies and chipmunks. Other attractions include: The Shadowstring Puppet Theatre, Wireless in the West Museum (a history of broadcasting), an adventure playground with two life-size galleon ships, a playground for the U5's and an indoor play castle with café.

## WWT Slimbridge

The Wildfowl and Wetlands Centre, Slimbridge, GL2 7BT
01453 891900, www.wwt.org.uk
Daily 9.30am-5.30pm, winter 9.30am-5pm
£8.75 adult, £4.80child, £24.40 family (2+2), FREE U4's (prices include voluntary Gift Aid Donation)
M5 Jct 13 or 14, follow brown tourist signs. Nearest station Cam & Dursley.

Spacious landscaped grounds offer the chance to get very close to and feed, exotic, rare and endangered water birds. You can also view from hides and towers. Humming birds can be seen at close range in the Tropical House. The swans feed is at 4pm every day. The visitor centre includes the Hanson Discovery Centre, a cinema and great views over the River Severn from the Sloane Observation Tower. There is also a wildlife art gallery. Many more events take place throughout the year (see their website or www.titchhikers.co.uk).

## Seaquarium

Marine Parade, Weston-super-Mare, BS23 1BE
01934 613361, www.seaquariumweston.co.uk
Daily 10am-4.30pm, (daily feeds at 2pm)
£6.15 adult, £5.15 child, £21.99 family (2+2), FREE U4's

Built on its own pier, the aquarium has a wide variety of marine life and an underwater walk through a tunnel. There are live presentations and feeds throughout the day. Tea room with views of Severn Estuary.

# Parks & Play Areas

## Contents

High quality outdoor play spaces have a huge impact on children's health and wellbeing. Now thanks to a successful City Council bid to the government's Play Pathfinder initiative, children and young people in Bristol will benefit from a massive £2.5m boost to the city play parks and play spaces over the next three years. Add to this all the major events and free activities that take place in our parks, and it becomes clear why parks are one of our most valued (yet free) resources.

Most of the events take place in the following parks - the 'Big Six':

Ashton Court Estate (see Walks, Woods & Picnics), Blaise Castle Estate, Eastville Park, Hengrove Park, Oldbury Court, & The Downs.

Almost every park listed here has a play area.

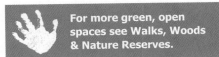

**For more green, open spaces see Walks, Woods & Nature Reserves.**

### Summer Events

Many of the parks hold exciting activities throughout the Summer months (April to September). See the contact details over the page, or watch out for events on www.titchhikers.co.uk.

## For all Bristol Park information:

**Bristol City Council Parks, Estates & Sport**

Department of Culture and Leisure Services, Colston 33, Colston Ave, BS1 4UA
0117 9223719, www.bristol.gov.uk/parks

Call the above number for information about your nearest park or play area, should it not appear in the following list.

# PARK EVENTS

The parks service runs a programme of events and activities, many taking place during the school holidays. See:

**www.bristol.gov.uk/events**

If you would like to organise your own community event in one of Bristol's 200 parks, call the Events Team: 0117 922 3538.

ALL PARK EVENTS ARE FREE

## Tips

Most Bristol parks do not have refreshment services or toilets onsite. If you plan a lengthy stay with small children make sure you pack a picnic (certainly a drink and snack) and check out the location of the nearest loo before you leave! (See www.bristol.gov.uk for help with this!)

# A-Z OF PARKS

## Ashton Court (BS41)

Long Ashton, BS41 9JN
0117 963 9174
8am daily throughout the year. Closing times vary with the season: Nov, Dec & Jan 5.15pm, Feb 6.15pm, Mar & Oct 7.15pm, Apr & Sept 8.15pm, May, June, July & Aug 9.15pm
Toilets & cafe at Visitor Centre, in the stable block of the mansion, and at golf kiosk.

Some pushchair & wheelchair friendly areas.

Ashton Court Estate is situated 2 miles from Bristol City Centre. Main entrances are off the A369 Portishead Rd at Kennel Lodge Rd, for mansion & centre of estate, & at Clifton Lodge for golf course and top of estate. There is unlimited free parking. The Avon Cycle Way runs from Long Ashton through the estate to Clifton Lodge.

Ashton Court is a parkland estate with 850 acres of grassland and woodland, a Grade I listed mansion, and wonderful views across the city. There is no play area as such but plenty of space for ball games, learning to ride a bike, or climbing over tree trunks.

**See Walks & Woods for more on Ashton Court.**

## Begbrook Green Park (BS16)

Off Frenchay Park Road, Frenchay (BS16 1HY area). Also access via Wren Drive (on road parking). Buses 4, 318, 319, 328, 329 and 519 all stop by the park.

Begbrook Green Park is open 24 hours.

Modern and friendly park. Two dog-free playgrounds. The park is very flat and, apart from the fact that the paved paths are in only linear (not circular) routes, is accessible for wheelchairs and pushchairs.

## Blaise Castle Estate (BS10)

Kingsweston Rd, Lawrence Weston, BS10 7QS
0117 3532268
Open 8am-dusk
Entrance and car park off the B4057 Kingsweston Rd
Accessible cafe and toilets by Kingsweston Rd car park

You will find the largest play area in North Bristol at Blaise. It attracts children of all ages from all over the city. There is a play area for toddlers and one for older children. Parents/carers must accompany their children. The spacious grass areas are great for picnics and

ball games, while recently resurfaced drives offer the opportunity to explore woodlands and water features. The Castle Folly is open on every third Sunday in the month, May to October, Bank Holidays from 2 - 4.30pm. Also take a look in the museum near the play area. **See Bristol Visitor Attractions, and Walks & Woods.**

*Summer Activities*

The Summer holiday events programme is fantastic, including puppet shows.

## Brandon Hill (BS8)

Entrances on Great George St (off Park St), Jacobs Wells Rd, Upper Byron Pl, Queens Parade, & Berkeley Square
Hilly site, access for wheelchairs difficult
Please note: Cabot Tower is currentky closed and should reopen late 2009

Climb Cabot Tower's many steps and see superb views across the city (opening times vary, normally 8am until 30 mins before dusk). From the tower, there is a network of pathways and steps with waterfalls, ponds and trees. Toilets are on the middle terrace. Fenced in play areas with toddler swings, sand pit and slide for younger children. Climbing structure and swings for older children. Often a Summer Sport programme (check out www.titchhikers.co.uk, www.bristol.gov.uk or call the Park Events Team for more information).

## Canford Park (BS10)

Entrance on Canford Lane, Westbury-on-Trym
5 gated entrances, each wide enough for wheelchairs or double buggies. On road parking. Bus stops nearby.

An attractive well-kept park. Fenced play area with a good variety of play equipment. The park itself has a large, flat lawn, excellent for ball games and picnics. There is also a sunken rose garden with a pond. The circular path around the park perimeter is popular for learning to cycle and skate. Tennis courts for hire by the hour (check the availability of courts by telephoning 0782 695 3264).

## Castle Park (BS1)

Castle Park is in the heart of Bristol with access from Bristol Bridge and the old city, Cabot circus shopping centre, and Broadmead. The park is open continuously throughout the year and admission is free. A cycle path runs through the park linking the city centre to the Bristol/ Bath cycle path. You can also access the park via ferry. Staffed public toilets with disabled facilities are situated near the remains of the old castle keep at the north east end of the park, opposite The Galleries shopping centre.

This is one of Bristol's newest parks, created on an ancient, riverside site. It is the biggest city centre green space with large wooded areas and the 'castle' play area, which is dog-free.

## Clifton Down (BS8)

Off Suspension Bridge Rd (next to the Suspension Bridge). Parking is difficult & is on road. Buses to Clifton Village.

This is an unfenced play area with a good mixture of assault course style wooden climbing equipment including slides, swings as well as natural rock faces — great for budding mountaineers. Toilets are on Bridge Road. Close to the Observatory and Bridge.

**www.avongorge.org.uk**
The website for The Avon Gorge & Downs Wildlife Project which was set up to protect the outstanding wildlife interest of the Avon Gorge and Downs and to raise awareness and understanding about the importance of this site for people and wildlife. Excellent kids section. **(Also see over page).**

## Cotham Gardens (BS6)

Entrance on Redland Grove, Nr Redland train station. The park is disabled accessible though there are some gentle slopes.

A small friendly park. Spacious fenced play area with large sand pit, swings and climbing apparatus. Also a grassed area for ball games and picnics. Great views of the trains passing on the railway line alongside.

## Dame Emily Park (BS3)

Dean Lane, Bedminster (BS3 1DD area). Short walk from Coronation Rd and East St. Buses 24, 25, 75, 76, 77, 89, 90, 503, 510, 511 all stop nearby. Open 24 hours. It has flat & wheelchair accessible areas.

A popular dog-free playground for the under 10s has been established together with an aerial runway for older children. Also a popular cycle park.

## The Downs (BS8)

Park anywhere along Ladies Mile. The Downs are open permanently. Nearly all parts of the grass areas of the Downs are flat and fully accessible to wheelchair users with no obstacles. Many of the paths along the western edge of the Downs bordering on the Gorge are narrow and have steep inclines or steps. Unfenced so children need to have a watchful eye on them

The Downs are made up of Clifton Down and Durdham Down. They are Bristol's most famous open space with grassland and some wooded areas. They are very popular with footballers, joggers, kite flyers and dog walkers. The Circular Road offers dramatic views of the Gorge and the Suspension Bridge. Toilets can be found near the viewpoint on the Sea Walls and at the Water Tower/The Downs Tea Room. The Downs usually hosts annual events such as the Children's Festival and circuses - **see Events & Festivals.**

### Park Developments
Many parks all over Bristol will be developed over the next couple of years. See www.bristol.gov.uk

## Avon Gorge & Downs Wildlife Project

c/o Education Department, Bristol Zoo Gardens, Bristol, BS8 3HA
0117 903 0609
www.bristolzoo.org.uk/events/avon

Set up in partnership with several groups to protect the wildlife and nature of the Avon Gorge and Downs. They run holiday activities, parent & toddler story telling picnics, wildlife trails and the popular Gorgeous Wildlife Family Fun Day, held each summer. For further information, pick up leaflets from the Downs Tea Rooms or at the Zoo.

**See also Walks, Woods & Nature Reserves**

## Easton Play Park (BS5)

Main entrance on Chelsea Rd (BS5 6AF area) next to The Mission. Access off the Bristol-Bath Cycle Path. Bus stops on Easton Rd.

This exciting and imaginative playground is really worth a visit. It is compact without being overcrowded, which makes it relatively easy to keep an eye on the children. There are climbing frames, slides, swings and a marvellous seesaw suitable for all ages. There is also an all-weather 5-a-side football pitch and a small area for picnics. The Bristol-Bath cycle path runs alongside.

## Eastville Park (BS16)

Alongside Fishponds Rd (A432) & adjacent to M32 J2. Car park in Park Ave, accessible from Fishponds Rd via Oakdene Ave (open 7.30am-dusk). Much of the park is accessible by wheelchair though the paths and landscape are slightly uneven.

A large area of grassland ideal for running about. There are two play areas, one of which is fenced and has a sandpit. Take a walk down to the lake, or walk through the woodland and along the river towards Oldbury Court. Toilets and ice-cream vans present in the summer.

Need Directions?
Use Google Maps or call Traveline on 0871 200 22 33

## Greville Smyth Park (BS3)

The park is at the junction of North Street and Ashton Rd, Bedminster. Buses 24 and 25 from Lockleaze via Broadmead stop outside the park. Greville Smyth Park is open 24 hours. The site is uneven and some of the paths are unsuitable for wheelchairs.

www.frogs.org.uk

Originally part of Ashton Court Estate, it is now a very popular local community park in South Bristol. Play equipment for all ages.

## Hengrove Play Park (BS14)

01275 836946
Entrance off Hengrove Way, BS14 0HR
Open: Summer: Mon-Fri, 10am-7pm, Sat/Sun, 10am-6pm, Winter: 10am-dusk
Wheels Park open: 10am-8pm

Next door to the leisure park on the site of the old Whitchurch airfield, this is the biggest free play park in the South of England. It features the innovative play dome, a 12 metre high domed frame with enclosing chutes and walkways. There is a skateboard/BMX zone, an area for sand and water play for younger children, plenty of open space plus seating, a café and toilets. Staffed during the day.

## Horfield Common (BS7)

Access off Kellaway Aveue. Bus stops of Kellaway Ave. The common is accessible and is open all the time and is criss-crossed by many paths. Disabled access generally good but there are some gently sloping areas.

Located in the quiet northern suburbs of Bristol with fantastic city views. Dog free play area.

## Mancroft Park (BS11)

BS11 0HX. Access is from Mancroft Ave, Hopewell Gardens and Moorend. 24 hour open access to the park. The park is sloping so may not be suitable for some wheelchair users.

Recently undergoing a major redevelopment, the playground uses natural elements to encourage children's interactions with spaces, rather than the more traditional, fixed, play equipment.

## Mina Road Park (BS2)

(BS2 9TJ area). Acces via Mina Rd, St Werburghs, or footbath Jubillee Rd

Dog-free playground in the park and a kickabout area with basketball hoops.

## Netham Park (BS5)

Avonvale Road, Redfield, Bristol BS5 9RN. Access is currently limited for wheelchair users but this should change over the next few years as footpaths are developed. On major cycle route. Public toilets.

A major park and area of open green space in built-up east Bristol with excellent new facilities for leisure, sport and recreational activities. Number of football pitches, cricket pitch, and more. New children's playground had been designed and will be under construction in the Autumn 2009 (after we have gone to print). Please give us your feedback for the next book.

## Oldbury Court Estate & Snuff Mills (BS16)

Entrances at Oldbury Court Rd and River View (cul-de-sac off Broom Hill, BS16 1DL)

Both entrances have car parks. This is a large park that extends from Snuff Mills to Frenchay, with the River Frome in its grounds. There is a large, well equipped, fenced off play area near the Oldbury Court Road entrance. Equipment includes a 9.6m high tower unit with tubular slides, several sand play areas, swings, long slides, trains, castles, a crows nest and lots more. There are pleasant walks by the river and woodland to explore. Toilets and a small café are situated by the Broom Hill entrance. There are also toilets next to the play area.

## Old Quarry Park (BS6)

Henleaze. Entrance off bottom of Henleaze Rd (BS9 4AS)

Great zip slide, climbing frames, big shady trees. Suitable for all. A little gem.

## Redcatch Park (BS4)

(Around BS4 2EP). Main entrance on Redcatch Rd and Broadwalk. Bus stops Redcatch Rd.

A pleasant, quiet park with a fenced play area. The park offers plenty of green space and also has tennis courts on-site which can be hired by the hour in season.

## Redland Green (BS6)

Access is from Redland Rd, Redland Green Rd, Cossins Rd and St Oswalds Rd, Redland. (BS6 &HE area).

Lovely green with a fenced, dog-free play area. There are swings, a whirligig and zip slide for older children, and a low-level climbing structure set over a large sandpit, which is particularly suited to toddlers but enjoyed by all.

## St. Agnes Park (BS2)

Thomas Street, Montpelier, Bristol
Access is from Davey Street and Thomas Street, St Pauls.

Community park in this densely built up area. There is a dog-free playground in the park. Due for improvement works in 2009. Let us know what you think.

## St Andrews Park (BS6)

Entrances on Effingham Rd, Leopold Rd, Maurice Rd, Somerville Rd and Melita Rd

Play area and an area of grass for ball games or picnics. The park also boasts Bristol's only functioning paddling pool (unsupervised). During hot weather the attraction of the pool makes the park extremely crowded (available for use in the Spring and Summer, from May Bank Holiday to 5 September. Call 0117 922 3719 to check whether the pool is open). Public toilets and tea rooms make this a really comfortable park for parents. It hosts Music in the Park in June, a fun family afternoon. Bristol City Council has received funding to develop the play area. Let us know what you think of the finished result.

## St George Park (BS5)

Entrances on Church Rd (A420), Park Crescent and Park View, with a car park off Chalks Rd

A large popular Victorian park with plenty of open space, as well as a lake with ducks and swans. There is a fenced play area with a variety of equipment, and a Wheel Park for skateboarding, roller-skating and BMX biking. Fishing is also permitted at the lake in St George Park but individuals should have an Environment Agency rod licence and are subject to the agency's regulations. Toilets by the main park entrance.

## Troopers Hill (BS5)

The site is in St George, east Bristol, and access is from Troopers Hill Road or Malvern Road (with pushchairs/wheelchairs)

A local Nature Reserve on a hillside. Troopers Hill has stunning views and is one of the most spectacular wildlife spots in the city. Holds regular events (see **Walks** for contact details and more information on Troopers Hill).

## Victoria Park (BS3)

Entrances from Fraser St, Somerset Terrace, Nutgrove Avenue, Hill Ave, St. Luke's Rd and Windmill Close

Plenty of open space with views over Bristol from the top of the hill. There are three play areas: Fraser Street play area for under-12s (not dog-free), St Lukes Road play area which has a five-a-side area (not dog-free), Nutgrove Avenue corner on top of the park has an adjacent trim tail. Small fenced playground with equipment for very small children set on a safety surface. There is a basketball backboard for older children, and a planned multi-sport facility off St Luke's Rd. The water maze is fun so bring your wellies! There are toilets next to Somerset Terrace.

# ADVENTURE PLAYGROUNDS

Children and young people can come and play in these free, open access, secure and safe, staffed quality play environments.

## Felix Road Adventure Playground

Felix Rd, Easton, BS5 0JW
www.felixroadplayground.org, 0117 9551265
Term time: Mon-Thur 1-5pm, Sun 10.30am-12.50pm, 2-5.30pm. Holiday time: Mon-Thur 10.30am-5.30pm, Sun 10.30am-12.50pm, 2-5.30pm. FREE
Bus route: 4, 5, 5a, 585, 586

This playground was established in 1972. It is a child-centred environment with staff available to inspire, support and supervise children on site. The playground is a large open space incorporating wooden structures (ramps, rope swings, features to climb, slides), a tarmac area, an outdoor stage, grassed areas with trees, a small nature area with a pond, a patio area and a sand pit. Under fives area has a safe fence around it, grassy green areas, play equipment, safe climbing frame,and shaded seating areas. All weather cover in the ground level play building, where there is a main hall with pool table, toilets/shower, quiet room and art room. Trips usually run in the Summer holidays at a subsidised cost.
Also downloadable information on their website.

## Lockleaze Adventure Playground

301 Romney Avenue, Lockleaze, Bristol, BS7 9SU
0117 979 8311
Mon-Thur 3.30-7pm, Sun 11.30am-2pm, 3.30-6.30pm. FREE
Buses 25 and 24 to Gainsborough Square.

Large children's play area with skateboarding/ bike facility. Organises many trips, camps and activities. Tuck shop selling drinks, snacks and sometimes, hot food. Drop-in.

## Southmead Adventure Playground

Doncaster Rd, Southmead, BS10 5PP
0117 950 3607
Tue-Fri 3.30pm-7.45pm in summer
Sats & sch hols 10am-12.45pm & 2pm-5.45pm

A variety of activities for under 16's including sport and craft. Facilities include an all-weather pitch, play area for U8's, a large soft play room for U8's and a climbing area. U6's must be accompanied by an adult. Trips/ camps and activities including arts, cooking sports plus lots more. There is a tuck shop which sells drinks, snacks and sometimes hot food where prices are good.

## St Paul's Adventure Playground

Thomas Street, St Paul's, BS2 9LL
0117 9542145, stpaulsapg.wordpress.com
Wed, Thur, Fri 3.30-6.30pm, Sat 12-5.30pm
School Holidays: Mon-Fri, 10.30am-5.30pm
FREE

St. Paul's Adventure Playground is an 'Open Access' play facility for children. This means that children and young people can come and leave as they please, join in with activities or choose something to play with by asking a member of staff.

The playground caters for 5-15 year olds, and provides an opportunity to play in a safe and stimulating environment. Parents must complete a Registration Form for the safety and security of children over 5 who are staying by themselves. Under 5's are welcome but need to be accompanied by adult (over 18). The playground is for disabled and non-disabled children.

Not listed your favourite park?

Please email us (mail@titchhikers.co.uk) with details of your favourite park if we have not listed it here. Remember, we only list recommendations.

# Fun for Free

Our **Top Ten** free things to do in Bristol.

1.  Visit the Bristol City Museum (at the time of going to print this was holding a free Banksy Exhibition). See **Bristol Visitor Attractions**.

2.  Join your local library. See **Reading and Storytelling** for more details

3.  Check out Bristol's many parks as well as the park events. Annual events such as the Kite Festival and the Balloon Fiesta, as well as Love Parks Week, are free. See this chapter and **Events**.

4.  All over Bristol City Centre you will find fountains. These are a great treat for hot toddlers on a Summer's day. The ones around Millenium Square are the most traffic free. (Tip - it's advisable to wear some sort of shoe in the fountains, just in case).

5.  Grab your bike and take to one of Bristol's cycle tracks. See **Travelling Around**.

6.  Stuck for something to do with your toddler? Why not go to an NCT Open House (or even start one up yourself). They're a great way to meet other parents and carers in your area. See **Parent and Baby/Toddler**.

7.  Visit one of Bristol's Community Farms. See **Animals**.

8.  Look out for seasonal events such as Christmas Markets, Light Shows (College Green). See www.titchhikers.co.uk and join our Mailing List to be kept up to date.

9.  After a big downpour of rain put some wellies on and jump in some puddles. Seriously - you'll love it!

10. Visit your local church or temple where you will find fun activities involving your local community.

# Walks, Woods & Nature Reserves

## Contents

## Tips

Take spare clothes for the kids if on a long walk, especially if it is wet

Always take food and drink

### Got a pushchair?

www.pushchairwalks.co.uk

www.walkswithbuggies.com

Family walks can be really good fun with children if you go at their pace and go somewhere interesting to them. This section lists just some family favourites. More walks can be found by looking at the details given throughout, or by going to: www.titchhikers.co.uk.

## The Country Code

Be safe - plan ahead and follow any signs
Leave gates and property as you find them
Protect plants and animals, and take your litter home
Keep dogs under close control
Consider other people

## Summer Events

Many events take place in the venues listed in this section. See www.titchhikers.co.uk for listings as they become available

## SOURCES OF INFORMATION

### www.ramblers.org.uk

Excellent website. Lists walks suitable for children and group walks going on in your area. Has lots of tips for family walks, for even the smallest ramblers.

### Forest of Avon

Ashton Court Visitor Centre, Bristol, BS41 9JN
0117 953 2141, www.forestofavon.org.uk

An amazing, user friendly website listing the woodlands, nature reserves, heritage sites and country parks within the Forest of Avon. Find out everything you need to know about walking, biking, kite flying, and much more, in this neck of the woods.

### Avon Wildlife Trust

32 Jacobs Well Rd, Bristol, BS8 1DR
0117 917 7270, www.avonwildlifetrust.org.uk

This charity is dedicated to protecting wildlife. It has two centres, one at Folly Farm, Chew Valley and one at Willsbridge Mill, Keynsham. There are regular events for families listed on the website as well as wildlife walks.

### Gloucestershire Wildlife Trust

01452 383333
www.gloucestershirewildlifetrust.co.uk

For nature reserves and walks for families, plus lots more interesting information and event lists.

### Somerset Wildlife Trust

01823 652400, www.somersetwildlife.org

Information about Reserves and much more.

## PLAN YOUR JOURNEY

The location of car parks are stated throughout. We would like to support the use of, and those families who rely on, public transport. Where possible we have therefore indicated other access options. Please also see or contact the following when planning your day out:

### Traveline

0871 200 22 33, www.traveline.org.uk

Plan travel by bus, train, coach or ferry.

And see **Travelling Around** chapter

Also see **Parks and Play Areas** for more ideas

### Kiddiwalks near Bristol & Bath

Nigel Vile, Countryside Books, £7.99

Excellent book with many walks around Bristol and the South West. Also see Nigel's quotes throughout this chapter.

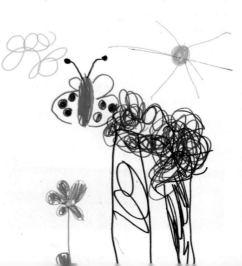

# BRISTOL WALKS

All over the city there are some great outdoor places to explore. Below are a few of our favourites. And why not combine your walk with a picnic, a pub lunch or one of Bristol's many free events, and make a day of it.

*"Never force children to walk – never – ever – never! Or when they get to an age when they can vote with their own feet they will stay firmly rooted in front of their PS3 or whatever."*

*Nigel Vile, 2008*
*(Author of Kiddiwalks)*

## Abbots Pool Wood

Manor Rd, Abbots Leigh, BS8 3RR
0117 9532141, www.forestofavon.org.uk
From the A369 turn down Manor Road. Car park is 70 metres from the main entrance to the Wood, off Manor Road. The Pool is 250 metres from the car park.
**Maps and information** are available from the Forest of Avon (call number above or see website)
**Accessibility:** Pushchair and wheelchair friendly

### Great for: **picnics, fishing, bike rides**

Abbots Pool is a small lake tucked away in Leigh Woods, and is an interesting place to explore. Surrounding the pool is idyllic mixed woodland, formerly part of the Robinsons Estate, and home to several species of bird such as the Green Woodpecker, Heron, and Kingfisher. The pool is stacked full of Roach and Perch. There are also picnic tables close to the pool.

## Ashton Court Estate

Long Ashton, BS41 9JN
0117 9639174, www.forestofavon.org.uk
2 entrances off the A369, one at Kennel Lodge Rd and one at Clifton Lodge (opp. Bridge Rd).
Third entrance off A370 at Church Lodge (opp. Long Ashton)
**Maps and information** are available from the Ashton Court Visitor Centre or can be downloaded from the Bristol City Council webpage.
**Accessibility:** Some pushchair & wheelchair friendly
**Toilets & refreshments:** Available at the Visitor Centre
**Open:** 8am-dusk

### Great for: **picnics, deer feeding, events, miniature railway, pitch & put, cafe, bike rides, woods**

Ashton Court Estate is a huge heritage estate with woodland, grassland and meadowland to explore. There is plenty of space for family games and picnics. There are many tracks that are suitable for toddlers or for walking with a backpack, and some suitable for buggies or wheelchairs. The Avon Cycle Way also runs from Long Ashton through the estate to Clifton Lodge. More info: visit the Ashton Court Visitor Centre, in the Stable Court Yard of Ashton Court Mansion & **see Travelling Around.**

### Deer Walks

These take place throughout the year and consist of a walk and talk with the Deer Keeper and the possibility of seeing the deer. Call the estate office on 0117 963 9176 for more information and to book as places are limited.

## Blaise Castle Estate

Henbury Rd, Henbury, Bristol, BS10 7QS
0117 353 2268, www.bristol.gov.uk
Park at Blaise Castle Estate car park on Kings Weston Road
**Accessibility:** Some pushchair & wheelchair friendly
**Toilets:** Kingsweston Rd car park
**Refreshments:** Cafe
**Open:** 8am-dusk

### Great for: **picnics, events, play area**

Pleasant wooded walks through the grounds, leading up to the castle folly and beyond into Coombe Dingle.

## Holiday Programmes

Events take place throughout the Summer Holiday on Tuesdays, Wednesdays and Thursdays.

See www.bristol.gov.uk & **Parks and Play Areas**

## The Downs

Stoke Rd, BS9

0117 922 3719, www.bristol.gov.uk

The Downs are situated on the North West of Bristol, about 2 miles from the City Centre, at the top of Whiteladies Rd (A4018). If travelling from north Bristol, Westbury Rd leads to The Downs.
**Accessibility:** Most of the grassy parts pushchair and wheelchair friendly
**Toilets:** Clifton Suspension Bridge & Stoke Rd
**Refreshments:** Ice cream van at the Sea Walls, a catering van on Parry's Lane, and The Downs Tea Room near the water tower on Stoke Road.
**Open:** permanently

**Great for: picnics, events, playing sports and games, short walks**

The Downs are 400 acres of grassed green space, consisting of Durdham Down and Clifton Down. From the Downs are fantastic views of the Avon Gorge, Leigh Woods, north Somerset, the Severn estuary and across to south Wales. You can also explore the Downs Tree Trail (download leaflet from website listed above).

## Events on the Downs

www.bristol.gov.uk

Regular events are organised on the Downs, such as firework displays, the Children's Festival, funfairs, circus, and the Flower Show.

## Avon Gorge & Downs Wildlife Project

0117 9030609, www.avongorge.org.uk

Run a popular programme of events throughout the year. With walks, talks, courses, children's events and family events.

Call the Avon Gorge & Downs Wildlife Project or see their website for more information and to book events on the Downs.

**Also see Parks & Play Areas, and Events.**

## Floating Harbour Walk

This walk can be combined with a ferry trip, **see Travelling Around.** It is possible to walk a complete circuit around the Floating Harbour (west of Prince Street Bridge), taking in the ss Great Britain, Industrial Museum, Arnolfini, Watershed, At-Bristol, Lloyds TSB building and the skateboarders! This walk is flat, so great for pushchairs and cyclists but watch the harbour edge with toddlers. A good place to start from is the car park at the ss Great Britain. The Floating Harbour extends beyond Prince Street Bridge, along Welsh Back towards Temple Meads.

**Also see Bristol Visitor Attractions.**

Hot day?
Let your children jump about in the many fountains.
See **Fun For Free.**

## Kings Weston Wood & House

Kings Weston Lane, Shirehampton, BS11 0UR
0117 938 2299, www.kingswestonhouse.co.uk
7 mins walk to house from the car park opposite Shirehampton Golf Course
**Accessibility:** Paths for pushchairs & wheelchairs
**Toilets:** Kings Weston House
**Refreshments:** Vaulted tea shop serving range of food and drink (9.30am-4pm).

**Great for: picnics, woods, cafe**

Paths through the woods lead to the grotto and to Kings Weston House, a Palladian mansion built in 1710. Pleasant grounds for picnics.

# Frome Valley Walkway

www.fromewalkway.org.uk, www.southglos.gov.uk

The Frome Valley Walkway is an 18 mile (29 km) footpath, taking in a variety of landscapes, and extending from Bristol's Castle Park to the source of the River Frome in the Cotswold Hills in South Gloucestershire. You can of course do the whole walk but parts of the walk are particularly child friendly and well recommended to us at Titch Hikers'. These encompass Eastville Park, Snuff Mills and Oldbury Court, which can be walked as a whole circuit or as individual, short, circular walks.

## Eastville Park

Fishponds Rd, BS5 6PN, www.bristol.gov.uk
Opposite the Royate Hill Turn off on the A432, Fishponds Rd. Car park in Park Avenue, accessible from Fishponds Road via Oakdene Avenue

**Great for: picnics, sport events, fishing**

Once in the park, descend the hill to the lake, then turn right and continue along the banks of the Frome for 1½ miles to Snuff Mills. This walk is suitable for pushchairs.

## Oldbury Court/Snuff Mills

Oldbury Court car park is off Oldbury Court Road, Fishponds BS16
Snuff Mills car park is at the end of River View, Stapleton BS16
www.bristol.gov.uk

**Great for: picnics, bike rides, fishing**

This is such a peaceful and beautiful walk that it is hard to believe you are only three miles from Bristol City Centre. The walk follows the River Frome through interesting woodland where children will delight at the many areas they can explore (but keep a close eye on them!) This walk is suitable for pushchairs although it can get muddy. Some unfenced areas next to the water. The walk can be shortened at various points.

**Accessibility:** Most pushchair & wheelchair friendly
**Toilets:** Eastville Park and Snuff Mills
**Refreshments:** Ice cream vans Eastville Park and Snuff Mills (summer), cafe Snuff Mills
**Play areas:** Located at Oldbury Court and Eastville Park
**Sites of particular interest:** Relics of a working stone saw mill at Snuff Mills with a double egg-ended boiler used in the past to power a saw for the stone quarry.

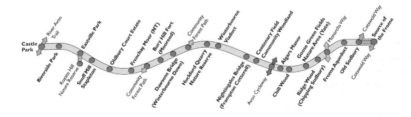

## See also Parks and Play Areas

Contact the Avon Frome Partnership 0117 922 4325 or South Gloucestershire Council 01454 863725 to receive the latest copy of the Frome Valley Walkway Booklet or download it from the South Glos website (above) which includes 5 additional short circular walks to interesting places in the Valley.

## Leigh Woods

The National Trust, Valley Rd, Leigh Woods, BS8 3PZ
0117 9731645, www.forestry.gov.uk
Open all year round
From Clifton take A369 towards Portishead, after
the traffic lights there is a large old archway on the
right, take right turn almost immediately after this,
car park ½km on the left
**Accessibility:** Paths for pushchairs & wheelchairs
**Refreshments:** Bring your own.

**Great for: picnics, bike rides, woods**

The Purple Trail, which begins and ends at the
car park, is a fully accessible 2½ km circular
route, hard-surfaced, mostly level and suitable
for pushchairs and wheelchairs. There are
also other hard-surfaced paths leading from
the Purple Trail which are marked on the
board in the car park and on a free leaflet
available from the Reserve Office on Valley
Road or from the website above. However,
not all are waymarked on the ground like the
Purple Trail.

## Oke Park Wood

Okebourne Rd, Brentry
www.forestofavon.org.uk
Access via Okebourne Road to the west, Chakeshill
Close to the east and Knole Lane to the south. No
designated car park.
**Accessibility:** Path for pushchairs & wheelchairs

**Great for: woods, views**

With excellent views across the Severn
Estuary and Ridge, Oke Park Wood is a
2.5 hectare new woodland located on the
northern fringe of Bristol. Trees planted are
all native broadleaves such as ash, oak, wild
cherry and hazel. There are also large areas
of grassed open space. The wood has full
public access, so you are welcome to visit at
any time.

# LOCAL NATURE RESERVES

If you want to see wildlife in the heart of the
city, look no further than Bristol's network
of Local Nature Reserves (LNRs). These are
places with wildlife or geological features
that are of special interest locally and offer
opportunities to study or learn about and
enjoy nature. Bristol has 11 nature in the city
sites.

## Badock's Wood

Doncaster Rd, Southmead, Bristol, BS10 5PL
0117 353 2268
www.forestofavon.org.uk, www.fobw.org.uk
Main entrances to the Wood are at Lakewood Rd
(off Lake Road) and Doncaster Rd. Car parking
is available on adjacent roads. Please park with
consideration for local residents.
**Accessibility:** Visitors with small wheelchairs and
pushchairs should use the Doncaster Rd entrance, as
other entrances have narrow kissing gates or stiles.
For visitors with larger wheelchairs, please phone
Bristol City Council for a key.
**Maps** available from the Forest of Avon.

Badock's Wood is a wildlife haven in the
north-west of Bristol. At least 400 years old
in parts, it is made up of woodland situated
in a limestone valley, with adjacent areas of
wildlife meadow. Look out for bluebells and
wood anemones in the Spring. It is named
after the local industrialist and landowner,
Sir Stanley Badock, who bought the wood in
1905. In 1937, he gave the wood to the City
of Bristol.

## Eastwood Farm Nature Reserve

Whitmore Ave, Brislington, BS4 4TQ
www.eastwoodfarm.org.uk
Access is via Whitmore Ave, off Broomhill Rd,
Brislington. Parking within the farm is free,
however vehicle access to the site only available
during working hrs on wkdays. Parking available at
Whitmore Ave, a short walk away. Or access by ferry
to Beeses Bar & Tea Gardens (**see Eating Out and
Travelling Around**)
**Accessibility:** Good footpaths throughout, with
certain areas wheelchair accessible. However, some
steep slopes and paths can be very muddy after rain.
**Maps** available from the Forest of Avon.
**Refreshments:** Beeses Bar & Tea Gardens next
door.

Eastwood Farm is situated by the side of the River Avon in Brislington and was designated as a LNR in Jan 2008. Formerly farmland, part of the site was also used as a landfill in the 1970s. Today, Eastwood Farm is a wildlife haven where you can see swans, buzzards, coots, kingfishers and more.

## Royate Hill Nature Reserve

Edward Street, Eastville, BS5 6LW
www.avonwildlifetrust.org.uk
Access is from Edward Street (next to Greenbank Cemetery) off Royate Hill. Very close to Bristol & Bath Railway Path (**see Travelling Around**)
**Accessibility:** There are steep steps leading up to a stony footpath which crosses the site.

Royate Hill is comprised of two disued railway embankments linked by a seven span brick viaduct, and spans a distance of 450 metres in total including a stream and an old orchard within its boundaries. A beautiful and unusual site, supporting many species of plants and wildlife, it was saved from development following a high profile public campaign in the 1990s. With its unique position it has amazing views across the city. Whilst there you may see badgers, butterflies and goats. Bristol Parks manages the site in partnership with Avon Wildlife Trust.

## Stockwood Open Space

Stockwood Rd, Brislington, BS4 5LR
0117 917 7270, www.avonwildlifetrust.org.uk
The two main access points are beside Brislington School at Hungerford Gardens and The Coots, Stockwood. Buses to Stockwood Rd and The Coots.
**Accessibility:** Tarmac paths give access to wheelchairs & pushchairs

An old area of farmland including a replanted old rubbish tip, Stockwood Open Space has survived development, and now supports a varied array of wildlife such as kestrels, owls, butterflies, glow-worms and foxes. There are wildflower meadows, woodland, and an old farm pond home to frogs, toads and newts.

## Troopers Hill

Troopers Hill Rd, St George, BS5 8BU
www.troopers-hill.org.uk
The site is in St George, east Bristol, and access is from Troopers Hill Road or Malvern Road. Easy walk or cycle to the site from Bristol along the River Avon Trail. Regular buses running between Bristol and Hanham or Bath stop at the north end of the site off Summerhill Rd.
**Accessibility:** The hill has good paths throughout, although beware of steep cliff edges. By accessing the site from Malvern Road, you can reach the top of the hill by avoiding a steep climb.

A winner of the prestigious Green Flag award in recognition of high environmental standards, Troopers Hill - characterised by the tall chimney standing on top of the hill - is a benchmark for excellence in recreational green areas. In the past, Troopers Hill was quarried for pennant sandstone and mined for coal and fire clay, and it is this unusual geology of Troopers Hill that is the reason for it's ecological importance. Today, it is home to ling and bell heather, over twenty species of butterfly, and mining bees. Many events aimed at promoting awareness and interest in the Local Nature Reserve and its varied flora and fauna are organised throughout the year by the Friends of Troopers Hill. The Friends are also keen to involve children and organise lots of events aimed at the younger age group. Stunning views across the city.

## Manor Woods Valley Nature Reserve

Vale Lane, Bishopsworth, BS3 5RU
www.bristol.gov.uk
Access is from St Peter's Rise or Vale Lane.
**Accessibility:** A tarmac track runs through the length of the site, offering good access for cyclists, walkers and wheelchairs. Footpaths through the woods are more informal.

This site is a mix of woodland, grassland and river habitats. With the River Malago running through this site, there is a chance that you may spot a heron or kingfisher on your visit. In Spring, the woodland is carpeted in bluebells and ramsons. And in the Summer, the Vale Lane end of the site is a mass of wildflowers.

## THE REST

### Callington Rd

Access from Callington Rd, close to where it joins the A37 Wells Rd. Also from Imperial Walk on the north west side of the reserve via the public right of way crossing the site.

**Rich mosaic of wildlife habitats**

### Lawrence Weston Moor

From Long Cross, Lawrence Weston, turn down Lawrence Weston Rd at the side of St Bede's Secondary School. Road ends at free car park in front allotments. Turn left out of car park onto lane to back of allotments and into the nature reserve.

**Ditches, ponds, wildflower grasslands**

### Narroways

Access path beside the climbing centre (the church) on Mina Road in St. Werburghs.

**Wildflower meadows**

### Northern Slopes

Daventry Road (beside St Barnabas Church), Wedmore Vale, Kenmare Road and Kingswear Road.

**Steep slopes but excellent views**

### Old Sneed Park

Entrance is in Glenavon Park.

**Fields, wooded slopes and lake**

To find out more about Local Nature Reserves see: www.bristol.gov.uk or www.english-nature.org.uk Or call: Bristol Parks on 0117 9223719

*"Keep it [the walk] short, let them play in rivers and streams, let them feed the ducks or whatever. And invent things like chocolate trees that are to be found on the top of steep hills!"*

*Nigel Vile, 2008*
*(Author of Kiddiwalks)*

## BEYOND BRISTOL

You don't have to travel very far out of Bristol to find a variety of places to stretch your legs, whether it's a gentle potter with toddlers or a proper hike you're after. Below you'll find some favourite spots (all within about an hour from Bristol), some requiring basic map reading skills, others just being nice places to wander around. Where possible we've tried to give an indication of age/pushchair suitability.

Many of the walks can be accessed by rail, so you could make a day of it (**see Travelling Around).**

*Tip:*
If there is a website, it is strongly advised that you look at it before heading out. They often contain really useful information and maps that can be downloaded.

## NORTH OF BRISTOL

### Three Brooks Local Nature Reserve

Near Fiddlers Wood Lane, BS32 9BS
www.forestofavon.org.uk, www.three-brooks.info
Three Brooks is 6 miles north of Bristol. The Reserve is accessible from Bradley Stoke Leisure Centre and Library where there is parking, toilets and a cafe. Buses stop nearby and Bristol Parkway mainline station is less than a mile from the southern entrance.
**Accessibility:** A well-signposted network of level, hard surfaced paths allows people to explore the reserve on foot or bike.
**Map:** Available from Forest of Avon.

**Great for: cycling, birdwatching**

The Three Brooks Local Nature Reserve is about 148 acres and comprises three bluebell woodlands, brooks, ponds areas of rough grassland, species-rich hedgerows and a lake. The rich mix of habitats provides a valuable home to a wide range of wildlife, including reed buntings, skylarks, great crested newts, slow worms, and kingfishers.

# NORTH EAST OF BRISTOL

## Coaley Peak

Nr Nympsfield, Stroud, Glouchesteshire
01452 425666/863170, www.gloucestershire.gov.uk
On the B4066 Stroud-Uley Rd, about ½ mile from
Nympsfield
**Accessibility:** Picnic table for wheelchair user

Great for: **picnics, kite flying**

Picnic site on the edge of the Cotswold
escarpment with panoramic views towards
the Forest of Dean – on a clear day, you can
see the Black Mountains in Wales. The 12-
acre area has been reclaimed as a wildflower
meadow (at its best in summer) with picnic
tables and open grassland good for flying
kites. It also includes Nympsfield long barrow,
a neolithic burial chamber. The Cotswold Way
runs the length of the site, and you can stroll
through the adjacent Stanley Woods.

## Forest of Dean Sculpture Trail

Log Cabin Symonds Yat, Near Coleford
01594 833057, www.forestofdean-sculpture.org.uk
B4226 between Cinderford and Coleford, follow
brown tourist signs
3 ½ miles long but shorter loop possible
**Maps & information:** From Beechenhurst Lodge
Cafe
**Accessibility:** Some parts suitable for pushchairs &
wheelchairs
**Open:** Dawn to Dusk, admission FREE
**Refreshments & Toilet:** Cafe

Great for: **art, scenery, children's play
area**

This is a beautiful and magical walk through
one of the country's oldest woodlands,
transformed by sculptures made by
international artists. The trail starts and ends
at the rear of Beechenhurst Lodge picnic site,
off the B4226, in the heart of the Forest of
Dean. Should children still have energy to
burn off, do not miss the inspiring play area,
designed by the sculptor Andy Frost. This
area is suitable for children up to 12 years
old with various play structures representing
aspects of timber production – children can
climb over an oak tree, an old wooden ship
under construction, a man and horse leading
an old cartload of logs, and woodmen with
a crosscut saw, modern lumberjack with
chainsaw. The history of mining in the Dean
is also portrayed; swings and a ropeway are
overlooked by a pithead cage tower, a sliding
pole is incorporated into a beam engine
used to pump mine water (the original is
in the Dean Heritage Museum). These are
augmented with various structures based on
animals to be found in the Forest.

## Minchinhampton Common

Stroud, Gloucestershire
01452 814213, www.nationaltrust.org
South of Stroud, between Minchinhampton and
Nailsworth

Great for: **picnics, flying kites**

A large open space on a hill-top plateau of
the Cotswolds with dramatic views over the
surrounding countryside. Great for picnics,
walks and flying kites. The common has a
special mix of wildflowers, including cowslips
and orchids, as well as a diversity of birds,
butterflies and other insects. It's also one
of the most important archaeological sites
in Britain, with prehistoric field systems, a
Neolithic long barrow, medieval roads and
military defences from the Second World War.

Don't be surprised to see free roaming cattle.

## Symonds Yat Rock

Log Cabin Symonds Yat, Near Coleford
01594 833057, www.forestry.gov.uk
Take B4432 north of Coleford
**Accessibility:**
**Refreshments & Toilet:** Cafe (Refreshment cabin:
Summer 10am-4pm, Winter: limited opening)

Great for: **picnics, bird watching**

Fantastic viewpoint high above the River
Wye. Log cabin with snack bar, information,
souvenirs and picnic area. Waymarked walks
start from here (see website - walks are
marked as easy). A pair of peregrine falcons
nest on the nearby cliffs and from mid April
to August, staff from the RSPB can tell you
all about the fastest birds in the world and
hopefully help spot them and even see right
into their nests, with powerful telescopes.
If you're walking, there are two useful hand
ferries (seasonal) which run from The Olde
Ferrie Inne on the west bank of the Wye to

the base of the Rock, and from the Saracen's Head Inn on the east bank. See website for summer activities.

## MORE OF NORTH EAST'S BEST

### Brackenbury Ditches, Cotswolds
www.visitthecotswolds.org.uk
Maps available to download at address above.
OS Map 162 Gloucester & Forest of Dean.
Access: Park on roadside 1 mile north of Wotton-under-Edge (map ref 757943 or 754941)

**Fairly level walk of 2-4 miles through mixed woodland. Suitable for all-terrain buggies. Aim for the fort and Nibley Knoll in a north westerly direction.**

### Leyhill Arboretum
HMP Leyhill, Tortworth, Wotton-under-Edge, GL12
01454 264345
Daily 9am-4pm
1/2 mile from M5, J12, on B4509 towards Wotton

**Short (1 mile) walk around this stunningly beautiful lake**

### Puzzle Wood
Near Coleford, GL16 8QD
01594 833187, www.puzzlewood.net
Mar w/e only 10am-5.30pm, Easter-Sep: 10am-5.30pm (last entry 4.30pm), Oct: 11am-4.30pm
£4.80 adult, £3.40 child, U4's FREE
B4228 0.5 mile south of Coleford
**Not suitable for pushchairs**

**An unusual maze and really weird scenery make for a great place to play - just don't get lost!**

# EAST OF BRISTOL

## Golden Valley
The main entrance to Wick Golden Valley is on the A420 near the Carpenters Arms, (OS Explorer 155, grid reference: ST 702 708). Bus services available along the A420 and bicycle locks provided near to the entrance. Also public footpaths that connect the reserve with nearby towns and villages. Visitors by car can use the Wick Village Hall car park, which is signposted off the A420 near the Rose and Crown pub. Blue badge holders can use two accessible parking bays at the Carpenters Arms.
**Accessibility:** The lower part of the reserve (Red Ochre Trail) is fully accessible.

### Great for: **the diverse habitat**

Wick Golden Valley is a Green Flag winning Local Nature Reserve at the foot of the Cotswold Hills in South Gloucestershire. The reserve contains a variety of habitats along the slopes and bottom of the valley, including a river corridor, woodland and grassland. These have been heavily influenced by the quarrying and production of refined ochre that took place in the 20th century (closing down in 1968). You can see the red ochre remains in the soil around the reserve. The Valley is home to a fascinating array of wildlife including Peregrine Falcons, Kingfishers, dippers, crayfish, bats and earth star fungi. The reserve is easily found with entrance signs and trail markers created by the Forest of Avon Wood Products Cooperative. The Red Ochre Trail, a circular walk, is about a mile long. Unsurfaced paths are steeper and narrower in other areas.

Free site leaflet available on request.

*"...take some matches and light a fire and cook beans and bacon in the open! I saw some families doing this recently and the children were having as much fun as you could imagine for free – collecting wood, scrambling on the rocks and generally getting very muddy in the process! Try the Frome Valley near Hambrook or in the Golden Valley near Wick".*

*Nigel Vile, 2008*
*(Author of Kiddiwalks)*

## Weston Big Wood

Nr Portishead, North Somerset
0117 917 7270
www.avonwildlifetrust.org.uk
mail@avonwildlifetrust.org.uk
From the B3124 Clevedon-Portishead road, turn into
Valley Road just north of Weston-in-Gordano. Park
in the lay-by 300m on the right, and walk up the hill.
Steps lead into the wood from the road
**Accessibility:** Access is difficult.
Open all year

### Great for: **the diverse habitat**

One of the area's largest ancient woodlands,
dating back to the last Ice Age, this Avon
Wildlife Trust nature reserve is rich in wildlife,
including butterflies, woodpeckers, tawny
owls, bats and numerous badger setts. In
spring, the ground is covered with wood
anemones, violets and masses of bluebells.
The old stones, ditches and banks are thought
to be medieval boundaries used to divide
the wood into sectors. The reserve is criss-
crossed with a network of (sometimes muddy)
footpaths; keep away from the quarry sides.

# SOUTH EAST OF BRISTOL

## Bradford-on-Avon to Avoncliff

Access: Bradford-upon-Avon Station car park.
**Accessibility:** Good for pushchairs & wheelchairs

### Great for: **accessing by train**

A canal-side walk between two villages.
Take the path at the end of Bradford-on-
Avon Station car park that leads into Barton
Country Park. Follow the river until it joins
the towpath. Walk along this for a mile or so
past narrow boats, until you come to Avoncliff.
Here you will find the Madhatter café and The
Cross Guns Pub (01225 862335). There is also
the Lock Inn Cottage

## Willsbridge Mill

Avon Wildlife Trust, Willsbridge Hill, Bristol, BS30 6EX
0117 932 6885
www.avonwildlifetrust.org.uk
A431 Bristol to Bath road, turn into Long Beach
Road. Car park on left.
**Accessibility:** Good for pushchairs & wheelchairs
**Refreshments & Toilets:** At Mill.
**Open:** Nature Reserve open all year, admission FREE

### Great for: **events & educational activities at the Mill, picnics**

This converted mill housing hands-on wildlife
and conservation displays is currently only
open when schools are visiting or events
are on, but there is plenty to do outside.
The Valley Nature Reserve which includes a
Heritage Sculpture Trail, a Wild Waste Garden
and plenty of lovely sculptural seating areas
for picnics is open all year. Pond dipping
equipment available for hire.

## Dundas Aqueduct to Avoncliff

Access: Take A36 from Bath to Monkton Combe, turn
left on B3108 and park at Canal Visitor Centre

This walk starts at Brass Knocker Basin (**see
Travelling Around** if you fancy hiring a
bike or taking a canal trip). It passes through
pretty cuttings and embankments. Take
towpath and follow the signs to Avoncliff. Lots
of wild flowers, ducks and cyclists. Fordside
Tea Gardens is about ¾ miles from the start
of the walk, open daily. The walk to Avoncliff
Aqueduct is about four miles. There are many
other walks that are possible along the Kennet
and Avon canal and it's easy for family cycling
(novice cyclists watch the edge). In the other
direction, it is about 4 miles to Bathampton
where The George is a child-friendly pub for
lunch.

More child friendly pubs can be found on our
website: www.titchhikers.co.uk

See also:
**Out & About West** and
**Travelling Around**

### Brass Knocker Basin

Brass Knocker Basin, Monkton Combe, BA2 7JD
01225 722292
www.bathcanal.com
Daily 8am-dusk, with seasonal variations
Take A36 south of Bath, at Monkton Combe turn left
at lights onto B3108
**See Travelling Around**

**Good point to orientate yourself whether
walking, cycling or boating. There's a visitor
centre and The Angelfish restaurant (scenic
and child friendly).**

# SOUTH OF BRISTOL

## Folly Farm

Nr Bishop Sutton, Bath & NE Somerset
01275 331590
www.avonwildlifetrust.org.uk, www.follyfarm.org
Open all year
Follow the A368 west from the A37 for about 1.5
miles. Folly Farm is signposted up a track to the left
**Map & information:** Available from Folly Farm.
**Accessibility:** Trail for pushchairs & wheelchairs
**Refreshments:** Plans for a cafe (Sept 09)
**Open:** Monday to Sunday

**Great for: events & educational activities**

A large nature reserve owned by Avon Wildlife
Trust including wildflower meadows, ancient
woodland and 17th-century farm buildings,
with spectacular views over Chew Valley
Lake and the Mendips. Visit in summer for
butterflies and meadows brimming with
flowers such as ox-eye daisies and orchids.
An Access for All trail through the old English
Woods over an impressive steel bridge
and overlooking an active badger sett, is
waymarked from the car park. You could bring
a picnic or visit the nearby Carpenters Arms at
Stanton Wick (see **Eating Out**).

*SOIL ASSOCIATION
ORGANIC FARMS*

Often have trails to follow.
See 'Animals & Wildlife'.

# SOUTH WEST OF BRISTOL

## Ashton Hill, Failand

0117 953 2141, www.forestofavon.org.uk
Get to Ashton Hill Plantation from the B3129 at
Failand. Car park at the site, (OS Explorer 154, grid
reference ST 518 710).
**Map:** Available from Forest of Avon
**Accessibility:** Paths for pushchairs & wheelchairs

A beautiful walk through woodland areas,
don't miss it in the autumn. There are several
walks of up to a couple of miles, through
mature woodland. The terrain can be rough
but there is a good network of surfaced and
unsurfaced paths.

## Blagdon Lake

Blagdon Visitor Centre, Blagdon Lake
0117 9536470, www.bristolwater.co.uk
**Map:** Available from Visitor Centre or online
**Accessibility:** Trail for pushchairs & wheelchairs
**Refreshments & Toilets:** Visitor Centre
**Open:** Visitor Centre, May-Aug: Sun 2pm-5pm

**Great for: picnics, nature trails, pony &
trap rides, family friendly open days**

Peaceful and pretty woodland walk along the
banks of the lake — but beware fishermen
casting. Good walking for toddlers. Discovery
trail leaflets available at the visitor centre or
online. Park on bridge abutting lake.

## Brockley Wood/Goblin Combe

Cleeve, North Somerset, BS49 4PQ
01934 833723, www.goblincombe.com
OS Map 172 Bristol and Bath
Take A370 towards Congresbury, turning left in
Cleeve immediately before the Lord Nelson pub,
down Cleeve Hill Road. Continue for approximately
600 yards and turn left into Goblin Coombe car park.
The X1 bus from Weston super Mare to Bristol stops
at the end of Cleeve Hill Road on the A370.
**Map:** Available from Forest of Avon 0117 953 214
**Accessibility:** Some surfaced paths
**Great for: events organised by the
environment centre**

Many pretty walks of up to four miles through
the woods, beautiful in autumn. No toilets,
but the Lord Nelson pub on the A370 is
close by.

## Burrington Combe, near Churchill

www.walkscene.co.uk
OS Map 172 Bristol and Bath
From A368 (Churchill to Blagdon) take the B3134.
Drive up the valley for nearly 2 miles to the plateau
and there is a car-park on the left
**Information:** Available from Visitor Centre or online
**Accessibility:** Not suitable for pushchairs/
wheelchairs

### Great for: **caves, streams, woodland walks, picnics**

A great starting point on the Mendips for young children. Fantastic views, wonderful heathland vegetation (wild grassy meadows, heather, bracken, gorse, silver birch etc.) and wildlife. Whether it's a quiet picnic, a gentle stroll or a few miles with the back-pack, there are lots of options available. For picnics and short walks take the path at the back of the car-park (north, towards Bristol) up 10 yards of rocky path and onto grassy meadow. For longer walks, walk up the road 30 yards and take the track on the right (going south) onto Beacon Batch and head right towards the peak. Continue west through Black Down, into Rowberrow Warren, Dolebury Warren to the Ancient Hill Fort above Churchill then back along the ridge in the direction of the car-park. This is about a seven mile circuit but can be shortened and there are other access points from Churchill and Shipham areas.

> If fishing is your thing, also see **Sharpness Canal, linking Bristol to Gloucester, for walks and Zander fishing.**

## Chew Valley Lake

Information Centre, Chew Stoke, BS40 8TF
01275 333345, www.bristolwater.co.uk
Daily 10.30am-5.30pm
Take change for parking or take a more leisurely pace on the bus (Service 672.674 Cheddar - Bristol, call Traveline on 0871 200 22 33)
**Map:** Available from Bristol Water, 0117 9536470
**Accessibility:** Suitable for pushchairs & wheelchairs

### Great for: **fishing, sailing, picnics, nature walks and bird watching**

This beautiful lake was constructed in 1950 to provide water for Bristol. It has wonderful views is a haven for birds, insects and animals. There are two lakeside trails suitable for buggies and wheelchairs - details available online or at the visitor centre (the main visitor centre is at Blagdon although there is a very small room at Chew Valley lake). There is also a gift and tea shop (nice menu, separate menu for children), and a play area near the cafe. Dogs on leads allowed.

## Clevedon Poet's Walk

Pay & Display at Salt House Fields or street parking
**Accessibility:** Some parts not suitable for pushchairs & wheelchairs

### Great for: **views across the Severn**

An inspiring, easy-going, short walk (about 1.5 miles) around the headland with good views across the Severn. Suitable for pushchairs (two flights of steps) with a nice clean public toilet. Start at the Salt House Fields car park, walk along the Front towards the headland, up the first flight of steps, and along the path. Continue along the undulating, fenced tarmac path on the top of the cliff to St Andrews Church. On the right hand side of the church you should see a sign for the walk, follow the path back towards your starting point. **See Beaches.**

> "In this day and age of environmental concern, why not let the train take the strain? Support the Severn Beach Line and travel out to the Severn Estuary, where the foreshore is littered with all manner of driftwood and sea weed, whilst low tide brings an abundance of wildfowl."
>
> Nigel Vile, 2008
> (Author of Kiddiwalks)

# The whole is only as good as the sum of its parts

## The Titch Hikers' Guide needs you.

The Titch Hikers' Guide is produced by parents and carers for parents and carers. We work on a not-for-profit basis as we want to keep the price of this book low so that it can keep reaching as many people who can benefit from it as possible. But checking and updating thousands of entries is a truly mammoth task. We therefore need mums, dads, carers, grannies, nannies, to help us produce the next edition of the Titch Hikers' Guide. We mainly need researchers, but other jobs come up from time to time. And you can give as much, or as little, of your time as you have. All we ask is that you are someone who truly believes in the integrity of the book.

**It's a good way to keep your CV ticking over, to meet new people, to develop new skills, and to earn a little pocket money.**

**Contact Elspeth at info@titchhikers.co.uk if you are interested.**

# Beaches

## Contents

**See also: Out & About West, Travelling Around, and Family Holidays.**

## SEASIDE CODE

Respect all marine life - do not poke or squeeze any animals you find, and put all creatures and rocks back where you find them.

Only collect empty shells.

Beware of cliffs and incoming tides.

Check public notice boards for information on water quality, currents and emergency phones. Swim parallel to the shore rather than out to sea, and do not swim after a meal.

Never leave young children unsupervised.

Take your litter home.

Consider other people.

If you see someone in trouble, alert the lifeguards, or call the Coastguard (999).

Tide times: www.easytide.ukho.gov.uk

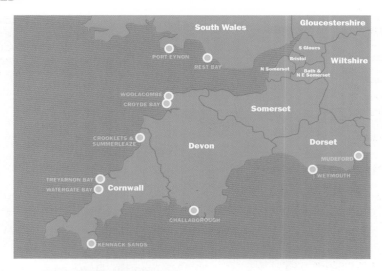

## TRAVEL TO...

The South West is blessed with beautiful beaches to suit everyone from budding surfers to paddlers. South Wales is about an 1¼ hr's drive from Bristol, North Devon and the Dorset coast both take just under two hours, and Cornwall just over 2 hours (you can also fly to Newquay from Bristol!) The beaches below are all recommended by the Marine Conservation Society for their clean water see: **www.goodbeachguide.co.uk**

### Port Eyon Bay, Gower

From Swansea. take the A4118 to Port Eynon.
A popular, sandy beach, backed by dunes and safe for swimming. Shop and café, toilets, lifeguard (May-Sept) and first aid.

*For more Gower beaches see www.enjoygower.com*

### Rest Bay

Porthcawl, Vale of Glamorgan, South Wales
M4 J37, take A4229 Porthcawl, follow signs to Rest Bay

Large, sandy beach backed by low cliffs and rocks that are just begging to be explored! Plenty of space but limited beach at low tide. Easy access with buggies. Grassy area next to car park and café to sit and watch the sun set. Lifeguard (May-Sept). Lost child centre.

## Woolacombe Beach and Barricane Bay

Woolacombe, North Devon
M5 J27, take third exit and follow signs for A361 to Barnstaple. Follow signs for Ilfracombe and Braunton. Stay on A361 to Mullacott Cross roundabout, take the first exit and follow signs to Woolacombe

The village beach has golden sand, backed by sandy hills. Excellent for sandcastles, paddling and surfing. In the summer there are miniature train rides and a bouncy castle. Woolacombe village is at the north end of beach. Lost child centre, lifeguard (May-Sept), car parks in Woolacombe. Barricane Bay is a lovely sand and shingle beach, smaller and quieter than the village beach. There is safe swimming and it is a great place to find unusual shells. Car park next to beach. Toilets at Village beach.

### Croyde Bay

nr Saunton, North Devon
Leave M5 at junction 27. Follow A361 to Braunton. From Braunton follow signs for Croyde. Car park next to beach

Pretty, small bay, with a lovely sandy beach, backed by sand dunes, and popular with surfers. There are good rock pools to explore and an enjoyable walk, with spectacular views, to nearby Baggy Point. Lost child centre. Beach lifeguard service May-Sept.

## Challaborough

Bigbury, Devon
At A379 between Modbury & Aveton Gifford turn onto B3392 towards Bigbury. At St Annes chapel turn right. Signposted Ringmore and Challaborough.

Fine sand and rocky cove family beach with rock pooling at low tide, and a coastal path along the cliffs. Toilets, shop, café, first aid, free parking.

## Crooklets and Summerleaze

Bude, North Cornwall
M5 J31, take A30, turn off at Okehampton, along A3079 and then the A3072. Bude signposted on the A39

Summerleaze is a huge sandy beach with a seawater pool at low tide. Ideal for sandcastles, rock pooling and paddling, it is also close to the town and its facilities. Crooklets is a safe, sandy beach, surrounded by sand dunes, with rocks to explore. Smaller and quieter than nearby Summerleaze beach, which can also be reached at low tide. Café, restaurants, lost child centre, toilets with disabled access, lifeguard service May-Sept.

## Kennack Sands

Helston, South Cornwall
From Helston. take the A3083 to the Lizard and then follow the signs to Kennack Sands.

Superb family beach. Lots of sand, a stream and rock pools. In an Area of Outstanding Natural Beauty (AONB), these two sheltered sandy beaches, east and west, form part of a National Nature Reserve. Toilets, café.

## Treyarnon Bay

Padstow, North Cornwall
Turn off the B3276 through Treyarnon.
Treyarnon is one of the most unspoilt beaches in North Cornwall. Its sandy bay lies in an Area of Outstanding Natural Beauty next to Constantine Bay. Toilets, car park, beach shop, cafe and hotel. Lifeguarded May-Sept.

## Watergate Bay

Nr Newquay, North Cornwall
Three miles north of Newquay towards Padstow.

While known as an excellent beach for surfing, Watergate Bay is truly stunning with azure water, a large open sandy beach, and plenty of rock pools for small children to paddle around in. Lots of facilities including excellent cafés Fifteen Cornwall is based here), a shop, toilets, and parking nearby.

## Mudeford

Bournemouth, Dorset
Access by foot, bicycle or land train from Hengistbury Head (parking available at Broadway, Southbourne, Bournemouth) or by ferry (seasonal) from Mudeford Quay and Christchurch Quay.

A spit adjoining the headland of Hengistbury Head, Mudeford Sandbank has a sandy beach against a backdrop of picturesque beach huts and views of Christchurch Harbour and the open sea. Café, shop, and toilets.

## Weymouth, Dorset

Signposted from junction 25 of the M5 or via the M27. A31. A35. A354. Pedestrian/visitor access to the beach is available from the promenade.

Lying within the "World Heritage Coast", Weymouth bay is good for children as it is sheltered, has a gradually sloping sea bed, and the beach is both sand and shingle. The central beach has lots going on in the summer months (it is easily located as it is adjacent to the town centre and harbour). Toilets, disabled facilities and access, first aid post, lost child centre, café/restaurants, shops, deckchair hire, pedalo hire and a promenade.

## MORE OF THE BEST

### Caerfai - St David's, Pembrokeshire

Just before St. David's on A487 turn left & follow the local signs. N.B. beach accessed by steep path. **Small rocky cove between spectacular cliffs, near St David's (where all facilities are). A sandy beach is revealed at low tide.**

### St Brides Haven - Pembrokeshire

Minor roads off B4327 Haverfordwest to Dale road. **Shingle and pebble, sheltered beach located in a cove.**

### Bournemouth Beaches

From Southbourne to Sandbanks
**Take your pick of these blue flag sandy beaches with all the facilities you could need.**

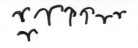

# AN HOUR AWAY

### Berrow - North of Unity Farm
Head to Burnham on sea, signs to Berrow & Brean. Access past Berrow on Berrow-Brean rd.
**Six miles of sand dunes and sand. Look out for the ship wreck at low tide!**

### Blue Anchor
Signposted off the A39 coastal road at Carhampton. east of Minehead.
**Sand & shingle beach great for finding fossils.**

### Doniford
Access through Watchet. Drive towards Haven holiday camp, unmarked turn-off takes you to a small carpark overlooking the beach.
**Stunning mud and sand beach with numerous rocks and rock pools.**

### Minehead Terminus
Turn off at junction 24 of the M5 and follow the A39 to Minehead
**Safe beach with lots of seaside amenities.**

# NEAR BRISTOL

It is possible to find a beach from as little as 20 minutes drive or train ride from Bristol. Also see **Out & About West.**

## Clevedon

The Victorian seaside town of Clevedon has a largely pebbled beach scattered with rock pools. There is a seafront promenade ideal for walks with toddlers and pushchairs. There are also donkey rides.

Best for... Exploring the rocky foreshore. The **Salt House Fields** at the opposite end of the promenade to the pier, where there are enclosed play areas for toddlers and older children. In season, there is a bouncy castle, miniature railway, crazy golf and snack bar. There are also various coastal walks around the area, such as **Poet's Walk** (some steps - may not be suitable for pushchairs, see **Walks, Woods & Nature Reserves**). Also **Boat trips** (see www.waverleyexcursions. co.uk).

Look out for... Summer Activities at the Grade 1 listed, Victorian **Pier** (01275 878 846, www. clevedonpier.com, open Mon-Fri 10am-4/5pm, Sat-Sun 10am-5/6pm, £1.50 adult, 75p child, FREE U3's)

### Clevedon Tourist Information Centre
Clevedon Library, 37 Old Church Road, BS21 6NN
01275 873498, www.somersetcoast.com

## Portishead

The beach at Portishead is probably not its highlight; it is very stony, more than a little muddy and not advisable for swimming! However, there is a small pebbled area for children to explore. There is also much more of interest in Portishead.

Best for...The spacious sea front park called the **Lake Grounds**. These were constructed in the early 20th century around an artificial lake. Here there is a boating lake, playground, inflatable slide, bouncy castle, tea cup ride and donkey rides. It's also possible to feed the ducks, and there's a nice cafe. Along the road from here is an open-air swimming pool (summer opening, 01275 843454).

Look out for...The large ocean-going vessels and coasters that sail past this coastline of geological and environmental interest.

## Weston-Super-Mare

The great British seaside tradition is exemplified in Weston-Super-Mare. There is a vast expanse of safe, flat, sandy beach. If you want to paddle, the tide is always in at Marine Lake at the North end of the seafront, or there is rock pooling at Anchor Head.

Best for... All the fun of the seaside from donkey rides, bouncy castles, crazy golf, miniature railway, putting green, horse drawn Thomas the Tank engine, to plenty of fish and chip shops! The **Grand Pier** is still closed following the tragic fire in 2008. It plans to reopen in 2010. See www.grandpierwsm.co.uk

### Weston-super-Mare Tourist Information
Beach Lawns, Weston-super-Mare, BS23 1AT
01934 888 800, www.somersetcoast.com
touristinfo@n-somerset.gov.uk

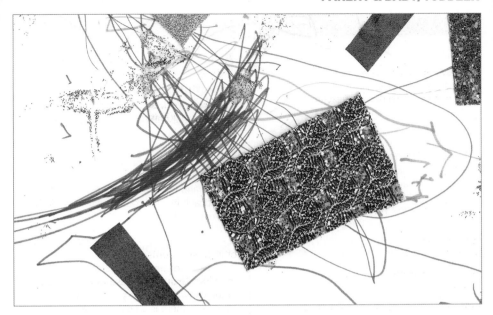

# Parent & Baby/Toddler

## Contents

For a new mum or dad, it can be really helpful to discuss the highs and lows of having a baby with others in the same situation. It is also nice to make the most of every minute with your baby knowing there is somewhere to go where you can indulge just being together. This chapter is all about being with your baby or toddler in safe, fun and accepting environments.

N.B Many groups are not open in school holidays.

### Good Website:

www.childcarelink.gov.uk
Online and telephone resource for finding toddler groups in your area.

For other ideas see:
**Storytimes & Reading, Get Physical, and Art, Craft & Cookery.**

Most health visitors run postnatal groups where you can go and chat to other mums, get your baby weighed and air any concerns.

## CHILDREN'S CENTRES

Children's Centres are for children and families during the early years. They provide family support, early leaning, activities and childcare to the local families. They are usually sited on or close to a primary school.

The following is a list of some of the Children's Centres in Bristol. (More will appear on www. bristol-cyps.org.uk as they open). Please contact your local centre for the full range of activities and facilities offered, (some will feature in our list of parent and toddler groups starting on page 121 but there are many, many activities taking place including baby groups, toddler and parent groups, PEEPs - peers early education partnership - and more):

| | |
|---|---|
| Bannerman Rd | 0117 377 2080 |
| Barton Hill | 0117 903 0407 |
| Brentry and Henbury | 0117 959 3800 |
| Broom Hill | 0117 353 4440 |
| Compass Point (Bedminster) | 0117 377 2340 |
| Filton Avenue | 0117 377 2680 |
| Footprints | 0117 303 9781 |
| Four Acres | 0117 903 0460 |
| Hartcliffe | 0117 903 8633 |
| Highridge | 0117 978 1028 |
| Lockleaze | 0117 377 2840 |
| Redcliffe | 0117 903 0334 |
| Sea Mills | 0117 968 8970 |
| St Anne's | 0117 377 3189 |
| South 2gether Knowle West | 0117 903 0214 |
| St Paul's | 0117 903 0337 |
| St Werburgh's | 0117 903 0323 |
| The Limes | 0117 903 0317 |

**More children's centres are opening (estimated to be by March 2010) to include the following areas and more:**
Avonmouth, Bishopsworth, Clifton/Cotham, Hengrove, Henleaze, Speedwell, Stoke Bishop, Whitchurch

For more information call 9037426 or see www.bristol-cyps.org.uk/early/family-information-service.html

## BABY GROUPS

### New Mums Club

www.newmumsclub.co.uk, rachel@boocoo.co.uk

Regular fun social morning for mums with bump or baby. Offers a chance to meet other mums, listen to a rolling programme of informal presentations covering topics such as complimentary health, weaning, childcare options and post natal welfare, and join in with local baby and toddler activities. Contact for venue details.

### Cairns Rd Baby Club

www.cairnsroad.org, 0117 9425669

Thursday afternoons: Baby Club for new mums and tiny babies, for chat and afternoon tea and cake. A time to share tips and get practical parenting advice. £1.50 per session. 1 to 2.45pm.

### Filton Avenue Nursery School

Blakeney Road, Horfield, Bristol, BS7 0DL
0117 377 2680, www.filtonavenuenursery.ik.org

Baby Groups - For children from birth until they are able to walk confidently.

Friday 9.00-11.15 - Premature babies with their parents/carers.

Tuesday 9.30-11.00 - Babies with their parents/carers.

### Highridge Play Centre

Lakemead Grove, Highridge, Bristol, BS13 8EA
0117 903 0460, www.fouracreschildrenscentre.co.uk
Mon 9.30-11.30am

Parents/carers and babies from 0-1 year.

### Redcliffe Early Years Centre

Spencer House, Ship Lane, Redcliffe, BS1 6RR
0117 903 0334
Mon 1-2.30pm

Baby Group - under 1's

# Tips

- You want to do a group with your baby or toddler but don't like the idea of coffee mornings. Try groups like Story Dance or Waterbabies where there is a firm focus on your baby.
- You want to meet other parents but aren't yet at a stage where you are happy to leave the house? Got a computer? Join **Netmums** and get chatting on the coffee house.

## Under One's Group

Charlotte Keel Health Centre, Seymour Rd, Easton, 0117 902 7100

Thu 12pm-1pm (runs through holidays), 20p

Small informal drop-in group for U1's in restricted area with stimulating toys. Good for a chat with new mothers. Open to local parents and carers.

## Under One's Group

Filton Clinic, Shield's Ave, South Glos, BS7 )RR
0117 969775
Mon 10am-12pm 12pm-1pm, 50p

## Windmill Hill Children Family Centre

Philip Street, Bedminster, Bristol, BS3 4EA
0117 963 3299, www.windmillhillcityfarm.org.uk
Mon 9.30-11am

£1.50 members, £2.50 non-members

Baby group.

# Did you know?

Early years drama, such as Debutots, starts from 6 months old.
See **Performing Arts** chapter.

# TODDLER TIMES AT MAIN ATTRACTIONS

## Bristol Zoo Gardens

Clifton, Bristol, BS8 3HA
0117 974 7399, www.bristolzoo.org.uk
For opening times, costs and directions see main listing in **Animals & Wildlife**

Toddler Time Every Weds 9.30-11am, Pelican Restaurant. Free to Zoo Members. (Non-Members pay for Zoo entry). FREE U3's.

A chance to meet other parents and children at the Bristol Zoo Parent and Toddler Coffee Mornings, where toys, games and activities are available and there is an offer on refreshments.

## Explore-At-Bristol

Anchor Rd, Harbourside, Bristol, BS1 5DB
0845 345 1235, www.at-bristol.org.uk
For opening times, costs and directions see main listing in **Bristol Visitor Attractions**

Toddler Time 2 – 5pm on Mondays. Under fives free, up to two carers get in half price

## Flying Saucers

9 Byron Place, Bristol, BS8 1JT
0117 927 3666, www.flyingsaucers.co.uk
For opening times, costs and directions see main listing in **Arts, Crafts and Cookery**

Toddler Time Every Tuesday is Toddler Tuesday. Go along with your pre-schooler or baby and receive 10% off and a free coffee. (Not during school holidays).

## PlaySpace

85 Barrow Road, St Philips, Bristol, BS5 0AE
0117 9550070, www.playspace.co.uk
For opening times, costs and directions see main listing in **Get Physical**

Toddler Time Every weekday morning, 10.15 onwards with a different arts and craft activity each week. Also holds regular baby fayres.

# PRE-SCHOOL MUSIC & MOVEMENT

## Baby Sensory

To find your local class call Keeley on: 01344 412072
www.babysensory.co.uk

Early learning for babies from 0-13 months. Includes activities designed to stimulate senses, which include combination of songs and rhymes to develop early communication skills. Classes held in various locations in Bristol. Contact for details.

## Boogie Beat

01934 741648/744272 Nicky or Lisa
www.boogiebeat.co.uk

Boogie Beat music and movement classes are energetic and fun, combining music, song and dance to give children a structured and enjoyable learning and development experience. Some props and percussion instruments are also used, and there is a wide range of music from classical to modern. Groups currently run in Clevedon, Backwell, Nailsea and Weston.

*"Excellent class. I have taken my daughter to many groups and classes and this one is the best. Energetic and great fun for children and mums too"*
*Local Mum at Little Monster Baby Show*

## Childs Play

The Crochet Factory Music Studio, Eastville, BS5 6LW
0117 951 8015, www.crochet-factory.co.uk

Offers preschool workshops, where under 3's are introduced to music through playing instruments, action songs and music games. (Also provides music workshops, group lessons and individual tuition for 4-8 yr olds.)

## Hum and Drum

28 Dublin Crescent, Henleaze, Bristol, BS9 4NA
0117 962 1328, penraw@blueyonder.co.uk

Introduction to basic musical concepts through playing a wide variety of instruments. Classes for 6mths-11yrs. Carers of younger children stay, but are encouraged to leave over 3's. Piano, violin & recorder lessons after school (up to 18 yrs).

## Jo Jingles

01454 610553 - Pamela Macleod
www.jojingles.co.uk/bristol, pam.jojingles@tiscali.co.uk
Venues: Redland, Emersons Green, Warmley, Yate, Bradley Stoke, Portishead, Clevedon, Thornbury and Mothercare at Eastgate

Weekly classes for pre-school children. Introduction to music, singing and movement including percussion instruments, action songs, sound games and nursery rhymes.

## Jolly Tots

St George Community Centre, St George, BS5 8AA
07970 - 678872 (Naomi Maggs)
jollytots.uk@blueyonder.co.uk

Singing workshops for children of pre-school age and their parents/carers. Sing songs with actions, props and puppets. Classes held at St George Community Centre on Fridays 2pm-2:45pm. £2.50 per child (pay as you go fees, not by term).

## Family Yoga

Bristol City Yoga
16 Backfields Lane, Bristol, BS2 8QW
0117 924 4414, www.bristolcityyoga.co.uk

Bring your auntie, your grampie and your sister too! Yoga poses suitable for the whole family. "The highlight for me is to see the children relax at the end. It's such fun to explore yoga and play in a creative way with them!"

# Jolly Babies/Music with Mummy/Three Four Time

www.musicwithmummy.co.uk
30 min sessions, payable half termly

Jolly babies is a chance to share your baby's first musical experiences, for ages 0-12 months. Music with Mummy classes are for ages 1-4yrs with carers. Fun with music through movement, games and using simple instruments. Some sessions during school holidays. Both classes take place at various venues. Call for further details: (J = Jolly Babies, M = Music with MUMMY, T = Three Four Time).

Lively sessions for babies and pre-school children.

For details of your nearest class call 0117 9574443
See our website www.musicwithmummybristol.co.uk

*Winner of the 2009 Little Monster Bristol's Best toddler class award*

**Bedminster/Brislington**
Hannah Kirby (JM)  0117 3778167
hannahspannah@blueyonder.co.uk
Jessica Stockwell (JM)  0117 9695466

**Bishopston**
Sophie Lincoln (JM)  01179 504913
sophielincoln908@mac.com

**Bitton & Longwell Green**
Kate Weldon (JM)  0117 9322430
kateweldon@btinternet.com

**Bradley Stoke**
Julie Thompson (JMT)  01454 619773

**Cotham**
Sue Richardson (JM)  0791 2627655
sueinbristol@hotmail.co.uk

**Downend/Emersons Green**
Deb Denny (JMT)  0117 9574443
sandddenny@blueyonder.co.uk
Katie Cox (JM)  0117 3738950
katiecox@blueyonder.co.uk

**Eastville**
Debbie Meachin (JM) 0117 9029145
imeachin@blueyonder.co.uk

**Fishponds**
Katie Cox (JM)  01173 738950
katiecox@blueyonder.co.uk

**Frampton Cotterell/Yate/ Winterbourne**
Wendy Howse (JMT)  01454 772711
wendyhowse@hotmail.com
Anne-marie Collier (JMT)
01454 773267
annemariecollier@yahoo.co.uk

**Hanham**
Ali Liddell (JM)  0117 9573842
alipabs@hotmail.com

**Henleaze/Clifton**
Fiona Reilly (JM)  0117 9510447
freilly73@yahoo.com

**Horfield**
Sophie Lincoln (JM)  0117 9504913
sophielincoln908@mac.com

**Iron Acton**
Anne-marie Collier (JMT)
01454 773267
annemariecollier@yahoo.co.uk

**Kingswood**
Ali Liddell (JM)  0117 9573842
alipabs@hotmail.com

**Knowle**
Jessica Stockwell (JM)  01179 695466

**Pill & Portishead**
Pip Hall (J)  01275 371767
jollybabies.bs20@btinternet.com

**Redland & Westbury Park**
Sue Richardson (JM)  0791 2627655
sueinbristol@hotmail.co.uk

**St George**
Debbie Meachin (JM)  0117 9029145
imeachin@blueyonder.co.uk

**Staple Hill**
Katie Cox (JM)  0117 3738950
katiecox@blueyonder.co.uk

**Totterdown**
Hannah Kirby (JM)  0117 3778167
hannahspannah@blueyonder.co.uk

**Warmley**
Deb Denny (JMT)  0117 9574443
sandddenny@blueyonder.co.uk
Kate Weldon (JM)  0117 9322430
kateweldon@btinternet.com

**Westbury Park**
Sue Richardson (JM)
0791 2627655
sueinbristol@hotmail.co.uk

**Whitehall**
Debbie Meachin (JM)
0117 9029145
imeachin@blueyonder.co.uk

## Kindermusik Classes

www.kindermusik.co.uk

**Bristol**
Hannah Loach                    0117 9245455

**Bristol City Yoga**
16 Backfields Lane, Bristol, BS2 8QW
Laura Chapman                   01454 853691
Kindermusik Village, babies 0-18 mths at 10.30 am
ABC Music & Me for toddlers to 4 years at 11.30am

**Stoke Gifford**
The Old School Rooms, St Michael's Church, The
Green, Stoke Gifford BS34 8PD
Laura Chapman                   01454 853691
Tuesdays at 10.15am

**Kingswood**
Rachel Georgeson 0117 307 9157
Park Centre in Kingswood, South Gloucestershire

Music and movement classes for young
babies - 7 yrs. Classes include singing, playing
instruments, gentle exercise and movement,
dance and music games.

## Mini Musicians

01275 394344 - Sarah Leong
www.mini-musicians.co.uk
Venue: Long Ashton Village Hall Club Room,  Keedwell
Hill, Long Ashton, Bristol. BS41 9DP. Disabled access.

Pre-school music class, suitable for children
aged 18 mths to 4 yrs. Classes held on Monday
mornings 9:30am & 10:25am. Singing, rhythm,
instruments, games, music and movement.
Classes given by a qualified music teacher.
Pre-instrumental music classes also offered on
Wed & Thurs afternoons within teachers own
home, (suitable for 4-7 yr olds). Includes an
introduction to playing the keyboard - phone or
see website for more details.

## Mmm Bopp

078999 21693, www.mmmbopp.co.uk
Music and movement classes offered for
babies up to 3 yrs. 45 minute classes including
creative music and movement, games and
songs. Classes held in various locations,
including St Christopher's Church Hall and
Jack & Jill Toy Shop (babies and walkers class)
and Playspace and St Christopher's Church
Hall (walkers up to 3 years).

## Music Bugs

0844 578 1012, www.musicbugs.co.uk
melanie@musicbugs.co.uk

40 minute classes involving singing nursery
rhymes, counting songs, knee bouncers,
action songs and finger play rhymes. Wide
range of props used. Classes held in various
locations across Bristol - contact or see
website to find your nearest class.

## Music Makers

33 Cornwall Rd, Bishopston, Bristol, BS7 8LJ
0117 924 1124

Introduction to music & movement for under
5's using accordion, percussion and additional
props. Children (18mth-4yr) attend sessions
according to age, lasting 30 to 45 mins.
Carersof older children settle them in the
group and can have a cuppa in the kitchen.
Occasional children's parties. Pre-booking
required.

## Rhymetime

Bedminster Methodist Church
(formerly Ebenezer Church), British Rd,
Bedminster, (off Clye Terr), BS3 3BW (free car park
Diamond St) & Tobbaco Factory, Southville, BS3 1TF
(go through theatre door, Raleigh Rd)

07751 - 022 902 (Esther), www.rhymetimebristol.co.uk

Lively music and action group, with separate
sessions for babies and toddlers. Sit in a circle
on the floor and sing along with the guitar to
favourite nursery rhymes and songs. Babies
join in with the action using the instruments.

Bedminster: Mon: Toddlers 10-10.30am &
Babies: 10.45-11.15am. £2.50 per session.

Southville: Thurs: Toddlers 10am-10:30am &
Babies: 10:45am-11:15am.

## La Leche League

See: www.bristollll.blogspot.com to find
out more about their coffee mornings and
meetings around breastfeeding issues.

## Rockin Babies

Henbury Library, Crow Lane, Henbury, Bristol. BS10 7DR.
0117 903 8522 Hayley, henbury.library@bristol.gov.uk

Fun singing, clapping and rhyme sessions for babies and toddlers aged 6 to 30 months. Every Monday (including school holidays) 10:30am - 11am.

## Shake, Rattle & Roll

0117 951 0396 , Clairelouise@rege.org.uk

Multi-sensory music, movement, drama and exercise classes for children aged 3-10 years. 1 hr sessions with relaxation at the end.

## Shake, Sing & Boogie

01275 891644, tanyabracey@blueyonder.co.uk
St Martin's Church Hall, Knowle

Music groups for U5's. Children learn a variety of nursery rhymes and action songs. They also get to play a selection of instruments. Classes last ¾hr, the first class is free.

## Sing and Sign

0117 950 0017 (Helen Hill), www.singandsign.co.uk
Course of ten sessions, £57.50, term time
Venues: Westbury-on-Trym, Portishead, Westbury Park, Hanham, Knowle, Keynesham, Redland and Horfield

Sing and Sign is a programme of songs and rhymes for babies from 6-18+mths, teaching simple gestures (derived from sign language) which parents can use to enhance communication with their babies. This course is based on three levels which move into phonics, the alphabet and colours as children progress. Older children welcome. Holiday/summer events held.

## Sing a Song and Movement and Music

Knowle Methodist Church, Knowle.
0777 9465 407, www.creatingtheway.com
debbielsmith@btinternet.com

Singing sessions for babies and toddlers (3 months - 4 years), every Monday 10-10:30am. Action songs, movement, finger rhymes and fun to live music. £2.50 per family - drop-in sessions, just turn up!

Bristol based **music** group for Mums, babies & toddlers...

**Wiggles & Giggles**

Fun sing-alongs with basket of puppets, props and percussion for every child

Classes held in colourful, stimulating environment

Group outings in school holidays and opportunity for Mums to meet up

Refreshments included

To book your place simply call Sadie on 0117 3732801

For more information please visit: www.wiggles-and-giggles.co.uk

## Starting Notes

Kirsty 0117 973 3965/07833 146576

A unique singing for pregnancy & early parenting group – running in Redland on Monday mornings. All pregnant parents & parents with babies (up to walking age), grandparents, and anyone working with birth & babies is welcome. The group aims to offer a chance to celebrate the parenting journey, to nourish parents, to encourage vocalising & singing for labour, soothing, relaxation, meditation, and fun, and also sharing & talking circle time. It's also a chance to refresh your memory of lullabies, playsongs & other lovely songs to sing with & to your baby.

119

## Story Dance

Cotham Parish Church, Cotham Rd, Cotham, BS6
Lucy Livingstone: 0117 924 9455
www.storydance.co.uk

Lucy uses themes from nature and appropriate props to inspire children to sing, move and dance in the ways that they feel comfortable. It is a part of the theme of the group that parents also join in with their child. For children aged 18mths-4yrs (grouped according to age). Classes take place on Tue, Wed & Fri mornings. Each group has maximum of 10 parents and children. Carers of younger children join in sessions but over 3's may stay on their own.

Lucy also runs groups for parents and babies aged 2-12 months (Fri am). These promise parents a chance to nourish themselves as well as their babies, through an activity-based group, using music, movement and props.

## Shake, Sing & Boogie

01275 891644, tanyabracey@blueyonder.co.uk
St Martin's Church Hall, Knowle

Music groups for U5's. Children learn a variety of nursery rhymes and action songs. They also get to play a selection of instruments. Classes last ¾hr, the first class is free Shake, Sing & Boogie

## Tatty Bumpkin

0117 952 0070, www.tattybumpkin.co.uk
www.pulabrown.tatty-bumpkin.com
Horfield Baptist Church - Mondays 9:30am & 10:30am.

Movement and story classes, with animal adventures, inspired by yoga. For ages 18mths-5yrs. With great music and ends with a lovely relaxation! Tatty Bumpkin is at various locations throughout the holidays/summer. Call for details.

Also see Paula's Advert on page 153, and read about 'Peas in a Pod Storytelling' on page 142.

## Toddler Tunes

0117 962 2336
Newman Hall, Grange Court Rd, Westbury-on-Trym
Horfield Baptist Church, Gloucester Rd

Singing classes with action songs and rhymes, instruments and puppets. Informal and fun atmosphere, parents/carers expected to participate. No pre-booking required. Suitable for all pre-school children. Pay as you go - just turn up!

## Wiggles and Giggles

0117 373 2801, www.wiggles-and-giggles.co.uk
£4.75 per session. Classes held at Westbury-on-Trym Methodist Church.

Music group for mums and babies/toddlers (4mths-3yrs). Sing-alongs with puppets, props and percussion. Small class sizes in homely environment. Refreshments included.

See Advert on previous page.

# PARENT & BABY CINEMA

## Curzon - CineMA and Baby

48 Old Church Rd, Clevedon, BS21 6NN
01275 871000 for recorded film information
www.curzon.org.uk
Wednesday mornings during school term time. Doors open at 10am, and the film starts at 10.30am.

Being a new parent does not mean that you have to miss out on watching new releases at the cinema, thanks to the Curzon in Clevedon. They run special parent and baby times where a great deal of effort is made to make the experience as stressfree as possible. The lighting is slightly higher than normal and the volume levels slightly lower so as to not frighten baby. Changing mats are provided in the auditorium for nappy changes before or during the film, as well as a microwave if you need to heat a bottle. Screenings are open to anyone accompanying a baby of up to 18 months old. You can bring older children in addition to your baby if the film's certificate permits. Adults unaccompanied by a baby will not be admitted. A really thoughtful service.

# PARENT & TODDLER GROUPS

Toddler groups are held during school terms and are for children under 5yrs. They are a good way for parents to meet up informally and for your child to socialise and try new skills under your supervision.

We have listed all the toddler groups by the day the group meets each week. They are listed alphabetically and some new groups to the book (recommended through the Bristol Family Information Service) are listed in a short section at the end of each day of the week. Please let us know if you have visited one of these groups and tell us more about them. Also, let us know if we haven't listed your favourite group.

A quick glance at the name and address of the groups will let you know if it is local to you. If you are unable to find a group in your area, one tip is to keep an eye on noticeboards in libraries, churches and doctors surgeries where they might be advertised. Let us know if you find one that should be listed here.

## Young Mums

There are various groups purely for young mums (under 20 years). Call Barton Hill Settlement (0117 9556971), Hillfields Young Mothers Group (0117 9586729) see Time For Mums (page 129) and Bumps & Babes Young Mums Group (page 127) and also contact your nearest children's centre.

# Daily Groups

## Bristol Children's Playhouse

Berkeley Green Rd, Eastville, BS5 6LU
Jackie Cutmore: 0117 951 0037, info@bcph.org.uk
Mon-Fri 9am-3.15pm

Informal drop-in for parents/carers open to all, every day, with extensive play equipment and playgrounds outside. Friendly, qualified, welcoming staff. Summer trips organised.

## Handprints

In Stoke Gifford, Bradley Stoke, Filton, & Little Stoke
01454 612128, www.myhandprints.co.uk
Mon-Sat 10am-12pm, £2.80 per session per family

Primarily support groups for parents and carers, but they also provide a planned play-programme which promotes imaginative play with toys, crafts, as well as singing. Drop-in basis. Special events in school holidays.

## Rowan Tree Kindergarten Parent and Toddler Group

Bristol Steiner School, Redland Hill, Bristol. BS6 6UX
0117 933 9990, www.bristolsteinerschool.org
Mon-Fri 9.30-12.15
£12 deposit on application, £6/session (1 siblings)

Part of Bristol Steiner Waldorf School's Kindergarten, sessions are held for parents and toddlers in homely surroundings with natural play materials. Sessions include crafts, break time and circle time.

## Sydenham Road Under Fives

Totterdown Baptist Church, Syndenham Rd, BS4 3DF
0117 907 4108, www.sydenhamroadunderfives.org
Mon-Fri 9.45am-11.30am

Toddler group for children aged 0-3yrs. Siblings under 5 also welcome. Baby area, craft activities and song time. Refreshments included. Parent pack available.

## PlaySpace

85 Barrow Rd, St Philips, BS5 0AE
0117 9550070, www.playspace.co.uk
Every weekday morning

Toddler Time with singalong & free cup of tea or squash and a biscuit.

# Monday

## Ashton Vale Toddlers

Ashton Vale Community Centre, Risdale Rd, BS3 2QY
0845 1297217, lhickery@aol.com
Mon & Thurs 9.30am-11.30am

£2 per family, includes refreshments

Drop-in session for children aged 0-4yrs. Spacious, friendly environment, lots of toys to enjoy and a different craft activity each week.

## Brentry & Henbury Children's Centre

Brentry Primary School, Brentry Lane, BS10 6RG
0117 9593800/9593900
www.bhchildrenscentre.org.uk
Mon 9.30-3.30, 50p

Family Drop In (under 5's). Come any time, bring packed lunch if staying over lunch period or lunch can be provided at a small cost (orders need to be in the week before).

## Barton Hill Family Playcentre

Barton Hill Family Playcentre, Barton Hill Settlement, 43 Ducie Road, Barton Hill, Bristol BS5 0AX
Elaine Iles, Family Playcentre Manager, on 955 6971
www.bartonhillsettlement.org.uk

Mon, Wed, Thur 9.30am-3pm, Fri 9.30am-2.30pm

Drop-in sessions covering the whole day. Tea, coffee, toast and snack time for the children. The activities include painting, dough, stories, outdoor play in the garden, and lots more fun. Contact for further information.

## Bright Sparks

St Mary's Magdalene Church Hall, Mariners Drive Stoke Bishop, Bristol, BS9 7QJ
Jenny Williams: 0117 968 3892/0845 129 7217
Mon 1.30pm-3.15pm

£1.50 per session

Informal drop-in group aimed at toddlers. Welcomes 0-4yr olds. Creative activity, lots of toys and separate baby play area.

Buy your ticket (under fives are free) to Brunel's ss Great Britain and enjoy a year of free entry. See **Bristol Visitor Attractions.**

## Cairns Rd Café with toddler zone

Cairns Rd Baptist Church, Cairns Rd, Westbury park, Bristol. BS6 7TH
www.cairnsroad.org (click on community page)
0117 9425 669 (Church Office)
Mon/Wed 9am-2pm, Fri 10.15am-2pm (reduced hours in holidays)

Free, fun soft play in large hall. Plenty of toys and a café with drinks and food, excellent toddler lunches (payable). Can be crowded but no booking required.

## Child's Play Toddler Group

Easton Christian Family Centre, Beaufort Street, Easton, BS5 0SQ
0117 955 4255, www.ecfc.org.uk
Mon, Wed, Thur, Fri 10am-12pm, £1 per family

Stay and play group for parents/carers and children under the age of 4 years. Large indoor play area and a newly developed outside play area encouraging the use of child's sensory abilities with sound, smell, touch and sight.

## Cotham Drop-in Playcentre

Cotham Parish Church, Cotham Road, BS6 6DP
Pauline: 0117 9734399
Mon 1.30-3.30pm, £1

Suitable from birth up to pre-school. Two halls, one for older and more mobile children. Sing song to finish. Refreshments included. Run by volunteers. Non denominational.

## Deutsche Spielgruppe

St Matthews Church Hall, Clare Rd, Cotham, BS6 5TB
0117 9441598
Mon 3.15-5.15pm (term time only)

German speaking group only.

## Early Learning Centre Toddler Art & Craft Group

Eastgate Centre, BS5 6X2
0117 951 8200
Tue 10.30am-12pm

Art and craft session so an opportunity to make a mess away from home! Meeting in the café where mums can relax with a drink. Toddlers are provided with juice and biscuit.

# Tips

Many groups will have messy play activities so wear old clothes

Most groups close during school holidays

Most groups will have a small entrance fee even if not stated here

Most groups will provide refreshments either free or for a small contribution

There are usually separate areas for babies

It's usually a good idea to phone first as some groups have waiting lists

## Filton Avenue Nursery School

Blakeney Road, Horfield, Bristol, BS7 0DL
0117 377 2680, www.filtonavenuenursery.ik.org
Mon, Wed, Fri 9-11.15am, Tue, Thur 1.15-3.15pm
Free

Stay and Play - A toddler group for children once they are walking confidently until they start nursery. This group introduces children to a wide variety of opportunities to learn through play and make new friends. It also helps parents/carers to feel more confident in their role as their child's first educator. These sessions are on a drop-in basis so you can arrive and leave when you want and choose to go to as many or as few sessions as you like.

## Parkway Parent and Child Project

Parkway Methodist Church, Conduit Place,
St Werburghs, BS2 9RU
0117 935 0205 info@parkwaypcp.org
Mon, Wed & Fri 9.30am-12pm
£1 per family

Drop-in sessions run throughout the year for children aged 2.5 to 5 years. Safe and stimulating environment with separate area for older children to ride bikes.

## Rainbow Tots

Kensington Baptist Church (Muller Hall), Seymour Rd, Easton, Bristol. BS5 0NX.
0117 951 1202
www.kenbaptist.org
Mon, Tues & Thurs 10am-12am (term-time).

Friendly church-run group meets three times a week for 0-4yr olds. Offers a craft activity every week, lots of toys plus baby area.

## Southmead Day Nursery

Doncaster Road, Southmead, Bristol, BS10 5PW
Liz Harper: 0117 377 2343
Mon, Wed, Fri 9.30am-11am

Free, informal drop-in sessions for children aged 0-4yrs. Parents can use the library or attend family learning activities, while children use the Sensory Room and outdoor play area.

## St Josephs Toddlers

St Josephs Church Hall, Forest Rd, Fishponds, BS16
Cathy Williamson: 0117 914 7173
Mon 1.45pm-3.15pm
£1.50 (second child 50p), annual sub £2

Variety of toys and activities, including baby area (carpeted) for children up to 4yrs.

## St Peter's Parent & Toddler Group

St Peter's Church Hall, The Drive, Henleaze, BS9 4LD
0117 962 8485
www.stpetershenleaze.org
Mon & Fri 10.30am-12pm. 50p per family per session

Children from bumps to nursery age, meets twice a week. Parents, grandparents, nannies are welcome to join. Action songs at the end.

## Redcliffe Early Years Centre

Spencer House, Ship Lane, Redcliffe, BS1 6RR
0117 903 0334

Mon 9.30-11am

Stay and Play. See Wednesday and Thursday for other sessions at Redcliffe Early Years Centre.

## Tiny Tots

All Saints Church Hall, Grove Rd, Fishponds, BS16
www.allsaintsfishponds.co.uk

Mon 10.30am-11.30am (term time)

Relaxed and fun group to inttroduce children to the Bible. Sing songs, listen to John tell a story related to the bible, then have an activity that connects to the story such as colouring pictures, making collages or mobiles. Time to play and for parents to chat. Also see Sticky Fingers - Thursday, and United Parents Toddler Group - Friday.

## Tots Time, Brislington

St Christopher's Hall, Hampstead Rd, BS4 3H
Alison Paginton: 0117 977 2016
Mon & Fri 9.30am-11.30am

£1.50 per session. Waiting list.

Popular group for children aged 0-3yrs. Lots of craft activity tables, dressing-up and books. Refreshments served mid-morning, followed by singing and then ride-on toys, trucks and parachute fun. Please ring for place.

## Trinity Tots ABC Club

Holy Trinity Church, Hotwells Rd, BS8 4ST
0117 983 8878
Mon 9.30-11.30am. Waiting list.

£1 per child with max of £2 for family

Drop-in friendly group for pre-school children offering variety of toys and music for all ages. Healthy snacks for children and adults.

## Tyndale Baptist Church Baby & Toddler Group

Tyndale Baptist Church, Whiteladies Rd, Clifton, BS8
Sue Garnier: 0117 924 5874

Mon 2-3.30pm (term time only).

Caters for children aged 0-4yrs.

## Victoria Park Toddlers

Victoria Park Baptist Church, St Johns Lane, Bedminster, BS3 5DA
Brendan Bassett: 0117 373 0477
Mon 9.30-11.30am & Thur 10-11.30am

£1 for one child, £1.50 for two or more.

Drop-in group for 0-4yr olds, with U1's area. Variety of toys, craft activities and sand. Fathers regularly attend.

## OTHER MONDAY GROUPS

### Bethesda Toddlers - Bethesda Methodist
Church Rd, Redfield, BS5 9HN
0117 9559118
Mon 10.30am-12pm, £1.25 per session

### Bright Sparks (St Mary's Church)
Mariners Dr, Stoke Bishop, BS9 1QJ
0845 1297217
Mon 1.30-3.15pm

### Headley Park Toddlers
Headley Park Community School, Headley Park Rd
0845 1297217
Mon 1.30-3pm, £1.50

### St Anne's PEEP group
Lichfield Rd, St Anne's, BS4 4BJ
0117 3773189, www.stannesparkcc.org.uk
Monday 1.30-2.30pm

### St Paul's Parent & Toddler Group
St Paul's Church, Coronation Rd, Southville, BS3 1AS
0845 1297217
Monday 10-11.30am (term time), £1 per session

### St Teresa's Parent & Toddler Group
Church Hall, Gloucester Rd North, Filton, BS34
0117 9793068
Mon 9.30-11.30am (term time), £1.30/carer & child
20p 2nd child

# Tuesday

## Brentry & Henbury Children's Centre

Brentry Primary School, Brentry Lane, BS10 6RG
0117 9593800/9593900
www.bhchildrenscentre.org.uk
Tue 1.30-3pm, 50p

Growing Together (1-2yrs old Peeps). Please ring to book place.

## Barton Hill One World Group

Barton Hill Family Playcentre, Barton Hill Settlement, 43 Ducie Road, Barton Hill, Bristol BS5 0AX
Elaine Iles, Family Playcentre Manager, on 955 6971
www.bartonhillsettlement.org.uk
Tue 1-3pm

For families with children from different countries. Chance to expand language skills in a fun way including singing and talking.

## Barton Hill PEEPS

Barton Hill Family Playcentre, Barton Hill Settlement, 43 Ducie Road, Barton Hill, Bristol BS5 0AX
Elaine Iles, Family Playcentre Manager, on 955 6971
www.bartonhillsettlement.org.uk
Tue 9.30am-12pm & 12-1pm (bring own lunch)

For parents and children. Fun activities and discussion to support a child's learning in everyday situations.

## Counterslip Baptist Church

648-652 Wells Rd, Whitchurch, Bristol, BS14 9HT
Jane Wood: 01275 833 377
www.counterslip.co.uk
Tue, Wed, Thur 10am-11.30am
£1, additional child 50p

Parent and toddler group held in a large carpeted area with wide variety of toys appropriate to age range. Small waiting list, please phone before coming.

## Filton Avenue Nursery School

Blakeney Road, Horfield, Bristol, BS7 0DL
0117 377 2680
www.filtonavenuenursery.ik.org
Mon, Wed, Fri 9-11.15am, Tue, Thur 1.15-3.15pm
Free

See Monday for full details.

## Horfield Methodist Church Toddler Group

Churchways Ave, Horfield, BS7 8SN
0117 952 0115, www.horfieldmethodist.org.uk
Tue 9.30am-11.30am
£1, £1.50 2+ children

Informal drop-in for parents and carers with children aged 0-3yrs. Free play and singing.

## Little Angels Parents & Toddler Group

6 Ashley Road, St Pauls, BS6 5NL
0117 9622321, www.bristolcitadel.org
Tue & Fri 10am-12pm, 50p

Small group meets two times a week, with space for 12-15 children, offering a variety of educational toys, trikes, tunnel, slide, dolls and prams. Storytelling & crafts. Refreshments. Fathers welcome.

## Long Ashton Toddler Group

Long Ashton Village Hall, Keedwell Hill, Long Ashton
www.longashtonparishcouncil.gov.uk
Tue 1.30pm-3.30pm £1, additional child 60p

Informal group held in Village Hall. Separate baby section and craft tables for toddlers. Entry includes light refreshments.

## Noah's Ark Stay & Play

Cairns Rd Baptist Church, Cairns Road, Westbury Park, Bristol. BS6 7TH
Carol de-Beger: 0117 944 6229
0117 9425 669 (Church Office)
www.cairnsroad.org (click on community page)
Tue 9.45am-11.15am £1.50 per session

Group for children aged 2-3yrs, plus their carer. Offers a Bible story craft activity and story. Numbers limited, please call for a place.

## Philip Street Chapel Toddlers

Philip Street, Bedminster, BS3 4EA
0117 953 9530, www.philipstreet.org.uk
Tue 10am-11.30am (term time) £1.30 per family
Entrance on Clarke Street

Well-equipped friendly group in large carpeted hall, aiming to provide a caring Christian environment. Wide range of toys available, book corner, craft activities, stories and singing. Welcoming to newcomers.

## Queen's Road Methodist Baby & Toddler Group

Queen's Road, Keynsham, BS31 2NN
0117 986 0271

Tue 2.30pm, £1 per family

Organised group for children aged 0-5yrs and their carers. Craft activity and lots of toys. Please call for a place.

## Rainbow Tots

Kensington Baptist Church (Muller Hall), Seymour Rd, Easton, Bristol. BS5 0NX
0117 951 1202, www.kenbaptist.org

Mon, Tues & Thurs 10am-12am (term-time).

See Monday.

## Redland Toddlers

Redland Parish Church Hall, Redland Green Rd, BS6
0117 946 4690, www.redland.org.uk

Tue & Fri 10-11.30am, £1

Spacious hall with good variety of toys and separate carpeted room for babies. Weekly craft activity and singing. Friendly and welcoming group. Dads, Mums and carers attend. Refreshments included.

## Rendezvous Parent, Baby & Toddler Group (Ebenezer Church)

286 Filton Avenue, Horfield, BS7 0BA
0117 979 1399, www.ebe.org.uk
Tue 10am-11:30am, (term-time).

£1 per family.

Well organised group (40+ children, age birth-3 yrs), with plenty of play equipment, craft activities and singing. Popular group with waiting list. Newcomers welcome.

## St Matthews Church Toddler Group

Clare Road, Cotham, BS6 5TB
0117 944 1598 (Church Office)
www.stmatthews-bristol.org.uk/children/toddlers
Tue 9.30-11.30am
80p/child, £1.20 for 2, £1.50 for 3 or more.

Fun group with a wide range of activities including craft, story time and songs based loosely around a theme for the term. Twice a term the group is taken up to the worship space for a very informal toddler service. Regular attendance is encouraged. Also see Saturday.

## St. Michael All Angels Church 'Piglets' Carers & Toddlers Group

St Michael All Angels Church Centre
160a Gloucester Road, BS7 8NT
Kay Crawford: 0117 924 1187
www.bishopstonandstandrews.org.uk

Tue, Wed, Thur 9.45am-11.15am £1.50 per family

Popular group for 0-4yr olds, plenty of toys, separate baby area. Price includes refreshments, stories, music and singing.

## Stockwood Free Church Toddler Group

Ladman Road, Stockwood, Bristol
Margaret Nash: 01275834 896

Tue & Thur 1.15pm-3pm, £1

Toddler and baby group held in church hall. Climbing frame, carpeted area for babies. Activity table for jigsaws, duplo or play dough. Coffee and tea.

## W-O-T Toddlers - Pat-a-Cake

Westbury on Trym Methodist Church
Corner of Waters Lane and Westbury Hill
Car park adjacent to the church.
Caroline Meaden: Tel 0117 9684894
Tue 1.15-2.45pm

£1 per family

Popular group for 0-4yr olds held in Church Hall. Large play area for older children with separate baby area. Weekly sing-song.

## White Tree Toddler Club

Westbury Park Methodist Church Hall, 4 North View, BS6 7QB
Alwyn Leverton 0117 962 5425
mobile 07804269289
www.whitetreepreschool.ik.org
10 -11.30

Drop in toddler club run by White Tree Preschool staff in groundfloor hall and rooms. One room has ride-on toys and other physical activities, one carpeted room is reserved for the babies, while the other has quieter activities for the slightly older children, including books, puzzles, small world toys, and construction sets.

## OTHER TUESDAY GROUPS

### Filton Little Folk
Filton Community Centre, Elm Park, Filton, BS34 7PS
0117 3305090
Tue 10am-12pm, £2.50 (includes refreshment)

### Tiddlers Play Sessions
Filton Fun Hanger, Filton Leisure Centre, Elm Park, BS34 7PS
01454 867076
Tue 9.30-11.30am

### Whitchurch Opportunity Group
112 Stockwood Lane, Stockwood, BS14 8TB
0117 9831298
Tue 10am-12pm

# NCT Open Houses

www.bristolnct.org.uk

The National Childbirth Trust (NCT) offers a way of meeting other parents and their children through open houses. Parents open their house (providing a drink and biscuit) for parents and their babies/children. Details are published in the quarterly NCT Bristol newsletter.

Open houses are a useful way of meeting other parents, especially if you are new to the area and can provide social contact through the baby and pre-school years. You do not have to be a member of the NCT to attend.

If there is not an NCT Open House in your area, why not think of starting one up. Have a look at the local website for more details.

# Wednesday

## Baby Comes Too
Key Centre, Charlton Rd, Keynsham, BS31 2JA
0117 987 7753
www.babycomestoo.ik.com
Weds 12.45-2.45pm, Fri 9.45-11am, £1 per family

For parents and carers of children aged 0-4yrs. Lots of toys, activities and singing session. Refreshments provided. Call as can be a waiting list.

## Barton Hill Family Playcentre
Barton Hill Family Playcentre, Barton Hill Settlement, 43 Ducie Road, Barton Hill, Bristol BS5 0AX
Mon, Wed, Thur 9.30am-3pm, Fri 9.30am-2.30pm

See Monday for more information.

## Brentry & Henbury Children's Centre
Brentry Primary School, Brentry Lane, BS10 6RG
0117 9593800/9593900
www.bhchildrenscentre.org.uk
Wed 9.30-11am & 1.30-3pm, 50p
Learning Together (Baby peeps under 1's)

## Bumps & Babes Young Mums Group
Clock Tower Association, Tower Rd North, Warmley, BS30 8XU
0117 9671655
Weds 10.30-12.30. Term time only.

Young Mums support/toddler group for ages 14-19 yrs with creche and social educational activities for mums.

## Cairns Rd Café with toddler zone
Cairns Rd Baptist Church, Cairns Rd, Westbury Park, Bristol. BS6 7TH

See Monday.

## Child's Play Toddler Group
Easton Christian Family Centre, Beaufort Street, Easton, BS5 0SQ
0117 955 4255
www.ecfc.org.uk
Mon, Wed, Thur, Fri 10am-12pm, £1 per family

For full details see Monday.

## Coffee Pot Parent & Toddler Group

St Peters Church Hall, Church Rd, Bristol, BS13 8JU
0117 964 5111
Wed 9.30am-11.30am, £1.50 1st child, 50p siblings

Well-organised group with craft activities every week, cooking, a puzzle area, sing-song, and plenty of bikes, prams and slides. Outdoor activities in nice weather. Tea, coffee, squash and biscuits are free, and toast & bacon butties can be purchased. Waiting list but drop in for more information.

## Counterslip Baptist Church

648-652 Wells Rd, Whitchurch, Bristol, BS14 9HT
Tue, Wed, Thur 10am-11.30am
For more information see Tuesday.

## Downend Baptist Church Toddlers

Salisbury Road, Downend, Bristol, BS16 5RA
Diane: 0117 956 7855
www.db-church.paradigmcomputing.co.uk
Wed 10am-11:30am and 1.30-3pm (term-time).
Thurs 10-11.30am

Mixture of Christian songs, nursery ryhmes, free play and craftactivites. Refreshments.

## Elmgrove Centre Mums & Tots

Redland Road, Cotham, BS6 6AG
0117 924 3377
Wed 10am-12pm, £1 per session

Drop-in group offering a variety of toys and activities including painting and games. Refreshments available. Use the side door which has no steps.

## Filton Avenue Nursery School

Blakeney Road, Horfield, Bristol, BS7 0DL
0117 377 2680, www.filtonavenuenursery.ik.org
Mon, Wed, Fri 9-11.15am, Tue, Thur 1.15-3.15pm
Free
See Monday for full details.

## Four Acres Children's Centre

Four Acres Primary School, Four Acres, Withywood
0117 903 0460, www.fouracreschildrenscentre.co.uk
Wed 9.30am-11.30am, Thur 1-2.45pm

Free informal drop-in for parents/carers with children aged 0-4yrs to stay and play.

## Hanham Folk Centre Parent & Toddler Group

High Street, Hanham
0117 967 4439, www.hanhamfolkcentre.co.uk
Wed 9.30am-12pm
£1.50 one adult + child, 25p per extra child, plus
£10.50 annual membership for folk centre

Group runs throughout holidays with organised trips in summer. Run by volunteers. Toys taken outside in good weather, plus weekly activities, refreshments included.

## Horfield United Reformed Church

139 Muller Road, Horfield, Bristol
0117 924 8689
Wed 9.30am-11.15am, Thur 9.30-11.15am

Informal group for 0-4yr olds, with craft activities, lots of toys and singing at the end.

## Imps

Henleaze & Westbury Community Church,
Eastfield Rd, Westbury-on-Trym, BS9 4AD
0117 962 0484/ 946 6807
www.the-community-church.net
Wed & Thur 9.45am-11.30am, £1 per session

Friendly welcoming group for 0-3yr olds with separate play areas, weekly craft activities and songs. Highly regarded. Please phone before attending.

## Mums and Tots

Leonard Hall, United Reformed Church,
Waterford Rd, Henleaze, BS9 4BT
0117 962 4196
Wed 1.30pm-3.30pm, 50p

Small, friendly and welcoming group with good range of toys.

## Parkway Parent and Child Project

Parkway Methodist Church, Conduit Place,
St Werburghs, BS2 9RU
0117 935 0205 info@parkwaypcp.org
Mon, Wed & Fri 9.30am-12pm

£1 per family

See Monday.

## Redcliffe Early Years Centre

Spencer House, Ship Lane, Redcliffe, BS1 6RR
0117 903 0334

Wed 10-11am

PEEP session. 1-5 yr olds. Call for details. See Monday and Thursday for other sessions at Redcliffe Early Years Centre.

## Rosemary Nursery School and Family Unit Stay & Play

Haviland House, St Jude's Flats, Bristol, BS2 0DT
0117 377 3297

Wed 1.30pm-3pm

Free informal stay and play for parents/carers with children up to 5yrs.

## Southmead Day Nursery

Doncaster Road, Southmead, Bristol, BS10 5PW
Liz Harper: 0117 377 2343

Mon, Wed, Fri 9.30am-11am

See Monday for full details.

## St Bonaventures Toddler Group

St Bonaventures Church, 7 Egerton Road, Bishopston
Wed 1.45pm-3.10pm

£1 per adult, 20p per child

Plenty of space for children aged 0-4yrs. A good variety of toys, weekly crafts and singing. Very friendly group, ideal place to meet locals, organic refreshments served.

## St George Baptist Church Parent and Toddler Group

St George Baptist Church, Summerhill Rd, BS5 8HH
0117 955 0512
Wed 1.30pm-3.15pm

50p including refreshments

Drop-in friendly group for 0-4yr olds. Large hall to run around in. Everyone welcome.

## St. Michael All Angels Church 'Piglets' Carers & Toddlers Group

St Michael All Angels Church Centre
160a Gloucester Road, BS7 8NT

Tue, Wed, Thur 9.45am-11.15am £1.50 per family

For more information, see Tuesday.

## St Patrick's Toddler Group

St Patrick's Community Centre, Blacksworth Rd, St George. (Adjacent to St Patrick's School).
0117 940 0482
Wed 8.30am-11am, £1

For children up to 5yrs. Includes painting, trains, bricks, play dough and jigsaws.

## St Peter's Parent & Toddler Group

St Peter's Church Hall, The Drive, Henleaze, BS9 4LD
Parish Office: 0117 962 3196

Mon & Wed 10am-12pm. 50p per family per session

See Monday for more details.

## Tiddlers & Toddlers

St Edyth's Church, Avonleaze, Sea Mills, Bristol. BS9 2HU 0117) 968 6965
9.30-11.30am (except school holidays)

Toddler group open to anyone with pre-school children. The group has a range of toys for the children to play with, and there is normally a craft activity to join in with. Refreshments are provided for children and adults. At the end of the session we have story and song time.

## Zetland Toddlers

Zetland Evangelical Church, 4&6 North Rd, St Andrews, BS6 5AE
Eirene Carey-Jones: 0117 982 4796
Wed 9.45am-11.15am

50p per family

Small and friendly church-based group for 0-4yr olds. Lots of toys, weekly craft activities and circle time.

## OTHER WEDNESDAY GROUPS

**Time for Mums**
The Sanctuary, 55 High Street, Staple Hil, BS16 5HD
07909892058 - ring for details
Wed 2-3.30pm, for mums under 20yrs only

# Thursday

## Ashton Vale Toddlers

Ashton Vale Community Centre, Risdale Rd, BS3 2QY
Lindsey Hickery 0117 963 9283
Thu 9.30am-11.30am
£2 per family, includes refreshments

Drop-in session in spacious, friendly environment for children aged 0-4yrs. Lots of toys, singing and various craft activities.

## Baby Break Parent & Toddler Cafe

Emmanuel Church Hall, Oxford Street, W-s-M
Sara Gray 07971421851

Thur 9.30am-2.30pm, £1 1st child, 50p siblings

Craft activities, bouncy castle, huge selection of toys and games, and a great choice of food.

## Barton Hill Family Playcentre

Barton Hill Family Playcentre, Barton Hill Settlement, 43 Ducie Road, Barton Hill, Bristol BS5 0AX

Mon, Wed, Thur 9.30am-3pm, Fri 9.30am-2.30pm

See Monday for more information.

## Brentry & Henbury Children's Centre

Brentry Primary School, Brentry Lane, BS10 6RG
0117 9593800/9593900
www.bhchildrenscentre.org.uk

Thurs 10-11.30, 50p - call to book place
Growing Together (1-2yrs old Peeps) session

Thurs 1.30-3pm, 50p - call to book place
Time Together (2-3yrs old Peeps) session

## Chatterbox (Toddler Group)

Horfield Baptist Church, 279 Gloucester Road, Bristol, BS7 8NY (Brynland Road entrance)
Valerie Harwood: 0117 924 3608
www.horfieldbaptist.net

Thur/Fri 1.00pm-3.00pm, £1.50

Church based group for 0-4 yr olds, running twice a week. Varied toys, craft table, climbing equipment and ride-ons finishing with a story.

## Chelsea Tots

Chelsea Christian Centre, Devon Road, BS5 6ED
Phillis Spratt: 0117 967 3920
0117 939 8498

Thu 10am-11.30am, £1

Happy, friendly and caring environment for 0-4yr olds, with 10mins singing each session. Occasional crafts. Open to all.

## Child's Play Toddler Group

Easton Christian Family Centre, Beaufort Street, Easton, BS5 0SQ
0117 955 4255, www.ecfc.org.uk

Mon, Wed, Thur, Fri 10am-12pm, £1 per family

For full details see Monday.

## Christchurch Toddlers

Christ Church Crypt, Clifton, BS8 4EE
Parish Office: 0117 973 6524 or Jane: 0117 9732593
www.christchurchclifton.org.uk
Ra Gibson gibson.ivywell@blueyonder.co.uk
or Jane Sykes pandj.sykes@blueyonder.co.uk
Thur 10am-11.30pm and 2-3.30pm

(Side entrance)

Friendly environment for 0-3yr olds, with blanket and toys for babies, dressing up, wendy house and bikes for toddlers. Different weekly craft activity and singalongs. Please phone, as there are restricted numbers.

## Clifton Cathedral Parent & Toddler Group

Clifton Cathedral House Clifton Park, Clifton BS8 3BX
0117 9738411
Thur 9.45-11.30am

For children 0-3 years. Informal, friendly group. Parking, refreshments for mum, dad and little ones. Craft table, singing time, ball pit. Drop in or call for more details.

## Counterslip Baptist Church

648-652 Wells Rd, Whitchurch, Bristol, BS14 9HT
Tue, Wed, Thur 10am-11.30am

For more information see Tuesday.

## Downend Baptist Church Toddlers

Salisbury Road, Downend, Bristol, BS16 5RA
Diane: 0117 956 7855
Thurs 10-11.30am
See Wednesday for more information.

## Emmanuel Chapel Toddler Group

Satchfield Cres, Henbury, BS10 7BN
Nikki: 0117 9501855
Thurs 10am, £1.50 for 1 child (25p each additional
family member)

Meets once a week. The group is centred
around music. Large range of toys including
ball pool tent, book corner, play kitchen area,
bikes, trikes and baby toys. Regular craft and
singing. Quiet space in one room. Newcomers
welcomed.

## Faith Space Parent and Toddlers

Stackpool Road Methodist Church, Southville, Bristol
Margaret Baber: 0117 963 7607
Thu 10.30am-12.30pm, £1.50

Corner of Stackpool Road and Howard Road

Popular and well-attended group with a
caring and warm atmosphere for children
aged 0-3yrs. Usually 60+ children, so can be
quite boisterous, held in two halls. Fathers
welcomed.

## Filton Avenue Nursery School

Blakeney Road, Horfield, Bristol, BS7 0DL
0117 377 2680, www.filtonavenuenursery.ik.org
Thur 9am-1pm. Free

**Childminder Stay and Play** - This group
runs just like the toddler Stay and Play but
is for childminders and the children they
care for. The childminders are able to access
support from each other and nursery staff.

Also **Stay and Play** - see Monday for full
details.

## Four Acres Children's Centre

Four Acres Primary School, Four Acres, Withywood
0117 903 0460, www.fouracreschildrenscentre.co.uk
Wed 9.30am-11.30am, Thur 1-2.45pm

Free informal drop-in for parents/carers with
children aged 0-4yrs to stay and play.

## Horfield United Reformed Church

139 Muller Road, Horfield, Bristol
0117 924 8689
Wed 9.30am-11.15am, Thur 9.30-11.15am

For full details see Wednesday.

## Imps

Henleaze & Westbury Community Church,
Eastfield Rd, Westbury-on-Trym, BS9 4AD
0117 962 0484/ 946 6807
www.the-community-church.net
Wed & Thur 9.45am-11.30am, £1 per session

See Wednesday for full details.

## Kebele New Families Group

Kebele Social Centre, 14 Robertson Rd, Easton
0117) 9399469, www.kebelecoop.org
12-3pm. Free

An informal drop-in group, open to children
from birth to four years accompanied by a
parent or guardian. Tea, coffee, juice and
cake available for a small donation.

## Kings Tots Parent and Toddlers

Bristol Community Church, Bourne Chapel,
Waters Road, BS15 8BE
0117 947 8441, www.bristolcommunitychurch.org
Fri 10am-11.30am

£1, includes refreshments

Children aged 0-3yrs can play in a safe
environment. Free play, crafts and
refreshments. Possible waiting lists.

Fancy Soft Play? See
Castaways in **Get Physical.**

## Little Acorns Parents and Toddlers

High Grove Church, Highgrove, Sea Mills, BS9 2NL
0117 968 5668, 0117 946 6807, 0845 1297217
www.highgrove.org.uk
Thur 9.30am-11.15am (term time)

80p per family

Coffee & chat for parent/carers with children
aged 0-4yrs. Good play equipment, craft
activity, singing and storytime. Occasional
outings.

## Parent and Baby Group

Knowle Clinic, Broadfield Rd, BS4 2UH
0117 919 0200

Thur 10.30am-12 noon

Free group (20p refreshments). Mats with toys for babies. Occasional speakers on health issues. Health visitor available.

## Rainbow Opportunity Parent and Toddler Group

The PAL House, Daventry Rd, BS3 1JG
0117 9300 303, nowen@bristol-mc.co.uk
Thur 12-2.30pm
Voluntary donation of £1

Playgroup for toddlers with delayed development or learning disabilities and their parents. Playtime with toys, craft and singing. Parents have an opportunity to chat and get the support they need. Makaton sign language is used.

## Rainbow Tots

Kensington Baptist Church (Muller Hall), Seymour Rd, Easton, Bristol. BS5 ONX.

Mon, Tues & Thurs 10am-12am (term-time).

See Monday.

## Redcliffe Early Years Centre

Spencer House, Ship Lane, Redcliffe, BS1 6RR
0117 903 0334
Thur 1.30-2.45pm (ages 1-3 only)

Wiggle and Giggle session. See Monday and Wednesday for other sessions at Redcliffe Early Years Centre.

## Redland Park Church Baby & Toddler Group

Redland Park Church, Whiteladies Rd, BS6 6SA
0117 973 5850, www.redlandparkchurch.co.uk
Thur 10am-11.30am

Small friendly group for 0-4yr olds. Money raised from the group supports orphans overseas.

## Scramblers

St Francis Church, North Street (opposite Aldi)
www.bedminsterchurches.net
Thur 11am-12.30pm £1.50 per session including refreshments

For parents/carers and their children (0-3 yrs). Fun family activities and support for parents.

## St. Michael All Angels Church 'Piglets' Carers & Toddlers Group

St Michael All Angels Church Centre
160a Gloucester Road, BS7 8NT

Tue, Wed, Thur 9.45am-11.15am £1.50 per family

For more information, see Tuesday.

## Sticky Fingers

All Saints Church Hall, Grove Road, BS16
0117 907 9064, www.allsaintsfishponds.co.uk
Thur 9.30am-11.30am

£2, additional child £1

Friendly, lively group for toddlers aged 1-3yrs. Wide range of activities, including sand and crafts along with construction toys. Small waiting list, regular attendance expected. Also see Tiny Tots - Monday, and United Parents Toddler Group - Friday.

## Stockwood Free Church Toddler Group

Ladman Road, Stockwood, Bristol
Margaret Nash: 01275834 896

Tue & Thur 1.15pm-3pm, £1

See Tuesday for full details.

## Victoria Park Toddlers

Victoria Park Baptist Church, St Johns Lane, Bedminster, BS3 5DA
Brendan Bassett: 0117 373 0477
Mon 9.30-11.30am & Thur 10-11.30am
£1 for one child, £1.50 for two or more.

Drop-in group for 0-4yr olds held twice a week, with baby area and toys for U1's. Variety of toys, craft activities and sand. Fathers regularly attend. Outdoor area used.

# Friday

## Baby Comes Too

Key Centre, Charlton Rd, Keynsham, BS31 2JA
0117 987 7753, www.babycomestoo.ik.com
Weds 12.45-2.45pm, Fri 9.45-11am, £1 per family

See Wednesday for full details.

## Barton Hill Family Playcentre

Barton Hill Family Playcentre, Barton Hill Settlement,
43 Ducie Road, Barton Hill, Bristol BS5 0AX
Mon, Wed, Thur 9.30am-3pm, Fri 9.30am-2.30pm

See Monday for more information.

## Bristol Twins & More

St George Community Centre, Church Rd, BS5 8AA
0117 9411882, www.bristoltwins.org.uk
Fri 10am-12pm, £1.50 per family

The group is open to all those expecting
multiples and those with pre-school multiple
children - all older and younger siblings are
very welcome. There is a vast array of toys for
ages from birth upwards. Fell free to drop in
at anytime during the 2 hours and you do not
have to come every week.

## Cairns Rd Café with toddler zone

Cairns Rd Baptist Church, Cairns Rd, Westbury park,
Bristol. BS6 7TH

See Monday.

## Chatterbox (Toddler Group)

Horfield Baptist Church, 279 Gloucester Road,
Bristol, BS7 8NY (Brynland Road entrance)
Valerie Harwood: 0117 924 3608
www.horfieldbaptist.net
Thur/Fri 1.00pm-3.00pm, £1.50

For full details see Thursday.

## Child's Play Toddler Group

Easton Christian Family Centre, Beaufort Street,
Easton, BS5 0SQ
0117 955 4255, www.ecfc.org.uk
Mon, Wed, Thur, Fri 10am-12pm, £1 per family

For full details see Monday.

## Filton Avenue Nursery School

Blakeney Road, Horfield, Bristol, BS7 0DL
0117 377 2680, www.filtonavenuenursery.ik.org
Mon, Wed, Fri 9-11.15am Tue, Thur 1.15-3.15pm

Free

See Monday for full details.

## Highridge Play Centre

Lakemead Grove, Highridge, Bristol, BS13 8EA
0117 903 0460, www.fouracreschildrenscentre.co.uk

Fri 9.30-11.30am

Informal stay and play run for 0-4yr olds.

## Little Angels Parents & Toddler Group

6 Ashley Road, St Pauls, BS6 5NL
0117 9622321, www.bristolcitadel.org

Tue & Fri 10am-12pm, 50p

See Tuesday for more information.

## Parkway Parent and Child Project

Parkway Methodist Church, Conduit Place,
St Werburghs, BS2 9RU
0117 935 0205 info@parkwaypcp.org
Mon, Wed & Fri 9.30am-12pm

£1 per family

See Monday.

## Redland Toddlers

Redland Parish Church Hall, Redland Green Rd, BS6
0117 946 4690, www.redland.org.uk

Tue & Fri 10-11.30am, £1

See full details under Tuesday.

## Southmead Day Nursery

Doncaster Road, Southmead, Bristol, BS10 5PW
Liz Harper: 0117 377 2343

Mon, Wed, Fri 9.30am-11am

See Monday for full details.

## St Pauls Day Nursery

Little Bishop St, St Pauls, Bristol, BS2 9JF
0117 903 0337
stpaulsdayn@bristol-city.gov.uk

Fri 9.30am-12.30pm

Free informal stay and play time for children
aged 0-5yrs and their parents/carers.

## St Peter's Parent & Toddler Group

St Peter's Church Hall, The Drive, Henleaze, BS9 4LD
0117 962 8485, www.stpetershenleaze.org

Mon & Fri 10.30am-12pm. 50p per family per session

For full details see Monday.

## Stay and Play

Filwood Community Centre, Barnstaple Rd,
Knowle West, BS4 1JP
Jane Yeoman: 0117 963 6475

Fri 10am-12pm, 50p

Group for parents and toddlers from the local
area. Emphasis on parents playing with their
children. Painting room, craft activities and
toys. Snack served half way through.

## Tots R-Us

Emmanuel Church, Forest Rd, Fishponds, BS16 3XQ
www.emmanuel-bristol.org.uk

Fri 10.15am-11.45am

Toddler group for families in the local area.
New craft activity every week and puzzles
and kitchen equipment. Move to new room
refreshments, singing and a story. Finish
with fun on the big toys, cars and trikes!
Refreshments available.

## Tots Time, Brislington

St Christopher's Hall, Hampstead Rd, BS4 3H

See Monday.

## United Parents Toddler Group

All Saints Church Hall, Grove Rd, Fishponds, BS16
Elaine Seretny: 0117 902 5257, www.
allsaintsfishponds.co.uk

Fri 10am-11.30am, £1.50

Friendly, well-established drop-in toddler
group, originally set up to support mothers
who may be experiencing isolation, loneliness
or stress often felt by new parents. Informal
atmosphere with plenty of toys, cars, art
activities and play dough. Also see Tiny Tots -
Monday, and Sticky Fingers - Thursday.

# Saturday

## Noah's Ark Dad's Club

Cairns Rd Baptist Church, Cairns Road, Westbury
Park, Bristol. BS6 7TH
Carol de-Beger: 0117 944 6229
0117 9425 669 (Church Office)
www.cairnsroad.org (click on community page)

Sat 9.30-11.30am. Runs once a term.

A taste of the Noah's Ark experience for dads
(grandads, uncles, male carers etc), their
pre-school age children and their siblings to
enjoy play activities together. Bacon butties
provided. Look out for leaflets for dates.

## Redland Dads & Toddlers

Redland Parish Church Hall, Redland Green Rd, BS6
0117 946 4690, www.redland.org.uk

Sat 9.30-11am, £2

Voluntary contribution includes grilled bacon
Sarnie, fairtrade filter Coffee, newspapers and
squash/juice.

## St Matthews Church Toddler Group

Clare Road, Cotham, BS6 5TB
0117 944 1598 (Church Office)
www.stmatthews-bristol.org.uk/children/toddlers
3rd Sat of month, 9.30-11.30am. £1 adult, 50p child

Saturday playtime with bacon sandwiches,
newspapers and lots of play activities. For
under 8's.

# Sunday Schools

A good place to meet new people and
for children to integrate into the local
community. Contact your local church.

# Reading & Storytimes

## Contents

## Look out for...

**Bristol Storytelling Festival**
www.bristolstoryfest.co.uk

**Library Reading Challenge**
www.bristol.gov.uk/libraries
www.southglos.gov.uk

Books develop children's emotions, imaginations, and appreciation of relationships, and it is probably never too soon to start your child's experience of reading. This chapter contains details of libraries, bookshops and storytelling events on offer in the Bristol region.

### Library Storytimes

Why not try one of the weekly pre-school sessions with your baby or toddler? Gone are the days of absolute silence in the library. Today libraries are bright, vibrant and occasionally noisy places where there is lots on offer for young children. The libraries listed in this chapter run a weekly storytime or baby bounce session that lasts about half an hour and includes stories, rhymes and sometimes a craft activity. All children no matter how young are very welcome with a parent or carer. Your baby or toddler can also have their very own library membership card, no matter how young they are. Please ask at your local library for details.

# LIBRARIES

Libraries are an excellent community resource for all ages, easy to join and free! All libraries have children's sections which are often brightly decorated and welcoming, providing a fun and stimulating environment to encourage your child's love of books. As well as story books, there are children's non-fiction books, music and story tapes, CDs, DVDs, videos and jigsaw puzzles which may be borrowed or used in the library. Libraries are also a great source of information on local groups for children and parents. All libraries have wheelchair access, although some are trickier to negotiate than others. All libraries also have free use of computers with internet access, as well as scanners.

### Bristol Libraries  Bristol Libraries

www.bristol.gov.uk

There is an interactive map to help you find your nearest library.

### South Gloucester Libraries

www.southglos.gov.uk

## Tip:

Bristol City libraries allow you to borrow and return books from different libraries.

### Please note:

Library opening hours are subject to change. Please check the above websites or call for details of opening hours if you are making a special trip.

**Most Bristol and South Glos libraries have children's activities during the holidays. See their websites or call for more details.**

## Children's Librarian

Bristol's Children/Young People's Librarian Janet Randall 0117 9037215

South Gloucestershire Children/Young People's Librarian 01454 868006

## Mobile Libraries

For people who are unable to visit their local library or for whom there is no other library access. Most mobile library facilities include: books and maps for loan, large print and talking books, community information, local history collection, DVDs for hire, jigsaws for loan.

### Bristol Mobile Library

0117 903 8531

mobile.outreach.library@bristol.gov.uk

### South Glos Mobile Library

C/o Yate Library on 01454 868006 or the mobile library on 07881813292

www.southglos.gov.uk

Tours South Glos on a two week timetable. A hydraulic lift is available for people who cannot climb the stairs.

Call or see website for the library routes.

*Where the Wild Things Are*, the classic by Maurice Sendak, cover drawn by William, age 6.

## A-Z OF LIBRARIES

Below is a list of local libraries with their storytimes. **Rhymetime** is a Bookstart initiative designed to encourage parents and carers to share rhymes and songs with babies from birth onwards. Sessions incorporate a mix of songs, rhymes, rhythm and movement. **Most activities are in term-time only.**

### Avonmouth Library

Avonmouth Rd, Avonmouth, Bristol, BS11 9EN
0117 903 8580
Mon 2pm-5pm, Wed 10am-1pm, Fri 2pm-6pm, Sat 9.30am-12.30pm
23, 528 & 530 buses stop opp the library car park.

*Storytime* Fri 2.15pm.

### Bedminster Library

4 St Peters Court, Bedminster Parade, BS3 4AQ
0117 903 8529
Mon/Wed/Fri/Sat 9.30am-5pm,Tue/Thu 9.30am-7.30pm, Sun 1pm-4pm
52, 75, 75a, 76,77, 89, 90, 503 & 511 all stop on Bedminster Parade or East St. Parking at large Asda car park always available during Asda opening hours.

No special provision for disabled parking.

*Baby Bounce & Rhyme* Tues & Fri 10.30am, term time only.

### Bishopsworth Library

Bishopsworth Rd, Bishopsworth, Bristol, BS13 7LN
0117 903 8566
Mon 9.30am-1pm & 2pm-7pm Tue/Thu/Fri/Sat 9.30am-1pm & 2-5pm
75, 75a, 76 And 77 buses stop on Bishopsworth Rd. 52 stops at Bishopsworth Swimming Baths 400m away. On-street parking available outside the library.

*Storytime* Tue & Fri 2pm, term time.

*Baby Bounce & Rhyme*

Tue 10.30am (NB: at Highridge Children's Centre, 2 Lakemead Gr, BS13 8EA. Term time)

### Bradley Stoke Library

Bradley Stoke Leisure Centre & Library, Fiddlers Wood Lane, Bradley Stoke, BS32 9BS
01454 868 006
Mon/Thu 10.30am-6pm, Tue/Fri 10.30am-8pm, Sat 9.30am-5pm, Sun 11am-3pm

*Storytime* Mon 11am with craft activity.

*Rhymetime* Thur 10.30am.

### Bristol Central Library

College Green, Bristol, BS1 5TL
0117 903 7215
Mon/Tue/Thur 9.30am-7.30pm, Wed 10am-5pm, Fri/Sat 9.30am-5pm, Sun 1-5pm.

*Baby Bounce & Rhyme* Weds 10am

*Rhymetime*

Weds & Sat 11.15am. Age 6mths+. Free.

### Cadbury Heath Library

School Rd, Cadbury Heath, Bristol, BS30 8EN
01454 868 006
Mon 9am-7pm, Thur/Fri 9am-5pm, Sat 9.30am-5pm
On-street parking outside the library

*Storytime*

Fri 2.15pm, term time only.

### Cheltenham Rd Library

Cheltenham Rd, Cotham, Bristol, BS6 5QX
0117 903 8562
Mon/Wed/Fri/Sat 10am-1pm & 2pm-5pm
70, 71, 72, 73, 75, 75a, 76 and 77 buses stop just outside the library. 20 and 21 stop nearby. Limited car parking available in the side street.

*Storytime*
Fri 10.30am, term time only. 50p/child, inc. juice and fruit.

### Chipping Sodbury Library

High Street, Chipping Sodbury, BS37 6AH
01454 868 006
Tue/Wed/Thur/Fri/Sat 9.30am-5pm. Closes lunchtime 12.30pm-1.30pm. On street parking in High Street.

*Storytime*
Tues 2.15pm, term time only.

### Clifton Library

Princess Victoria Street, Clifton, Bristol, BS8 4BX
0117 903 8572
Mon/Wed/Fri 10am-5pm, Sat 10am-4pm
8, 8A, 9, 9A, 586 and 587 stop on Clifton Down Road within 200m. Parking is difficult in Clifton.

*Storytime*

Mon 10.30am with colouring, term time only. Coffee, squash and biscuits 30p.

## Downend Library

Buckingham Gardens, Downend, Bristol, BS16 5TW
01454 868 006
Mon/Thu 9.30am-7pm, Wed/Fri/Sat 9.30am-5pm.
Car park at rear.

*Storytime*

Thurs 10.30am, term time only. Rhyme-Time
Wed 10.30am.

## Eastville Library

Muller Rd, Eastville, Bristol, BS5 6XP
0117 903 8578
Mon/Wed/Fri/Sat 10am-1pm & 2pm-5pm.
24, 25, 585, 586, 587 buses stop on Muller Rd. 4,
4A pass along Glenfrome Rd approx 400m away. On-street parking in side streets. Bike rack at the library.

*Storytime* Mon 2.15pm, term time only.
50p per child inc. squash and biscuits.

## Emersons Green Library

Emersons Way, Emersons Green, BS16 7AP
01454 868006
Tue/Thu 10.30am-8pm, Fri 10.30am-6pm
Sat 9.30am-5pm, Sun 11am-3pm.

*Storytime* Tue 2.15pm, term time only.

*Rhymetime* Thur 2pm, term time.

## Filton Library

The Shield Retail Park, Link Rd, Filton, BS34 7BR
01454 868 006
Mon/Thu 9.30am-7pm, Tues/Fri/Sat 9.30am-5pm.
Parking in front of library.

*Storytime* Tue 2pm, term time only, with
story related craft activity.

## Filwood Library

Filwood Broadway, Bristol, BS4 1JN
0117 903 8581
Mon/Tues/Wed/Fri 9.30am-1pm & 2pm-5pm,
Sat 9.30am-1pm. 52, 89 and 90 buses run past end
of Filwood Broadway, the stop being less than one
min walk away.
On street parking nearby.

*Storytime* Mon 2.15pm, term time.

*Baby Bounce* Fri 2.30pm.

## Fishponds Library

Fishponds Rd, Fishponds, Bristol, BS16 3UH
0117 9038560
Mon/Tue/Fri/Sat 9.30am-5pm, Thu 9.30am-7pm.
5A, 48, 49 and 587 buses stop outside the school
next door travelling from Bristol and across the road
just past Morrisons travelling into Bristol. On-street
parking nearby and in Morrisons car park (2hr max).l

*Storytime* Tue 2pm, term time, with
nursery rhymes, craft activity, drink & biscuit
(50p). Booking advisable.

## Hanham Library

High Street, Hanham, Bristol, BS15 3EJ
01454 868 006
Mon/Thur/Fri 9am-5pm, Tues 9am-7pm, Sat 9.30am-5pm. Car park at rear.

*Storytime* Thur 2.15pm.

*Bounce & Rhyme* For babies and
toddlers, Mon 9.15am.

## Hartcliffe Library

Peterson Square, Hartcliffe, Bristol, BS13 0EE
0117 903 8568
Mon/Fri 9.30am-1pm & 2pm-5pm,
Sat 9.30am-1pm.
Buses 36, 75, 75A, stop at Bishport Ave, 76, 77 stops
at Hareclive Road. Both routes stop approximately
200m away. On-street parking nearby; staff car park
for disabled users.

*Bounce & Rhyme* Fri 10.30am

## Henbury Library

Crow Lane, Henbury, Bristol, BS10 7DR
0117 903 8522
Mon/Tue/Thu/Sat 9.30am-1pm & 2pm-5pm,
Fri 9.30am-1pm & 2pm-7pm
1, 40, 40A and 77 buses stop Crow Lane & 54 stops
Wyck Beck Rd. Car parking at the rear of the library.

*Bounce & Rhyme* Mon, 10.30am.

## Henleaze Library

Northumbria Drive, Henleaze, Bristol, BS9 4HP
0117 903 8541
Mon/Fri 9.30am-7pm, Tue/Wed/Thu/Sat 9.30am-5pm.
54 bus (& U5 Mon - Fri see www.uwe.ac.uk/hsv/transport/bus.shtml for timetable). 586 & 587 run along Coldharbour Lane approx 400m from Library. On-street parking nearby; small car park to rear. Bike racks at library. Toilets at Wairose across rd.

*Storytime* Thurs 10.45am & Tues 2pm, term-time. Please book in advance.

## Hillfields Library

Summerleaze, Hillfields, Bristol, BS16 4HL
0117 903 8576
Mon/Wed/Fri 10am-1pm & 2pm-5pm,
Sat 10pm-1pm & 2pm-4pm.
6 and 6a buses. On-street parking.

*Storytime* Fri 10.15 am.

*Baby Bounce & Rhyme* Fri 11am. Term-time only.

## Horfield Library

Filton Avenue, Horfield, Bristol, BS7 0BD
0117 903 8538
Mon 9.30am-1pm & 2pm-7pm,
Tue/Thu/Fri/Sat 9.30am-1pm & 2pm-5pm.
70, 71, and 73 buses stop on Filton Ave at junction with Toronto Rd approx 100m from library. On-street parking nearby; library has own small car park.

*Storytime* Tues 10.30am. Term-time.

## Kingswood Library

High Street, Kingswood, Bristol, BS15 4AR
01454 868 006
Mon/Tue/Sat 9.30am-5pm, Wed/Fri 9.30am-7pm.
Limited on-road parking in front of library, car park to the left of the building.

*Storytime* Tues 2.15pm, term-time only.
*Rhyme Time* For babies and toddlers and their parents or carers, Weds 10.30am.

## Knowle Library

1st Floor, Broadwalk Shopping Centre, Wells Road, Knowle, Bristol, BS4 2QU
0117 903 8585
Mon/Fri 9.30am-7pm, Tue/Thur/Sat 9.30am-5pm.
The 36 bus stops at Broadwalk shopping centre, the 511 runs along Redcatch Rd and the 51, 52, 54, 55, 558 and 559 stop on Wells Rd at Broadwalk shopping centre. Parking at Broadwalk multi-storey car park. Library access for wheelchair users via roof car park. Lift from Mall to car park. Please note - the lifts near Mall entrance to library not considered large enough to take wheelchairs, you may need to use the ones near Somerfield. Double buggies may find it easier to access library via the roof car park.

*Storytime* Fri 2.15pm.

*Baby Bounce & Rhyme* Fri 11am.

## Lawrence Weston Library

Broadlands Drive, Lawrence Weston, BS11 0NT
0117 312 5696
Mon-Fri 9.30am-5pm, Sat 9.30am-1pm.
The 40 bus stops approx 300m away on the Longcross at the bus turning point near Ridingleaze shops. Park at City of Bristol College Lawrence Weston Centre car park available to library users.

*Storytime* Thurs 11am.

## Marksbury Road Library

Marksbury Rd, Bedminster, Bristol, BS3 5LG
0117 903 8574
Mon 10am-1pm & 2pm-7pm,
Wed/Fri 10am-1pm & 2pm-5pm, Sat 10am-1pm.
The 510 and 511 bus stop nearby on Bedminster Rd. On-street parking nearby.

*Storytime* Weds 10.45am.

## Patchway Library

Rodway Rd, Patchway, Bristol, BS34 5PE
01454 868 006
Mon 9am-7pm, Weds/Fri 9am-5pm, Sat 9.30am-5pm. Own car park. Public toilets next door.

*Storytime* Weds 10.30am (term time). Tea, coffee, soft drinks.

*Rhyme Time* For babies and toddlers - first and third Mon of every month at 10.30am (term time only).

## Redland Library

Whiteladies Rd, Redland, Bristol, BS8 2PY
0117 903 8549
Mon/Tue/Fri/Sat 9.30am-5pm, Thu 9.30am-7pm,
Sun 1pm-4pm. 1, 8, 9, 40, 40A, 41, 54, 55, & 99
buses run along Whiteladies Rd. Bus stops outside
Clifton Down shopping centre approx 2 mins from
library. On-street parking difficult; multi-storey car
park at Clifton Down Shopping Centre, entrance in
Alma Rd. Toilets at Clifton Down shopping centre.

*Storytime*

Mon 2.30pm with craft activity.

## Sea Mills Library

Sylvan Way, Sea Mills, Bristol, BS9 2NA
0117 903 8555
Mon/Tue/Fri/Sat 9.30am-1pm & 2-5pm,
Thur 9.30am-1pm, 2-7pm.
40, 40A, 57 , 523 and 585 buses run along
Shirehampton Rd just off Sylvan way and the 41 and
517 stop in Westbury Lane. All stops are around five
mins walk away. On-street parking available.

*Storytime*

Mon & Thur 2.30pm.

## Shirehampton Library

Station Rd, Shirehampton, Bristol, BS11 9TU
0117 903 8570
Mon/Wed/Fri 10am-1pm & 2pm-5pm,
Sat 10am-1pm & 2pm-4pm.
40, 40A, 41, 57 and 523 buses stop at Shirehampton
Green just off Station Road. On-street parking.

*Storytime* Alternate Mon, 12-12.15pm.

*Baby Bounce & Rhyme*

Mon 11.20-11.40am

## Southmead Library

Greystoke Ave, Southmead, Bristol, BS10 6AS
0117 903 8583
Mon/Wed/Thur/Fri 9.30am-1pm & 2pm-5pm,
Sat 9.30am-1pm.
54, 55, 76 & 585 buses stop Greystoke Ave. Large
free car park with disabled spaces nearby at Aldi.
Toilets at Aldi.

*Storytime* Weds 10am, term time.

## St George Library

Church Rd, St George, Bristol, BS5 8AL
0117 903 8523
Mon 9.30am-1pm & 2pm-7pm,
Tue/Wed/Fri/Sat: 9.30am-1pm & 2pm-5pm.
40, 40A, 41, 44, 45 and X67 buses run along Church
Rd. Small car park to rear of library; on-street
parking nearby; large car park nearby.

*Storytime* Tue 2.15pm including singing
and craft activity (50p) term time only,
booking necessary.

## St Pauls Library

Grosvenor Rd, St Pauls, Bristol, BS2 8XJ
0117 914 5489
Mon/Thu 1pm-7.30pm, Tue/Fri 10am-1pm, Wed
1pm-5pm, Sat 10am-12pm & 1pm-5pm.
The 5A and 25 buses run along City Rd and Sussex
Place approximately 300m away.

*Storytime* Thurs 2pm, Tues 11am.

## Staple Hill Library

The Square, Broad St, Staple Hill, BS16 5LS
01454 868 006
www.southglos.gov.uk/libraries
Tues/Fri 9.30am-7pm, Thu/Sat 9.30am-5pm.
Public car park and on-street parking nearby.
Disabled toilet facilities.

*Storytime* Fri 11am, term time only.

*Rhyme Time* For pre-school children - 1st
Thursday of the month 11am.

## Stockwood Library

Stockwood Rd, Bristol, BS14 8PL
0117 903 8546
Mon/Thu/Fri/Sat 9.30am-1pm & 2pm-5pm,
Tue 9.30am-1pm & 2pm-7pm.
54 and 57A buses stop in Holloway Rd outside the
shops 100m away travelling from Bristol and outside
Bowmead Elderly Persons Home travelling into
Bristol. The 636 stops 50m away on the opposite
side of road travelling from Bristol and outside the
library going into Bristol. Free car park nearby

*Storytime* Fri 9.30am term time only.

*Baby Bounce & Rhyme* Term time
Mon 2.30pm.

## Thornbury Library

St. Mary Street, Thornbury, South Glos, BS35 2AA
01454 868 006
Mon/Tue 9.30am-5.30pm, Wed/Fri 9.30am-7pm,
Sat 9.30am-5pm. Next door is a signposted, short-stay car park. Toilets opposite at Safeway.

*Storytime* Mon 2.15pm term-time only,
except for last Monday in month. Dads' pre-school storytime, Sat 2.15pm (fortnightly).

*Rhyme Time* Last Mon of month,
2.15pm, term time only.

## Trinity Road Library

Trinity Rd, St Philips, Bristol, BS2 0NW
0117 9038543
Mon/Wed/Fri 10am-1pm & 2pm-5.30pm,
Sat 10am-1pm & 2pm-5pm.
4, 24, 48 and 49 buses stop on Stapleton Rd near
Trinity Rd. The 6, 7, 36, 41, 43, 44, 45 and 585
travel along Trinity Rd on way out of city and down
Clarence Rd and West St on return. Limited on-street
parking nearby, large car park short walk.

*Storytime* Friday, 11.05am.

*Baby Bounce & Rhyme* Fri 10.30am.

## Westbury-on-Trym Library

Falcondale Rd, Westbury-on-Trym, Bristol, BS9 3JZ
0117 903 8552
Mon/Tue/Wed/Sat 9.30am-5pm, Fri 9.30am-7pm.
1, 20, 21, 55, 517, 523 and 585 buses stop on
Canford Lane. The 55 stops on Falcondale Rd. On
street parking in Abbey Rd and/or Canford Lane by
Canford Park.

*Storytime* Mon 2.15pm. Storytime with
crafts. Term time only. Wed 11am. Baby
bounce and rhyme. Term time only.

## Wick Road Library

Wick Rd, Brislington, Bristol, BS4 4HE
0117 903 8557
Mon 9am-1pm & 2pm-7pm, Tue/Wed/Fri 9am-1pm &
2pm-5pm, Sat 9.30am-1pm & 2-5pm.
Number 1 bus stops at top of Allison Rd, with the
stops opposite each other. The 36 stops in Wick Rd
outside the cafe travelling from Bristol and outside
the chemist travelling into Bristol. The 558 and 559
run along Sandhurst Rd and Sandy Park Rd approx
300m away. On-street parking nearby.

*Storytime* Wed 2.15pm, term time only.
50p per child.Fri 9.30am, term time only. 50p
per child. Baby bounce and rhyme, Weds
10am and 11am. Term time only.

## Winterbourne Library

Flax Pits Lane, Winterbourne, South Glos BS36 1LA
01454 868 006
Tue/Fri 9.30am-7pm, Wed/Sat 9.30am-5pm. On-road
parking in front of the library.

*Storytime* Wed 2.15pm, term time
only. Rhyme Time for babies and pre-school children, Tues 9.30am, followed by
refreshments.

## Yate Library

23 South Parade, Yate, BS37 4AX (temp address)
01454 868 006
www.southglos.gov.uk/libs.htm
Mon/Tue/Thu/Fri 9.30am-7pm, Sat 9.30am-5pm,
Sun 11am-3pm

At the time of going to print, major
refurbishment and extension to the library
was being carried out and it was located at
this temporary address.

Look at our website:
(www.titchhikers.co.uk) for details of
Storytelling Walks on the Downs

Also see YogaSara, Debutots and Tatty
Bumpkin for more storytelling fun.

# Other Bristol Storytimes

## Borders

48-56 Queens Rd, Clifton, BS8 1RE
0117 922 6959
www.bristol.borders.co.uk
Sat 11am & 3pm, Sun 3pm

Children's Storytime. Also many holiday storytelling events.

## Bristol Zoo Gardens

Bristol Zoo Gardens, Clifton, BS8 3HA
0117 9747385, www.bristolzoo.org.uk
For more details see **Animals.**
First Wed of every month. £4 per adult, child free.

In the Terrace Theatre. Pre-Booking advisable.

## Explore-At-Bristol

Anchor Rd, Harbourside, Bristol, BS1 5DB
0845 345 1235, www.at-bristol.org.uk
For more details see **Bristol Visitor Attractions.**
2pm-5pm, entry for carers half-price during these sessions (max 2 adults per child). U5's free.

Toddler afternoons with story-telling sessions.

## Peas in a Pod Storytelling

www.peasinapodstories.co.uk

Peas in a Pod storytelling brings (oral) storytelling sessions to schools, nurseries, festivals, theatres, and children's parties. Stories can be adapted from any age from 2 to 10 years and can fit with curriculum topics, the seasons and your child's favourite subjects. Many of the stories are drawn from traditional folk tales, many are magical and celebrate the natural world, and all draw from stories from other cultures.

## ALSO TRY

### Jack & Jill Toyshop
192 Wells Rd, Totterdown, BS4 2AX
0117 958 8860

### Martin Maudsley
07761 026460, www.storysoup.co.uk

# Has your child received their bookstart pack?

Bristol Libraries has a big role to play in delivering Bookstart packs to all children in Bristol. Bookstart aims to provide a free pack of books to every baby in the UK, to inspire, stimulate and create a love of reading that will give children a flying start in life. We deliver the first free pack of books to babies, usually when they're aged around 8 months old. These packs are usually given out to babies at around 7 to 9 months by their health visitor. If your baby has not received this pack then it can be collected from any Bristol Library. The second Bookstart pack is for children 15-35 months and you can receive this pack from your health visitor or once again collect it from any Bristol Library. The third and final pack is the Bookstart Treasure Chest which is normally gifted through a child's nursery, pre-school, or any other early years setting that they attend. If your child does not go to nursery or day care then once again their Bookstart Treasure Chest can be collected from any local library. For more information visit www.bookstart.org.uk.

If you have any questions about Bristol Libraries or Bookstart then do not hesitate to contact Roxanne the Early Years Librarian for Bristol Libraries on 0117 3772718 or email bookstart@bristol.gov.uk

## Good Websites

**Talk to your baby**
www.literacytrust.org.uk

**Child Literacy Centre**
www.childliteracy.com
Website to help parents learn about the reading process and encourage their pre-school children to develop the skills needed to read and write.

# bookstart
est. by booktrust 1992

143

# BOOKSHOPS

Bristol has some great book shops, offering a good range from birth upwards. Staff are usually very knowledgeable and helpful, with ordering services offered by the majority. There are also some excellent books sold through local agents and online:

www.barefootbooks.co.uk

www.usbornebooksathome.co.uk

www.thebookpeople.co.uk

## Blackwell's

89 Park Street, Clifton, BS1 5PW
0117 927 6602, www.blackwell.co.uk
Mon-Sat 9am-6pm, (Tues 11am-6pm) & Sun 11am-5pm.

Friendly, expert staff. The various departments are on several levels, staff can help with buggies. The array of books, CDs and academic publications is impressive. Within the shop is the popular Cafe Nero where shoppers can browse books and take refreshments. There is a good selection of children's books in a pleasant reading corner.

## Borders

Clifton Promenade, 48-56 Queens Rd, BS8 1RE
0117 922 6959, www.borders.co.uk
Mon-Sat 9am-10pm, Sun 12am-6pm

A huge book shop catering for all ages and tastes. There is a large, bright children's section with regular story time (U8's). There is also a kids' club, contact store for details. This store is very popular with new parents with its Starbucks Coffee Shop, so you can browse while drinking coffee!

## Durdham Down Bookshop

39 North View, Westbury Park, Bristol, BS6 7PY
0117 973 9095
Mon-Sat 9am-6pm

For a small bookshop, it has a large section of children's books for all ages. Also books on parenting, health and well-being. 24 hour ordering service.

## Stanfords

29 Corn Street, BS1 1HT
0117 929 9966, www.stanfords.co.uk
Mon-Sat 9am-6pm, Tue 9:30am-6pm.

This is a great shop for young explorers. Stanfords specialise in maps, but also stock a wide range of travel and guide books. There is a small children's section with soft baby globes and puzzles for the younger ones, and children's/teen's guide books for the young traveller and those taking gap years abroad. Online ordering is available.

## Waterstones

www.waterstones.com
The Mall, Cribbs Causeway & The Mall Galleries, Broadmead
0117 950 9813/0117 925 2274
Mon-Fri 9:30am-9pm, Sat 9am-9pm & Sun 10:30am-5pm (Cribbs) & Mon-Sat 9am-6pm & Sun 10:30am-5pm (Broadmead)

Full range of books available for children, teenagers and parents. Large children's sections where children are welcome to browse. Ordering service available.

## WH Smith

www.whsmith.co.uk
The Galleries, Broadmead and The Mall, Cribbs Causeway
0117 925 2152/0117 950 9525
Clifton Down Rd, Clifton Village and Clifton Down Shopping Centre
0117 973 3255/0117 973 5063

Range of books to suit all ages. Also stocks stationery, CDs and toys. An ordering service is available.

# Get physical

## Contents

Also see **Performing Arts, Parent and Baby/ Toddler,** and the out and about chapters for more physical actviity ideas.

Children at the older end of the age group catered for in this edition can enjoy almost every kind of physical activity available in the region. A four or five year old can take group lessons in rugby, horseriding, tennis and even golf! For babies and toddlers, there are lots of fun, safe, supervised activities to burn energy and help development.

## FOOTBALL

The 2018 World Cup, which Bristol has bid to host, will probably come too soon for readers of this edition to take a competitive part in. Still, begin living the dream through the opportunities on offer to young children, some of which cater for those who have yet to take their first steps!.

### Little Dribblers

Silas Youth Centre, Stockwood, BS14
07877 287072 - Jeff Dickens

Offer football sessions where childen are introduced to the basic skills of football such as dribbling, control, passing and shooting. Lessons for 4-5 year olds held every Sunday 9:30-10:25am.

### Socatots

07795 411707, northbristol@socatots.com
www.socatots.com/northbristol

Socatots provide popular football coaching lessons for children aged 6 months - school aged. The sessions include teaching of basic football skills, as well as developing physical skills of agility, balance and co-ordination. Sessions held across Bristol, including Southville Community Centre, Bishop Sutton Village Hall, St. Peter's Church hall in Henleaze, Horfield Baptist Church, St Bats Church Hall in St. Andrews, Clevedon YMCA, Portishead Parish Wharf Leisure Centre, Bradley Stoke Community Sports Hall, Elmgrove Centre in cotham/Redland and Flax Bourton Village Hall.

## GOLF

After many generations of being kept well apart, golf and children are becoming increasingly acquainted. Many local clubs are welcoming kids with fun and imaginative introductions to this most challenging – but completely gripping - of sports. Play this sport from age 4 to 104!

*Tips:*

For information on the practicalities of children getting involved with golf, from what they can expect of the sport and what the sport expects of them, see www.englishgolfunion. org; www.golf-foundation.org. For a list of clubs, see www.juniorgolfleague.org. The clubs below are a selection of the clubs which place the greatest emphasis on child golfers.

### Bristol & Clifton Golf Club

Beggar Bush Lane, Failand, Bristol
01275 393474, mansec@bristolgolf.co.uk
www.bristolgolf.co.uk

This club welcomes members and non-members to its younger kids coaching sessions, called TRI-Golf. The emphasis is on learning basic skills in a fun and friendly environment, catering for the 4-9 year old. Regular six week courses run on Saturdays throughout the summer.

# GYMNASTICS

## Bristol Hawks Gymnastic Club

Gymnastics World, Roman Rd, Lower Easton, BS5
0117 935 5363/973 7481
www.bristolhawksgymnastics.org

Offer Parent & Toddler sessions for children aged 18 mths-5 yrs. 45 min classes held on Tues, Wed & Thurs mornings. Classes include play phase, group exercises, using apparatus and finishing with a song. (£3.90/ session or £20.10 for six weeks). 'Play Sessions' on Sat mornings (30 mins). No formal teaching, however an experienced coach is on hand to guide and advise (£2.25/session).

## Bristol School of Gymnastics

Old Bishopston Methodist Church,
245 Gloucester Rd, Bristol, BS7 8NY
0117 942 9620
www.bristolsg.pwp.blueyonder.co.uk

Under and over 3's classes. Under 3's include many types of apparatus, such as floor level trampoline, climbing frames and soft play. First half hour free play and last 15 mins songs and group activities. £30.40 for 8 weeks (Mon, Wed, Thurs & Fri mornings). Over 3's classes start with a group activity and then the children work on 3 pieces of apparatus with a coach. £33.60 for 8 weeks, (Mon, Wed, Thurs & Fri).

## Fromeside Gymnastics Club

Watleys End Rd, Winterbourne, Bristol, BS36 1QG
01454 776 873/777 749
www.fromesidegymclub.co.uk
Bradley Stoke Leisure Centre, Fiddlers Wood Lane, Bradley Stoke, Bristol. BS32 9BS. 01454 - 867050

Offer variety of pre-school classes, which teach basic co-ordination, imporve confidence and help general development. Classes include 'Jelly Tots' for under 2's, Parent & Toddler classes for 2-3 year olds and 'Gym Tots' for 3-4 year olds. Jelly Tots and Parent & Toddler classes are held Tues & Wed mornings. Gym Tots is on Tues & Wed mornings and Mon & Fri afternoons. 'Jelly Tots', £2.50 per week (payable on door). 'Parent & Toddler & Gym Tots', £15 per term & £3.50 per week (payable on door).

## Gymnastic Pre-School Gymnastics Club

Esporta, Hunts Ground Rd, Stoke Gifford, BS34 8HN
0117 - 910 9563, www.gymnastic.co.uk
gymnastic.ltd@btinternet.com

Offer weekly classes for toddlers to 5 yrs (grouped according to age). Various sessions held throughout week (Mon-Fri mornings). Weekly themed sessions are varied, challenging and fun.

## High Jinks

227th Scout Headquaters, Old Quarry Park, 18 Eastfield Terrace (back of), Henleaze, Bristol.
07743 - 540 973, high_jinks@hotmail.co.uk

Offer fun fitness session for 3-5 year olds. Sessions include selection of equipment and games. Thurs 2-2:45pm (term-time only). £3.50 per session, (pay as you go).

## Jack In a Box

Waterford Hall, Waterford Rd, Henleaze, Bristol
0117 - 962 3758 Kate Wright
www.jackinabox.info, kate@jackinabox.info

Popular and friendly pre-school gym club for children aged 3mth-4yrs, (term-time only). 'Bouncing Babies' (10wks-crawling), Wed afternoons, 2:25-3pm, £4.20. 'Soft Play for Tinies' (9mths-20mths), Tues, Wed & Fri mornings 9:25am-10:15am, £3.80. 'Mini-Gym' (20mths-2yrs 3mths), Tues, Wed & Fri mornings 10:45-11:25am. (2 years 3mths-nearly 3yrs) 11:35-12:15am, £4.20. 'Pre-School gym' (3-3yrs 6mths), Fri 1:15-2pm. (Over 3yrs 6mths), 2:15-3pm, £4.50.

## Kingswood Gymnastic & Trampoline Centre

The Wesley Studios, Kingswood Foundation Estate, Britannia Rd, Kingswood, Bristol. BS15 8DB
0117 947 6449

Call for times and details.

Lots of places listed in **Animals & Wildlife** also have soft play

## City of Bristol Gymnastics Centre

c/o Hartcliffe Engineering Community College, Teyfant Rd, Hartcliffe, BS13 0RL
0117 377 3420, www.bristol-city.gov.uk

'Gym Tots' (12mths-4yrs). (Continued over)Class helps to develop confidence, balance, strength & co-ordination. Thursdays 9:30-10:30am & 10:45-11:45am - £3.50 per session. 'Trampoline Tots', (18mths-4yrs). Offers an introduction to trampoling. 6 week course, Mondays 1:30-2:30pm (term-time only), £18. 'Gymnastic Classes' - fun gym for boys & girls 3-5 yrs. Offers introduction to gymnastic apparatus and basic skills. 6 week course £20 or £3.80 per session, Mon 4:30-5:30pm, Wed 4-5pm & 5-6pm & Thurs 4:30-5:30pm.

## Mini Champs

Westbury on Trym Methodist Church, Westbury on Trym, Bristol. BS9 3AA
01275 395272, ljoslin@hotmail.co.uk

Pre-school sports class for children aged 2+. Teaches basic game skills, including throwing, catching, hitting, kicking and striking. Parents/carers stay and work with children during sessions. Mon 10-10:40am & 11-11:40am, (term-time only). £3.70 per 40 min session. Classes also held in Long Ashton on Tue am.

## Star Jumpers

Emersons Grenn Village Hall, Emerson Way, Emersons Green, Bristol. BS16 7AP
0117 957 0009 Steve Denny
starjumpersgymclub@blueyonder.co.uk

Pre-school gym club. Offers a variety of classes for children aged 5mths-5yrs. Classes include gymnastics and physical play. 'Twinkling Star's (5mths-confident walking), follows 'British Gymnastics Fun 4 Baby syllabus. 'Little Stars' (confident walking-2 1/2 yrs). 'Big Stars' (2½ - 3½yrs) & (3½yrs-5 yrs). Mon/Tue - Emersons Green Village Hall. Weds- Page Community Centre, Staple Hill. Thurs- Quakers Rd Church Hall, Downend. Fri - Pucklechurch Community Centre.

For Cycle Hire and Cycle Routes, see **Travelling Around** chapter.

## Trymkids

Coombe Dingle Sports Centre, Coombe Lane, BS9 2BJ
0117 968 2252 Sarah Power

A multi-skills sports course for pre-school children aged 3-5 years. Classes held Tues & Fri 1:30-2:30pm, £3.50. Also offer 'Trymharmony' classes, which combines yoga and pilates - (see yoga section in book for further details).

# HORSE RIDING

## Kingsweston Stables

Kingsweston Rd, Lawrence Weston, BS11 0UX
0117 982 8929
www.kingswestonstables.com

Stables of up to twenty five horses, with an indoor arena and beautiful surrounding woodland. Escorted pony trekking for smaller children (from age 4yrs upwards). Offer group and private lessons for children aged 6yrs+.

## Urchinwood Manor Equitation Centre

Urchinwood Manor, Congresbury, Bristol, BS49 5AP
01934 833248
www.urchinwoodmanor.co.uk

Teaching centre, offering lessons for all ages and stages, including working towards competitions and BHS exams for those that want to compete. Also caters for disabled and special needs riders.

# MARTIAL ARTS

## Bristol Dojo

74-78 Avon Street, St Phillips, BS2 0PX
0800 756 6990, www.bristoldojo.com

Sessions for children of all ages. Mini Imps is designed for Pre-School children aged 3 & 4, to help build confidence in a safe environment. It is especially beneficial to children on the build up to starting school as it encourages the learning of colours, counting and social skills.

See also **Parties** chapter and **Soft Play** in this chapter).

## SOFT PLAY

### 123 Jump

22 Concorde Road, Cribbs Causeway, BS34 5TB
0117 9312 733, www.123jump.co.uk

Jump is a huge soft play venue with areas for babies and children of all ages. There is an enormous adventure play-frame, a space zone, a galleon and an enchanted castle. There are also huge inflatables, an indoor football pitch, ten pin bowling and an enormous zone just for toddlers. Contact for prices and opening hours. See **Advert.**

### Castaways

Bourne Chapel, Waters Rd, Kingswood, BS15 8BE
0117 9615115, www.bristolcommunitychurch.org

Owned and run by the Church, Castaways is a safe and friendly purpose built play system, with two levels of ramps, a slide and lots of random spongy shapes and places to hide. There's also a great café area. Contact for prices and opening hours.

### Bristol DoJo

74-78 Avon Street, St Phillips, BS2 0PX
0800 756 6990, www.bristoldojo.com

For pre-School Children aged 4 years and under. Sessions take place on a fully matted floor area and include mini soft contained play structures, ball pools and a variety of soft play items in all shapes and sizes. Bristol Dojo Soft-play sessions can be combined with use of the Fitness Zone (cross trainers and treadmills) for adults sessions whilst watching your child having fun. Contact for prices and opening hours.

### Noah's Ark Play Centre

828 Bath Rd, Brislington, BS4 5LQ
0117 971 2599, www.noahsarkplay.com

Fun packed soft play area with climbing, sliding, swinging, jumping, hiding, bouncing, rolling, wriggling and much more. Also a dedicated toddler area and a café with tasty hot and cold food. Contact for prices and opening hours.

**England's Largest**
Dedicated Indoor Softplay

- Enormous Toddler Zone
- Free Sing and Dance Sessions
- Full Café Facility
- Ages 0-12 Years
- Ball pits, inflatables, sport pitch and so much more

Patchway Trading Estate,
22 Concorde Road,
Cribbs Causeway,
Bristol BS34 5TB
tel: 0117 931 2733
www.123jump.co.uk

## ALSO TRY...

**Playzone at Riverside Leisure Club**
Station Rd, Little Stoke, BS34 6HW
01452 413214, www.riversidesports.co.uk

Excellent indoor play area attached to the Leisure Club. Good café (with magazines). See parties.

**Playspace**
85 Barrow Road, St Philips, BS5 0AE
0117 9550070, www.playspace.co.uk

Separate areas for babies through to juniors. This is a well thought out venue with a nice and well located (for viewing) café. See other entries in Parent & Baby/Toddler, and Parties.

**Tiny Tearawayz Soft Play**
Unit 31 Broadwalk Shopping Centre Knowle BS4 2QU
www.tinytearawayz.co.uk

Good soft play area catering for toddlers through to juniors. See Parties.

# SWIMMING

Safety and confidence in the water is important for everyone. See also **Leisure Centres** in this section.

## Swim for Free

Bristol Community Sport
www.bristol-city.gov.uk/sport

The free swimming initiative is part of a national campaign to promote swimming, general fitness, more active lifestyles and well-being. All children under the age of 16 can access free swims, subject to normal admissions policies, such as being accompanied by an adult if under the age of 8yrs (see Bristol City Council Website for more information). In order to receive your free swims, you need to purchase an Everyone Active Discount Card, which costs £3.50 per year for Bristol residents and £30 for non-residents. You also need to fill in an application form for the Everyone Active Discount Card. This can be downloaded from the Council website or you can collect one from your nearest Everyone Active swimming pool. Take your completed form to any of the Everyone Active centres or pools for processing and they can take you to the next step in obtaining an Everyone Active Discount Card. You will need to take proof of residency and your National Health Service Card with you - this proves your eligibility for the scheme. Free swims will end in March 2011.

**Participating pools:**

Bishopsworth Swimming Pool - 0117 903 1600

Bristol South Swimming Pool - 0117 903 1618

Easton Leisure Centre - 0117 903 1628

Henbury Leisure Centre - 0117 353 2555

Horfield Leisure Centre - 0117 903 1643

Jubilee Swimming Pool - 0117 903 1607

## Dinky Dolphins

Filton Sports & Leisure Centre, Elm Park, BS34 7PS
Gareth Hughes: 01454 866 686
Mon 9.30-10.30am, Thur 10-11am, Fri 10-11am (term time only)
£3.18 per adult and up to 2 children under 5 years

Lively music, singing and play session with inflatables in the kiddies pool. From 6mths-5yrs, party packages available.

## Puddle Ducks

0117 - 971 7165, www.puddleducks-swimming.co.uk
bristolandbath@puddleducks-swimming.co.uk

Offer swimming classes for babies (from birth), toddlers and pre-school children across Bristol, Somerset and South Gloucestershire. Classes include music and rhyme and help to teach your child to swim and be safe in the water. See **Advert** over page

## Splash 'n' Swim

Freeways Hydrotherapy Pool, Abbots Leigh, BS8 3RA
07976 - 558 260 - Alison, www.splashnswim.co.uk

Offer range of parent & child swim classes for newborn and toddlers up to pre-school age. Half hour sessions, 10 week block (during school year). Sessions include songs, floats and toys to help teach water safety skills and enable children to gain confidence in water. Lessons take place Tues, Thurs, fri & Sat - times vary.

## Water Babies

0117 946 6919 - Bryony Johnstone
www.waterbabies.co.uk
underwater@waterbabies.co.uk

Award winning swimming lessons designed to introduce babies, under 1yr, to water. Word association, repetition, games and songs are used to encourage the development of natural swimming skills including the ability to swim underwater. All are taught without the use of armbands. Lessons take place at various pools in the Bristol and Bath area. Half hour sessions.
See **Advert** on the back page of this book.

# You can take a horse to water but only a DUCK will swim!

Develop your child's confidence in water the natural way. By engaging your child's abilities and affinity with the water, we offer simple steps to a lifetime love of swimming. Join at any age from birth.

**Tel 0117 971 7165  Email bristolandbath@puddleducks.com**

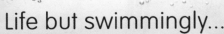

Life but swimmingly...
www.puddleducks.com

## OPEN AIR POOLS

### Clifton Lido

Oakfield Place, Bristol BS8 2BJ
0117 933 9530
www.lidobristol.com

Wonderful restoration of this Victorian,
Community leisure facility complete with a
poolside bar and restaurant. But there are
limited swimming times for families.

### Greenbank Outdoor Pool

Wilfrid Rd, Street, Somerset, BA16 0EU
01458 442468
www.greenbankpool.co.uk

This pleasant heated outdoor pool surrounded
by grass is less than five minutes' walk
from Clark's Village. There are two pools, a
separate children's area, a new Wet Play
Area and refreshments. Picnics welcomed.
Small car park. Open May 2nd - Sept 13th,
10am-6pm (school holidays) & weekdays 12-
6:45pm & 10am-6:45pm weekends
(term-time).

### Portishead Open Air Pool

Esplanade Rd, Portishead, BS20 7HD
01275 843454  Open: May-Sep

Heated open air swimming pool with separate
toddler pool. Indoor changing rooms, showers
and sunbathing terraces. U8's must be
accompanied by an adult. 1:1 ratio for U5's.

### Sandford Parks Lido

Keynsham Rd, Cheltenham, Gloucestershire, GL53
01242 524430 Open: 2nd May-27th Sep (Childrens
pool open 11am-7:30pm daily. Main pool opening
times vary - contact or see website for full details).
www.sandfordparkslido.org.uk
swim@sandfordparkslido.org.uk
M5 J11, A40 to Cheltenham then follow tourist signs.

Large heated outdoor pool set in landscaped
gardens with spacious terraces for sunbathing
and a café. Separate children's pool for
U8's, paddling pool for toddlers and slides.
Two children's play areas, table tennis and
basketball. Lockers in the heated changing
rooms. Pay and display car park next door.

## RUGBY

### Rugby Tots

0845 313 3250 David Hughan, www.rugbytots.co.uk
david@rugbytots.co.uk

Weekly play sessions for children aged
between 2-5 yrs. Classes combine the multiple
skills used in rugby, with a fun structured play
programme.

## TENNIS

With an impressive 22 venues for developing
your tennis skills practically everyone in the
area is within easy access of an excellent
tennis programme. It is a interesting fact
that if you are fortunate enough to be based
in the tennis heaven of Bishopston, Cotham,
Henleaze, Horfield and Westbury Park, you
are better off than almost anywhere else
in Britain. According to the Lawn Tennis
Association, your seven venues within a mile
of the doorstep is more than is on offer to
families in SW19, the home of British tennis.

Tips:

For useful information on  your nearest club
plus what you need to make the most of this
sport, check out Avon Tennis at:
www.avon.totaltennis.net, 0117  9626723

Check with the clubs concerned to see what
specific facilities are provided and whether
they are open to non-members.  Also the
age that they are willing to start your child
at (this is often dependant on the individual
child's abilitiy). Do not assume membership
will be out of your reach, because great steps
are being taken to make junior membership
affordable and accessible to all.

## YOGA

### Tatty Bumpkin

www.paulabrown.tatty-bumpkin.com
Horfield Baptist Church - Mondays 9:30am & 10:30am.

Movement and story classes, with animal adventures, inspired by yoga. For ages 18mths-5yrs. With great music and ends with a lovely relaxation! Tatty Bumpkin is at various locations throughout the holidays/summer. Call for details.

### Yoga Stars

07976 350564, www.yoga-stars.co.uk
hello@yoga-stars.co.uk
Covering Bristol/Bath/South Glos

Yoga Training for Kids aged 3 plus

For thousands of years, yoga has been recognised as having a multitude of benefits for people. Now these benefits are available to children in the form of Yoga Stars. Yoga can improve a child's self-esteem, confidence, sleep patterns, concentration and memory retention. Traditional yoga postures help keep young bodies flexible, strong and active. Breathing and relaxation techniques help children to learn to control their emotions and boost energy levels.

Yoga has also been proven to aid children with autism, ADHT and learning difficulties. The combination of postures, breathing and deep relaxation will strengthen the child's nervous system, increase overall health and facilitate the development of body awareness and concentration.

## Older Children?

If your child is age 5 plus, they can join in with many more Kids Yoga sessions. These give your child an opportunity to explore their imagination while relaxing. Yoga is also thought to help with many conditions such as ADHT and learning difficulties.

See: Bristol City Yoga (page 7) and YogaSara (page 7) for recommended classes.

# BRISTOL LEISURE CENTRES

For more details see: www.bristol-city.gov.uk/sport or www.filton-town-council.co.uk — classes are subject to change. Contact for details.

| Leisure Centres Open daily | Phone/web | Aerobics | Badminton | Basketball | Boxercise | Crèche | Cricket Nets | Dance | Football | Gymnastics | Gymnasium | Holiday | Martial Arts | Netball | Outdoors | Parties | Softplay | Squash | Swimming | Tennis | Trampolining | Volley Ball | Yoga |
|---|---|---|---|---|---|---|---|---|---|---|---|---|---|---|---|---|---|---|---|---|---|---|---|
| Ashton Park Sports Centre — Ashton Park School, Blackmoor's Lane, Bower Ashton | 0117 377 3300 | ✓ | ✓ | | | | ✓ | ✓ | | | ✓ | ✓ | ✓ | ✓ | ✓ | ✓ | | | | ✓ | ✓ | | ✓ |
| Easton Leisure Centre — Thrissell Street, Easton | 0117 955 8840 | ✓ | ✓ | ✓ | | | | | ✓ | | ✓ | ✓ | ✓ | | | ✓ | | | ✓ | | | | ✓ |
| Filton Sports & Leisure Centre — Elm Park, Filton | 01454 866686 www.filton-town-council.co.uk | | ✓ | | | ✓ | | | | | | ✓ | ✓ | | | | ✓ | | ✓ | ✓ | | | |
| Henbury Leisure Centre — Avonmouth Way, Henbury | 0117 353 2555 | ✓ | ✓ | | | | ✓ | ✓ | ✓ | ✓ | ✓ | ✓ | ✓ | ✓ | ✓ | ✓ | | ✓ | ✓ | ✓ | | ✓ | ✓ |
| Horfield Sports Centre — Dorian Road, Horfield | 0117 903 1643 | ✓ | ✓ | | | ✓ | ✓ | ✓ | ✓ | ✓ | | ✓ | ✓ | | ✓ | ✓ | ✓ | | ✓ | | ✓ | ✓ | ✓ |
| Kingsdown Sports Centre — Portland St, Kingsdown | 0117 942 6582 | ✓ | ✓ | | ✓ | ✓ | | | ✓ | ✓ | ✓ | ✓ | ✓ | ✓ | | ✓ | ✓ | ✓ | ✓ | | | | |
| St Paul's Community Sports — Academy Newfoundland Road, St Paul's | 0117 377 3405 | ✓ | ✓ | ✓ | | ✓ | ✓ | | ✓ | ✓ | ✓ | ✓ | ✓ | ✓ | ✓ | ✓ | ✓ | | ✓ | ✓ | | ✓ | ✓ |
| Whitchurch Sports Centre — Bamfield, Whitchurch | 01275 833911 | ✓ | ✓ | ✓ | | ✓ | | ✓ | ✓ | | ✓ | ✓ | ✓ | ✓ | ✓ | ✓ | ✓ | | ✓ | | | ✓ | ✓ |
| Withywood Sport Centre — Withywood Community School, Molesworth Drive | 0117 377 22294 | ✓ | ✓ | | | | | | ✓ | | | ✓ | | ✓ | | ✓ | ✓ | | ✓ | | ✓ | | |

# BRISTOL SWIMMING POOLS

For more details see: www.bristol-city.gov.uk/sport except Filton Sports and Leisure see: www.filton-town-council.co.uk

| Leisure Centres Open daily | Phone | Pool Size | Aquafit Classes | Swimming Sessions for U5's | Lessons | Swimming Club | Learner Pool | Off Poolside Changing Rooms | Spa Facilities | Playpen and Baby Changing | Disabled Facilities | Parking | Public Transport | Sub-aqua | Water Slide | Parties, floats & inflatables | Other Swimming Activities |
|---|---|---|---|---|---|---|---|---|---|---|---|---|---|---|---|---|---|
| Bishopworth, Whitchurch Lane, Bishopworth | 0117 964 0258 | 25m | ✓ | | ✓ | ✓ | | ✓ | | ✓ | ✓ | ✓ | ✓ | ✓ | | ✓ | |
| Bristol South, Dean Lane, Bedminster | 0117 966 3131 | 30m | | ✓ | ✓ | ✓ | | | | ✓ | | | ✓ | ✓ | | ✓ | water polo, canoeing |
| Easton Leisure Centre, Thrissell St, Easton | 0117 955 8840 | 25m | ✓ | ✓ | ✓ | ✓ | ✓ | ✓ | | ✓ | ✓ | ✓ | ✓ | | ✓ | ✓ | |
| Filton Sports and Leisure Centre, Elm Park, Filton | 01454 866686 | 25m | ✓ | ✓ | ✓ | ✓ | ✓ | ✓ | ✓ | | ✓ | ✓ | ✓ | | | ✓ | |
| Henbury, Avonmouth Way, Henbury | 0117 353 2555 | 25m | ✓ | ✓ | ✓ | ✓ | ✓ | ✓ | ✓ | ✓ | ✓ | ✓ | ✓ | ✓ | | | |
| Horfield Sports Centre, Dorian Rd, Horfield | 0117 903 1643 | 25m | ✓ | ✓ | ✓ | ✓ | ✓ | ✓ | | ✓ | ✓ | ✓ | ✓ | | | ✓ | |
| Jubilee, Jubilee Rd, Knowle | 0117 977 7900 | 25m | ✓ | ✓ | ✓ | ✓ | | ✓ | | ✓ | ✓ | | ✓ | | | ✓ | |

# SOUTH GLOUCESTERSHIRE LEISURE CENTRES

For more details see: www.southglos.gov.uk/LeisureCulture/sportcentres — classes are subject to change. Contact for details.

| Leisure Centres Open daily | Phone | Aerobics | Badminton | Basketball for U12's | Boxercise | Crèche | Cricket Nets | Dance Classes | Football for U12's | Gymnastics | Gymnasium | Holiday Timetable | Martial Arts | Netball | Outdoor Facilities | Parties | Softplay | Squash Courts | Swimming | Tennis | Trampolining | Volley Ball | Yoga |
|---|---|---|---|---|---|---|---|---|---|---|---|---|---|---|---|---|---|---|---|---|---|---|---|
| Bradley Stoke Leisure Centre, Fiddlers Wood Lane, Bradley Stoke | 01454 867050 | ✓ | ✓ | ✓ | | ✓ | | ✓ | ✓ | ✓ | ✓ | ✓ | ✓ | ✓ | | ✓ | ✓ | ✓ | ✓ | | ✓ | ✓ | ✓ |
| Downend Sports Centre, Garnett Place, Downend | 01454 862221 | | ✓ | ✓ | | | ✓ | | ✓ | | | ✓ | ✓ | ✓ | ✓ | ✓ | | | | | | ✓ | |
| Kingswood Leisure Centre, Church Rd, Staple Hill | 01454 865700 | ✓ | ✓ | | | ✓ | | | | | ✓ | ✓ | ✓ | ✓ | ✓ | ✓ | | | ✓ | | ✓ | | ✓ |
| Patchway Sports Centre, Patchway Community College, Hempton Lane, Almondsbury | 01454 865890 | | ✓ | ✓ | | | ✓ | | ✓ | ✓ | ✓ | ✓ | ✓ | ✓ | ✓ | ✓ | | ✓ | ✓ | | ✓ | ✓ | |
| Thornbury Leisure Centre, Alveston Hill, Thornbury | 01454 865777 | ✓ | ✓ | | | | ✓ | ✓ | | ✓ | ✓ | ✓ | ✓ | ✓ | | ✓ | ✓ | ✓ | ✓ | ✓ | ✓ | ✓ | ✓ |
| Yate Leisure Centre, Kennedy Way, Yate | 01454 865800 | ✓ | ✓ | | | | ✓ | ✓ | | ✓ | | ✓ | | | | ✓ | ✓ | ✓ | ✓ | ✓ | ✓ | ✓ | ✓ |
| Yate Outdoor Sports Complex, Behind Brinsham Green School, Yate | 01454 865820 | | | | | | | | ✓ | | | ✓ | | ✓ | ✓ | ✓ | | | | ✓ | | | |

# NORTH SOMERSET LEISURE CENTRES

For more details see: www.n-somerset.gov.uk. Classes are subject to change. Contact for details.

| Leisure Centres (Open daily) | Phone | Aerobics | Badminton | Basketball for U12's | Boxercise | Crèche | Cricket Nets | Dance Classes | Football for U12's | Gymnastics | Gymnasium | Holiday Timetable | Martial Arts | Netball | Outdoor Facilities | Parties | Softplay | Squash Courts | Swimming | Tennis | Trampolining | Volley Ball | Yoga |
|---|---|---|---|---|---|---|---|---|---|---|---|---|---|---|---|---|---|---|---|---|---|---|---|
| Backwell Leisure Centre, Farleigh Rd, Backwell | 01275 463726 | ✓ | | | | | | | | | | | | | | ✓ | | ✓ | ✓ | | | | |
| Churchill Sports Centre, Churchill Green, Weston-super-Mare | 01934 852303 | ✓ | ✓ | | | | | | | | ✓ | ✓ | ✓ | | ✓ | ✓ | | ✓ | ✓ | ✓ | ✓ | | |
| Gordano Sports Centre *, Gordano School, St Mary's Rd, Portishead | 01275 843942 | ✓ | ✓ | ✓ | | | ✓ | | ✓ | ✓ | | ✓ | ✓ | | ✓ | ✓ | | ✓ | ✓ | ✓ | ✓ | | |
| Hutton Moor Leisure Centre, Hutton Moor Rd, Weston-super-Mare | 01934 425900 | ✓ | ✓ | ✓ | | ✓ | | ✓ | ✓ | | ✓ | ✓ | ✓ | ✓ | ✓ | | ✓ | ✓ | ✓ | | ✓ | | ✓ |
| Parish Wharf Leisure Centre, Harbour Road, Portishead | 01275 848494 | ✓ | ✓ | ✓ | | ✓ | ✓ | ✓ | ✓ | | ✓ | ✓ | ✓ | ✓ | | ✓ | | | | | | | ✓ |
| Scotch Horn Leisure Centre, Brockway, Nailsea | 01275 856965 | ✓ | ✓ | ✓ | | | | ✓ | | | ✓ | ✓ | ✓ | ✓ | ✓ | ✓ | ✓ | ✓ | ✓ | | | ✓ | ✓ |
| Strode Leisure Centre, trode Way, Clevedon | 01275 879242 | ✓ | ✓ | ✓ | | | ✓ | ✓ | | | ✓ | | | ✓ | ✓ | ✓ | | | ✓ | ✓ | ✓ | ✓ | ✓ |
| Swiss Valley Sport Centre *, Clevedon School, Clevedon | 01275 877 182 | | ✓ | ✓ | | | ✓ | ✓ | | | ✓ | | | | ✓ | ✓ | | ✓ | | | | | |
| Wyvern Sports Centre *, Marchfields Way, Weston-super-Mare | 01934 642426 | | ✓ | ✓ | | | | | | | | | | ✓ | ✓ | ✓ | | | ✓ | ✓ | ✓ | ✓ | |

*Leisure centre attached to a school so restricted opening times during school hours

# BATH AND NORTH EAST SOMERSET LEISURE CENTRES

For more details see: www.aquaterra.org — classes are subject to change. Contact for details.

| Leisure Centres Open daily | Phone/web | Aerobics | Badminton | Basketball for U12's | Boxercise | Crèche | Cricket Nets | Dance Classes | Football for U12's | Gymnastics | Gymnasium | Holiday Timetable | Martial Arts | Netball | Outdoor Facilities | Parties | Softplay | Squash Courts | Swimming | Tennis | Trampolining | Volley Ball | Yoga |
|---|---|---|---|---|---|---|---|---|---|---|---|---|---|---|---|---|---|---|---|---|---|---|---|
| Bath Sports and Leisure Centre North Parade Road, Bath | 01225 462565 | ✓ | ✓ | ✓ | ✓ | ✓ | | ✓ | ✓ | ✓ | ✓ | ✓ | ✓ | ✓ | ✓ | ✓ | ✓ | ✓ | ✓ | ✓ | ✓ | ✓ | ✓ |
| Chew Valley Leisure Centre * Chew Lane, Chew Magna | 01275 333375 www.chewvalleyleisurecentre.co.uk | ✓ | ✓ | ✓ | | | ✓ | | | ✓ | ✓ | ✓ | ✓ | ✓ | ✓ | | | ✓ | | | | ✓ | ✓ |
| Culverhay Sports Centre * Rush Hill, Bath | 01225 486902 Mon-Fri 01225 480882 Eve/WE's | ✓ | ✓ | ✓ | | | ✓ | | ✓ | | ✓ | ✓ | ✓ | ✓ | ✓ | ✓ | | | ✓ | ✓ | | | ✓ |
| Keynsham Leisure Centre Temple St, Keynsham | 01225 395161 | ✓ | ✓ | ✓ | | ✓ | | ✓ | | ✓ | ✓ | ✓ | ✓ | | | | ✓ | ✓ | | | | ✓ | ✓ |
| South Wansdyke Sports Centre Rackvernal Rd, Midsomer Norton. | 01761 4015522 | ✓ | ✓ | ✓ | | ✓ | ✓ | ✓ | ✓ | ✓ | ✓ | ✓ | ✓ | | ✓ | | ✓ | ✓ | | | ✓ | ✓ | ✓ |
| Writhlington Sports Centre Radstock, Knobsbury Lane | 01761 438559 www.writhlingtonsportscentre.co.uk | ✓ | ✓ | ✓ | ✓ | | ✓ | ✓ | | ✓ | ✓ | | ✓ | ✓ | ✓ | ✓ | ✓ | ✓ | ✓ | | ✓ | ✓ | ✓ |

*Leisure centre attached to a school so restricted opening times during school hours

# Performing Arts

## Contents

This chapter contains details of where in Bristol your child can join other children in dance, drama and circus activities. There are drama classes for children upwards of six months, and dance from 18 months. As for plate spinning, your young entertainer can look forward to workshops from age three.

### Bristol's got talent

Watching your charismatic two year old sing and dance with impressive confidence and grace may prompt thoughts of your child having a glittering career on the stage. One practicality is to make a network of contacts through reputable organizations such as Spotlight (www.spotlight.com) and Phoenix Casting Agency (www.phoenixagency.biz). Then there is the serious matter of children's health and safety issues, mental and physical. These are regulated by child employment legislation. The Employment of Children Act 1973 sets out the relevant legal framework. You should note that paid acting is generally unlawful without your child's contract being licensed by the local education authority.

# CIRCUS SKILLS

## Circus Maniacs

Office 8A, The Kingswood Foundation, Britannia Rd,
Kingswood, BS15 8DB
0117 947 7042
www.circusmaniacs.com

Circus unites aspects of both sport and arts,
providing the creative freedom to be original
and unique. 'Caterpillars Club' (3-5 yr olds),
held Sat mornings (term-time) 10-10:45am.
£40 per term & annual membership £10.
Taster session £5. Parents/carers are required
to stay & assist. Club teaches wide variety
of circus skills, including plate spinning,
acrobatics and many more. Holiday and
summer events held - contact or see website
for further details.

# DANCE

## 344 Dance School

Alexandra Pk, Fishponds, Bristol, BS16 2BG
0117 965 5660, www.dancestation.org.uk
Branches at: Bradley Stoke, Long Ashton, Wick,
Knowle and Fishponds

Full range of term-time classes for children
aged 2 ½yrs onwards. Mums & toddler
classes held Fri 10am. Holiday/summer
classes/events held - contact for further
details.

## Annette Adams School of Dance

0117 968 4879
www.annetteadamsschoolofdancing.com
info@annetteadamsschoolofdancing.com

A range of classes are held during term time
(children aged 3 yrs onwards), at Horfield
Methodist Church and the Kelvin Players
Drama Studio, both on Gloucester Road.
Offers wide range of classes, including ballet,
modern, tap, jazz and hip hop. Holiday/
summer events held - see website or contact
for further details.

## Bristol School of Dancing

Lansdown Rd, Clifton, Bristol, BS8 3AB
0117 973 3487
www.thebristolschoolofdancing.co.uk
From £38 per term, dependent on age.

Hold classes at various locations across
Bristol and North Somerset, including Clifton,
Southville, Redland, Nailsea, Backwell and
Clevedon. Offer holiday/summer events - see
website or contact for further details.

## Classique Academy of Dance

07887-992 451
www.classiqueacademyofdance.co.uk
info@classiqueacademyofdance.co.uk

Dance classes offered for children aged 2½
onwards. Classes held at Emersons Green Hall
and Wickwar Village Hall. All types of dancing,
including ballet, tap, modern and hiphop.

## Danceblast@the Tobacco Factory

Tobacco Factory, Raleigh Rd, Southville
0117 964 6195
www.danceblast.co.uk
anne@danceblast.co.uk

Sat 3-18 yrs, £4 per 1½hr session

All types of dancing: ballet, jazz, lyrical and
hip hop as well as some singing and acting
included, working towards an annual show.
Sessions are drop-in.

## Mini Movers Dance Academy

Little Stoke Community Hall, Little Stoke Lane, Little
Stoke, Bristol. BS34 6HR
07926 730420 Lula, lula1@hotmail.com

Fun pre-school dance session offered for
children aged approx 18mths-4 yrs. Class held
on Tuesdays 10:30-11:10am (term-time only).

## Pre-School Ballet Classes

Avonmouth Community Centre, 257, Avonmouth Road,
Avonmouth. BS11 9EN
07754 827888 Eve Brewer

eve_brewer@yahoo.co.uk

Pre-school ballet classes for ages 2 ½
years upwards. Friday afternoons 4:15 pm
(term-time only). Children learn basic dance
movements and are introduced to ballet, dance
and different types of music in a fun way.

## Stapleton School of Dancing

01453 834 211
www.stapletonschoolofdancing.co.uk
Classes held at Begbrook Primary School, Stapleton
Christ Church Hall, Quaker Road, Downend and The
Ridgewood Community Centre, Yate.

Ballet, modern and tap classes for children
aged 2+ yrs.

## The Big Act

0870 8810367, www.thebigact.com

Classes in acting, singing and dancing for
children aged 4 up to 18yrs. There are no
auditions, places are offered on a first come
first served basis. New students can come for
a free trial lesson. Students regularly perform
shows in Bristol. There are various venues in
Bristol.

## The Kathryn Hurley Dance Academy

Iron Acton Parish Hall, Iron Acton, South
Gloucestershire.
07968 378995
www.thekathrynhurleydanceacademy.com
hurleykat@hotmail.com

Ballet, tap and modern dance classes for
children aged 3+. Classes held on Monday,
Tuesday and Thursday from 3pm during term-
time.

## Toddlers Creative Dance

Redland Parish Church Hall, Redland Green, Bristol.
07879 483106 Emma, foxyfossil2003@yahoo.co.uk

Fun dance classes for pre-school children
from 2yrs, accompanied by an adult. Every
Wed 9:30-10:15am, including half-terms
and Easter. During summer holidays, classes
held at Horfield Quaker Meeting House 10-
10:45am.

## Westbury Park Dance Centre

St Albans Church Hall, Westbury Park, Bristol, BS6
0117 968 3682,
westburyparkdancecentre@hotmail.com

Classes following RAD ballet and ISTD Jazz/
Modern / Tap syllabuses. Children (all ages,
from 3 yrs) work towards occasional shows.

## Wingfield School of Ballet

0117 950 3916, wingfieldschool@ninety.plus.com
Venues: Patchway, Little Stoke, Thornbury,
Almondsbury, Brislington & Bradley Stoke
Leisure Centre

Offer classes in ballet, jazz and tap for
children aged 3 yrs and onwards. Holiday/
summer events held - contact for further
details.

## Yasmin's Fun Dance for Under 6's

St Nicholas Youth Centre, Chargrove, Yate, BS37 4LG
01454 883162,  lisa_carps@hotmail.com

Modern dance classes for under 6's. 2 classes
held every Sat 9:30am-10:am (£2) and
10:15am-11am (£2.50).

## Young Performanze Dance & Drama Arts Foundation

Hillcrest Primary School, Knowle, Bristol.
07745 099472 Rosie, www.performanze.co.uk

Classes in ballet, tap, modern and street jazz.
Suitable for children aged 3yrs+. Classes held
on Saturdays.

**TITCH HIKERS'
RECOMMENDED**

We want to know who
you think are great.

Please email us at info@titchhikers.co.uk.

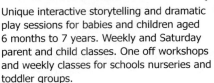

# DRAMA & THEATRE SKILLS

## Debutots Early Years Drama

Bristol and South Gloucestershire
01454 612063, www.debutots.co.uk

Unique interactive storytelling and dramatic
play sessions for babies and children aged
6 months to 7 years. Weekly and Saturday
parent and child classes. One off workshops
and weekly classes for schools nurseries and
toddler groups.

## Helen O'Grady Drama Academy

(Regional office) Saville Court Business Centre, 11
Saville Place, Clifton, Bristol, BS8 4ES.
0117 900 1602, www.helenogrady.co.uk

Popular drama classes offered for children
across Bristol, aged 5yrs onwards. The
programme offered at the academy aims
to provide on-going confidence and skills in
verbal communication through drama.

## Little Sunshines - Shine through Arts

St. Bartholomew's Church, Wick, S Glouc, BS30
0117 961 9720 Beth Morgan
littlesunshines@btinternet.com

Fun music, drama and craft classes held
for babies, toddlers and preschoolers. Held
every Thursday morning during term-time. 3
separate classes available according to age.

## Stagecoach

0117 953 2500
www.stagecoach.co.uk
bristolsouthwest@stagecoach.co.uk

Offer classes involving drama, dance and
singing for children aged 4 onwards. 'Early
Stage' classes for 4-6 yr olds held at Birdwell
Primary School, Long Ashton, (1 1/2 hrs on
Sat mornings). Classess split by age and
ability. Other sessions also held at Portishead
on fri afternoons and Clevedon on Sat
mornings.

# Art, Craft & Cookery

## Contents

Bristol has masses for young children who wish to express themselves artistically, whether through arts and crafts, pottery, painting, or food. This chapter provides information on venues, and lots of ideas of fun things do to within the home.

## Good Websites for Ideas

### Children and the Arts
www.childrenandarts.co.uk
Subscribe to this site to be notified of upcoming events.

### Netmums
www.netmums.com
Lots of fun ideas.

Many toddler groups have art and craft activities. See
**Parent & Baby/Toddler**

## ARTS & CRAFTS

### Baby Skills

Westbury Baptist Church, Reedley Road
Philpa: 07931708474 or Archna: 07956800520,
www.babyskills.co.uk
Thurs: 3-12 mths 1.30-2.30pm, 12-24 mths 3-4pm

Baby development classes with different activities each week (craft, structured play, sand play, singing, painting and more).

### Busy Fingers

Scotch Horn Leisure Centre, Brockway, Nailsea, North Somerset, BS48 1BZ
01275 856965
Weds 1.15-2.45pm, ages 2½-5 years all year round

Busy fingers is a fun session where your child is encouraged to cut and stick and create their own masterpieces based around the theme for the week. There is also water play, dressing up, play doh and painting as well as a selection of toys for them to play with.

### Children's Scrap Store

Scrapstore House, 21 Sevier Street, Bristol BS2 9LB
0117 914 3025, www.childrensscrapstore.co.uk

#### Super Saturday Sample Sessions

FREE sessions
11am-12.30pm & 1.30-3pm every other Sat.

A chance for members and the public to try out the products on sale in the Artrageous shop. A Craft Expert is on hand to show you what to do but children must be supervised by an adult. Drop-in but places are limited.

### Mini Art

The Old School Rooms, Stoke Gifford, BS34 8PD
01454 777450, Mini-Art@kcit.co.uk (Karen)
Tuesday and Friday morning from 10.15-11.00.
Suitable Age 18 months to 5years
£4 per session

Arts, crafts and messy play group for toddlers, preschoolers and their carers. Each week there is a theme with crafts based around this. Also, lots of free play, painting, sand, water, playdough, cutting, sticking and more.

### Mucky Pups Arts & Crafts

07780 607899/0117 963 8316, www.mucky-pups.com
Long Ashton Village Hall, Keedwell Hill, Long Ashton, Bristol, BS41. Tues 10-10.45am
Southville Methodist Church, Faith Space, Stackpool Road, Southville, Bristol, BS3. Fri 9.45-10.30am
Both are term time only. Booking essential. 0-5yrs.

The above sessions are run by Karen, who believes that most children love to make 'masterpieces' but don't always get the opportunity as adults can be afraid of the mess. By encouraging them to have a go with a wide range of materials, children gain confidence and deveop everyday skills, such as fine motor control. Mucky Pups is based around weekly themes and ends with a circle time. Summer & Easter sessions for children up to 8 years. Also see **Parties**.

Notes: Taster sessions £6. Weekly £5.50 payable/ term in advance. Registration Fee, £12.50 includes the I'm a Mucky Pup t-shirt. Aprons provided.

### Sticky Fingers

07803749408 & 07830377971
St Stephens Church Hall Church Rd BS15 1XD
07803749408 & 07830377971
School Holiday sessions (need pre-booking).
Mon 9.30-10.30am. £2.50 (siblings £2) U1 free.

Creative and messy play sessions for children aged 5 and under. Different art and craft materials are provided to inspire your child to explore and express their ideas and feelings.

## HAD YOU THOUGHT OF?

The following places provide art and craft as part of their overall experience.

### Arnolfini - p.49
**Often has craft days during school holidays.**

### Bristol City Museum - p.49
**Art and craft areas & holiday activities.**

### Playspace - p.149
**Activity Room with drop-in arts & crafts sessions, messy play & more (10.30am/2pm).**

### Brunel's ss Great Britain - p.48
**Regular art and craft workshops.**

# POTTERY

## Absolute Ceramics

66 High Street, Hanham, South Glos, BS15 3DR
0117 947 8878, www.absoluteceramics.com
Paint your own pottery, make baby prints and casts, have a pottery painting party, or cast finger prints in solid silver. Also see **Parties.**

## Flying Saucers Painting Pottery Café

9 Byron Place, Bristol, BS8 1JT
0117 927 3666, www.flyingsaucers.co.uk
Open: Tues-Sat 11am-6pm, Sun 11am-5pm
Release your and your child's inner artist or capture your child's hand or footprint forever at this friendly, fun, pottery painting café. Great for creating special, individual gifts for Granny and Grandad too. Also see **Parties.**

*Tip*

Every Tuesday is Toddler Tuesday. See Parent and Baby/Toddler for more information.
Also see **Advert** below.

## The Village Pottery

70 Princess Victoria Street, Clifton, BS8 4DD
0117 973 4343, www.thevillagepottery.co.uk
Open: Tues-Sat 10am-5pm, B/Hs 10am-5pm

Pottery teaching to children and adults. Baby imprinting and also birth plates and other personalised gifts such as boiled egg and soldier plates. One-to-one lessons available for older children and adults. Also has a lovely coffee bar with home made cakes. See **Advert** above.

## COOKERY

### Tickle Your Tastbuds Courses

Alphabet Childcare,
184a Henleaze Rd, BS9 4NE 0117 962 2897,
www.connectmedical.com/tyt/index.html

**Run by Amanda White (a Teacher), and Caroline Grant (a Health visitor).**

Fun fruit and vegetable activity sessions for children aged 1-5yrs. These sessions allow your child to explore fruit and vegetables in imaginative ways. Each week there is a different fruit and vegetable to explore, chop and taste, as children prepare their own simple dishes. There are also stories, singing and puppets activities; children may even help with some simple gardening. Amanda and Caroline try to use local, seasonal produce, and to get over the recycling message wherever possible. Everything is provided for the packed hours session, and there are goodie bags and nutition tips and hints.

### Cookwise

North Wootton, Nr Wells, BA4 4AA,
01749 890017, www.cookwise.co.uk

Workshops and resources to get children cooking.

# Crafty ideas

1. Make your own play dough (see below).
2. Do a treasure hunt by hiding clues around the house (picture clues for non-readers).
3. Make your own pizza - either buy a dough mix or make the dough then give your child lots of toppings to pile on. Lunch sorted!
4. Flower pressing. Then make into a card or piece of art.
5. Make a puppet out of an old sock. Then put on a puppet show.
6. Easy cakes e.g. rice krispie cakes.
7. Make a shaker (toilet roll and pasta/rice).
8. Playing restaurants - let your children make some 'food' (see play dough) and serve it to you! (You get to sit down!)
9. Make a junk model - bottles, boxes, etc.
10. Make your own bubble mixture with diluted washing up liquid then test what you can make the bubbles with.

## Tip

The Early Learning Centre have produced some fabulous cards with play ideas on. Visit their shops or see www.elc.co.uk/play.

# Play Dough Recipe

**The easiest recipe around and guaranteed fun. Can be baked to keep creations!**

You will need:

2 cups flour, 1 cup salt, 1 tablespoon cooking oil, 1 cup water with food colouring.

Mix together flour, salt and oil. Add water until mixture forms a ball. Knead. Make your model or roll out and use cutters to make hanging decorations. Bake at 180°c for approx. 35-40 minutes. Cool, paint and varnish if required.

# Children's Theatre

## Contents

### Theatre Company Listings for Parents to Check out

**www.creakingdoor.co.uk** - e.g. Adaptations of Grimm's fairy tales.

**www.heartbreakproductions.co.uk** - e.g. Peter Pan at Tyntesfield.

**www.lingo.co.uk** - e.g. The Fish's Wishes, What a Wonderful World.

**www.oldvic.ac.uk** - Bristol Old Vic Theatre School, 0117 9733535 (sometimes at Redgrave Theatre) e.g. traditional pantomimes, Nativity.

**www.puppet-lab.com**

**www.tallstories.org.uk** - e.g. Adaptation of Julia Donaldson's Room on the Broom.

**www.travlight.co.uk** - e.g. The Ugly Duckling

**www.tuckedin.org** - e.g. Jackajack.

Don't think of theatre as a daunting thing to do with children, nor something that is out of reach financially. This chapter introduces you to the Bristol venues, many of which are affordable, and all of which are committed to putting on shows whose length and content make them a lovely experience for young children.

## Tips

- Phone to find out in advance how long the performance is and try to allow enough time to go to the toilet before the show starts, bearing in mind that it's sometimes quite a long walk to the toilet.

- Theatres do not usually apply age restrictions, like the cinema, but not all material is going to be suitable for your child. Take note of the theatre companies' recommendations about age.

# THEATRES

## Bristol Old Vic

King Street, Bristol, BS1 4ED
Box office: 0117 987 7877
www.bristololdvic.org.uk

In September 2009, the Bristol Old Vic will reopen under the new artistic directorship of Tom Morris. The admirable **Travelling Light Theatre Co.** are programmed to show 'How cold my Toes' in the Studio, and for slightly older siblings, world renowned **Kneehigh Theatre Co.** are bringing a retelling of 'Hansel and Gretel' to the Main House. Check out the website for other events for young children; there may, for example, be a return to the Fri/Sat storytelling sessions.

## Hen and Chicken

210 North Street, Bedminster, BS3 1JF
0117 9663143
www.henandchicken.com

The Hen and Chicken is a pub with an upstairs entertainment venue, usually associated with shows for adults (particularly 'The Company Box') but look out for children's productions in the holidays.

## Redgrave Theatre

Percival Rd, Clifton, Bristol, BS8 3LE (near the Zoo)
0117 3157666
www.cliftoncollegeuk.com/ccsl/redgrave
For details of upcoming performances take a look at the school's website or phone for details

This is a purpose-built school theatre attached to Clifton College that stages productions by school groups, touring companies as well as local amateurs. It hosts various seasonal shows for a younger audience and productions from Clifton upper school, prep school and pre-school. The Old Vic Theatre School also performs at the Redgrave. It can be difficult to find out what's on there as the box office is not open full-time but you can join the mailing list: redgrave@clifton-college.avon.sch.uk. Don't assume the refreshment bar will be open after the show for a drink or snack, so stock up before.

## The Bristol Hippodrome

St Augustine's Parade, Bristol, BS1 4UZ
0117 3023333 (enquiries)
0844 847 2325 (bookings)
www.bristolhippodrome.org.uk
Parking nearby at Millenium Square car park.

The Hippodrome is Bristol's west end theatre. Its large stage allows for spectacular productions.

## The Tobacco Factory

Raleigh Rd, Southville, Bristol, BS3 1TF
0117 902 0344, www.tobaccofactory.com
Closed in August

The Tobacco Factory strives to offer productions that are innovative and unusual. Children welcome in the Green Room area of the café bar and in the theatre bar. Refreshments for children are inexpensive. The toilets are quite a long walk downstairs, so we recommend children 'go' before the show starts. There is also a Sunday market from 10.30am-2.30pm.

## The Egg at The Theatre Royal

Sawclose, Bath, BA1 1ET
01225 448844, www.theatreroyal.org.uk

This is a fabulous, modern, purpose designed space attached to the main house (one of the oldest working theatres in the country). There is an impressive range of kids' shows. Join the Egg Club to find out about all the weekday sessions for little people. There is an excellent cafe for pre/post refreshments (child sized plain sandwiches and healthy drinks) supplied by Bristol's Chandos Deli. There are little toilets and low sinks - but 'go' before the show because they are in the basement. Visit by train - only a 10 minute walk from Bath Spa station. But beware of the cost of parking at Temple Meads!

Got a budding actor on your hands?
See **Performing Arts**

# Why take children to the theatre?

By Gillian Sweet Bartley

Does the idea of 'theatre' conjure up images for you of a high stage with huge swishing curtains and tickets you have to save up for all year? If so, let me tell you about the affordable and fun studio venues which we are lucky to have in the Bristol area, sometimes in places you might not expect. For example, The Tobacco Factory in Bedminster has a commendable commitment to performances for children. And did you know that just down the road the Hen and Chicken Pub hosts an upstairs entertainment room? The local *Creaking Door* theatre company performed there this year and made our Anna's three year old eyes shine to see her brothers impromptu roles as Snow White's dwarves, complete with Sleepy and Dopey hats. Of course, your child may be shy, and not all theatre for children indulges the star-struck or actively encourages them to join in, but these days it is often a participative and even intimate experience, particularly for the under fives. The gentle 'What a Wonderful World', written and performed by the duo from *Lyngo* theatre, begins by giving every child a little cloth bag of interesting objects to find and use during the 45 minute show.

Performances for the young are often no more than an hour, with no interval, which makes them easy on both attention span and bladder capacity. Also, the actors are sometimes milling around and interacting with the children before the actual performance begins, which usually helps to get the children relaxed. *Tall Stories* theatre co. play hide 'n seek in the audience before the start of 'Room on the Broom' which little children (and me) find hilarious.

This kind of shared experience is clearly very different from watching TV, DVDs or going to the cinema. I invited Mike Akers, Education Director of Bristol's highly acclaimed *Travelling Light Theatre Company*, to share some of his views about how children can benefit from theatre visits.

"...The Theatre experience is very different to the other forms you mention. The thing they have in common is that they're all mediums for storytelling but, beyond that, seeing a play has so much more to offer. For a start, it's live, so you get a connection between the audience and the performers that you can't get on film or TV. This is a unique experience that will never be repeated in exactly the same way again. It's also a much more active process. Theatre makes you think and you often have to make connections or fill in the gaps... The direct connection between the audience and the performers and the closeness to the action, also means good theatre can provide a more vibrant and powerful experience. An amazing piece of theatre is the kind of thing a child will remember for life."

Mike's right, and children delight to 'fill in the gaps'. I love to see how willingly my grandchildren become absorbed in the theatrical make-believe world. Film, in contrast, tends to aim for visual realism, but the credulity of children doesn't depend on authentic costumes, location details and special effects. Imagination is something children use all the time in their own play; a crown makes a king, a branch is a forest, and magic can happen because they say so.

See our theatre listings for venues, and also our selection of touring theatre companies who might be performing in our area soon. Some are outdoor too and you can take a picnic. Join their mailing lists so you don't miss out. Sometimes they might only do two shows on a single day in Bristol.

And remember, film has its place, but there's nothing like the real thing!

# Parties

## Contents

Please let the entertainers or businesses listed in this book know where you heard about them.

Let's party! Whether the mere thought of a kids party leaves you exhausted, or your appetite for such things knows no bounds, the event ideas and organisers highlighted here will help you make an informed decision.

## Tips

**Think laterally. Many of the people and places listed in this book (but maybe not this chapter) will also do parties.**

**Book the venue in advance.**

**Give directions to the venue.**

**Tie balloons to your gate.**

## Summer Events

Watch many of the performers for FREE in Bristol during the Summer. See www.titchhikers.co.uk for details

# CHILDREN'S ENTERTAINERS

## Cassandra, Storyteller

0117 966 3864, 0797 107 7774
www.storiesinmotion.co.uk
cassandrawye@yahoo.co.uk

An internationally-acclaimed storyteller, Cassie creates an exuberant and vividly expressive performance, involving the audience in every twist and turn of the story. "Children and adults' imaginations are totally engaged by her unique and participative style of storytelling."

## Cats Whiskers

0117 3706147 (Bristol)
01454 806349 (South Glos)
www.catswhiskers.biz, enquiries@catswhiskers.biz

Face painting, body art, temporary tattoos, balloon modelling. Events and promotions. Strict code of practice regarding hygiene and use of safe professional paints (for sensitive skin). A maximum of 24 children for a two-hour party session.

## Clementine Parties

07867 542942, 07806
www.clementineparties.co.uk
Clare and Emma organise art activity parties. There are a wide range of themes to choose from, and a choice of four types of party packages depending on your budget. Examples of activities include T shirt or jewellery box decorating, puppets, min-makeovers, and face painting. Both Clare and Emma are mums themselves and so know what it takes to make a good party. For boys and girls aged 2+

## Jack Stephens Magician

42 Netherstreet, Bromham, Chippenham, SN15 2DW
01380 850453, www.jackstephens.co.uk
jackstephens@abra-cadabra.co.uk

Jack's fun show features magic, puppets, singing with a guitar, games, balloon modelling and "above all lots of audience participation". Gears the performances for all venues and occasions.

## Magical Mandy

01225 442223, 07841 627013
www.magicalmandy.co.uk, amanda.farrell@sky.com

Wonderful magic shows with a choice of themes. Mandy organises games, prizes, balloon modelling, even dressing up, as well as the magic show. Fancy dress competition optional. Mandy is a member of the Magic Circle. For Bristol & Bath.

## Mr Brown's Pig — Puppet Shows and Pirate Pantomine

15 Vicarage Road, Southville, Bristol, BS3 1PD
0117 963 4929, www.puppetsonline.co.uk
chris@puppetsonline.co.uk

These excellent puppet shows are for children aged 3+yrs, featuring an elaborate puppet booth with lights and music. The shows have lots of audience participation and humour. The Pirate Pantomine features puppets, comedy, music and magic. See advertisement.

*Summer Fun*

See Mr Brown's Pig at events around Bristol during the Summer months.

## Pizzazz

Covering Bristol/Avon/Wilts area
07721 831 263
www.gamesagogo.co.uk
gamesagogo@hotmail.com

Circus skills parties/workshops with balloon modelling, face painting, caricatures, giant bubbles and parachute games. "Steve manages to include all children (and adults) with patience and humour!"

## Punch & Judy

Pogles Wood, 8 Marjoram Place, Bradley Stoke
Bristol BS32 0DQ
0117 965 7761 (Trevor), 01454 613 796 (John),
0771 447 8327, www.punchandjudy4u.co.uk

Traditional English Punch and Judy for 3+yrs.
Entertainment can also include magic and/or
balloons depending upon the individuals
requirements. Shows last up to 1hr and the
costs vary.

## Tallulah Swirls

0117 377 4543, www.tallulahswirls.co.uk

Amy's beautifully hand-crafted puppets
perform to all ages. "Lots of audience
participation, singing and laughing followed by
a chance for everyone to see how the show
operates." Workshops also offered. Also see
**Advert**.

Summer Fun

Amy often performs during the Summer Parks
programme. See **Parks & Play Areas**.

## Tatty Bumpkin

0117 952 0070, www.tattybumpkin.co.uk
paulabrown@tattybumpkin.com

Children's parties based on music and
movement for ages 18mths-6yrs. Can be
tailored to your child, incorporating favourite
places, people and a theme into an animal
adventure, with certificates and stickers and
a party game. **See Tatty Bumpkin around
Bristol and the West. Dates and times on
our website - www.titchhikers.co.uk.**

## The Pink Strawberry Puppet Co.

01275 544576, 07914 187737
monkeybpirate@aol.com

Anthony Churchill is a puppeteer who both
teaches and performs. Performances can be
geared to audience age and size. Workshops
and puppet clubs teach puppet making,
performing and its history. Available for
birthday parties over the summer.

## Wastenot Workshops

0117 941 4447
Within Bristol area

Children can create their own masterpieces
from recycled materials, anything from
puppets to costumes and masks. Themes
include mermaids, pirates, dragons and
princesses. Face painting can also be included.

## Wizzo the Wizard

01291 424 385, 07748 772 686
www.wizzothewizard.com

Magic for children of all ages; there are
puppets, balloon modelling and prizes for all.
Wizzo also does Educational Road
Safety Shows.

# HIRE OF INFLATABLES

## Absolute Bounce

01275 540731, www.bouncycastlesbristol.co.uk
info@absolutebounce.co.uk

Variety of bouncy castles, ball pools and other inflatables (such as soft play equipment) for hire. Available for delivery to Bristol, Clevedon, Portishead, Nailsea, Weston-Super-Mare, Taunton, Wells and all surrounding areas.

## Adams Castles

0117 9834280, 07720 846945
www.adamscastles.co.uk

Castle and ball pool hire throughout the year. Extremely friendly. Free delivery, set-up and collection. Added safety features.

## Bristol Bouncy Castles

07796 775522, 01454 321566 (Mr Paul Tree)
www.bristolbouncycastlesltd.co.uk

Assorted bouncy castles, slides, ball ponds, gladiators for indoor and outdoor parties and events. They even have a 'baby bounce' for 1-3 year olds. Delivery (within 25 miles of Bristol) and set-up are free. Free insurance.

## Bristol Fun for Hire

01173 302943 or 07545 185027
www.funforhirebristol.co.uk

Provide bouncy castles and wide range of other inflatables and games for hire.

## Bristol Inflatables

Bristol Inflatables, P O Box 250, BS16 5WX
0117 9564380, 07971 325307
www.bristolinflatables.com

Bouncy castles for hire, for all occasions.

## Bristol Partyhire

07912 422300, www.bristolpartyhire.co.uk

Bouncy castles, inflatable slides and ball pools for hire. Free delivery within 15 miles of BS34 FREE - delivery further afield extra.

# PARTY GOODS

## Balloon Clusters

Collette Taylor, Charnwood House, Frog Lane, Felton Bristol, BS40 9UN
01275 475611, www.ballooncluster.co.uk

Professional balloon decorating service.

## KidzCraft

01793 327022, www.kidzcraft.co.uk
Office open 9am-5pm, Mon-Fri

The Kids Craft Party Shop. Creative fun Craft Party ideas and supplies for children's parties.

## Party Pieces

01635 201844, www.partypieces.co.uk
Mon-Fri 8.30am-6pm, Sat 9am-5pm

Mail order service selling everything that you could need for your child's party, including unusual plates, invitations, prizes, and cake kits.

## Partysmartys

07918667843 or 01275 818971
www.partysmartys.co.uk, partysmartys@yahoo.co.uk

Partysmartys is a small family business, creating unusual party bags, party tablewear, fancy dress costumes, party games, and more. In fact, everything that you could need to make your child's party go swimmingly. The party bags are guaranteed to have the 'wow' factor, are fun, safe and affordable. Based in Portishead, Somerset. Customers who live locally are invited to look through the box of small party items, choosing exactly what they want and then deciding on colours or theme. Customers who are not so local can browse the ever changing selection from the website. See Advert opposite.

## Tips

Why not think about an entertainer or party bags for another special event such as a Christening or Naming Day? See **PartySmartys** above.

## CAKES & PARTY FOOD

### Bib & Tucker

077612 78031, www.bibandtuckerfoods.co.uk
rachael.symons@btinternet.com

Home-cooked party food and celebration cakes. (Also does a range of children's frozen foods, using free range and organic ingredients. See website or call for details).

### Cakes by Alison

01454 315742, 07801 336213
www.cakesbyalison.co.uk
From £20

Cakes for all occasions. Personalised to your requirements. Will deliver free within 20 miles of Bristol.

### Tots Teas

Vicky Duffield, 5 St Agnes Close, Nailsea, BS48 2UB
01275 544198 or 07802 810897

Small and friendly catering company, taking care of everything from the cake to the entire catering. The top quality party food can be delivered to your home or the party venue.

## PARTY VENUES

### ANIMALS

### Bristol Zoo Gardens

Clifton, Bristol, BS8 3HA
0117 974 7300, www.bristolzoo.org.uk

"Zooper" birthday parties. As well as all the usual zoo events, activities and animals, face painting can be booked (additional charge), or a private activity session in the Education Centre (can include face to face encounters with small animals and role play). Children's lunch bags can be provided by the Pelican restaurant. Also see **Animals** chapter.

### Horseworld

Staunton Lane, Whitchurch, Bristol, BS14 0QJ
01275 893030 , www.horseworld.org.uk

Parties for a minimum of 10 children. Food and party bags are provided. Ask about Horace making a special appearance at your party. Also see **Animals** chapter.

**See more ideas over the page...**

## ALSO TRY...

### Noah's Ark
Failand Rd, Wraxall, Bristol, BS48 1PG
01275 852606, www.noahsarkzoofarm.co.uk

### Windmill Hill City Farm
Philip Street, Bedminster, BS3 4EA
0117 963 3252

## ART

### Mucky Pups Arts & Crafts
07780 607899/0117 963 8316
www.mucky-pups.com

Bespoke birthday parties. See **Arts, Craft & Cookery** for more information.

## CIRCUS

### Circus Maniacs
Office 8a, Kingswood Foundation, Britannia Road, Kingswood, Bristol, BS15 8DB
0117 9477042, www.circusmaniacs.com

Range of party workshops available for children from 3 years. Food is not provided but there is an independent cafe on site, or you can picnic on the grass outside. Circus maniacs will also come to your venue. Contact or see website for more details.

## COOKING

### Cookwise
North Wootton, Nr Wells, BA4 4AA,
01749 890017, www.cookwise.co.uk

Cooking parties where children cook their own party food from locally produced, raw ingredients. Suitable for all age ranges although under 7's usually require an adult to stay. Parties normally held in North Wootton Farm but DIY parties in your own venue can be arranged. 2½ hours and party bag provided.

## GYM

Gym parties are always popular with small children (and Dads who seem to find joining in irresistable). They usually involve a similar theme of lots of soft play and exploration of gym equipment under supervision. Contact the Gyms on page 147 to find out what they have to offer children.

## POTTERY

### Absolute Ceramics
66 High Street, Hanham, South Glos, BS15 3DR
0117 947 8878, www.absoluteceramics.com

Pottery painting parties. Parties last approximately 1 hour 30 mins. You can bring your own cake, drinks and party food.

### Flying Saucers
9 Byron Place, Bristol, BS8 1JT
0117 927 3666, www.flyingsaucers.co.uk
See main entry in **Arts, Craft and Cookery**

A superb party venue for children of all ages. The party takes place in a private party room which you have exclusive use of for up to 2 hours (seats up to 20). You can bring your own party food and cake, but squash, plates and napkins can be provided. The birthday child also receives a standard plate as a gift; often all of the children help personalise this as a really special reminder of the day. Contact for pricing. Download your invitations from the website.

## SOFT PLAY

### 123 Jump
22 Concorde Road, Cribbs Causeway, BS34 5TB
0117 9312 733, www.123jump.co.uk

Fantastic, action packed, themed parties, tailored to children of all ages. These are incredibly well organised parties, from the greeting the minute you step through the door of Jump, to the friendly and accommodating play workers, to the range of activities (vary depending if you opt for the premier package or the straightforward one). Party host, unlimited play, hats, balloons, cake and food, invitations and more are all included.

## Noah's Ark Play Centre

828 Bath Rd, Brislington, BS4 5LQ
0117 971 2599, www.noahsarkplay.com
Paries last up to 2 hours with the first hour spent in soft play followed by food and more playing afterwards. Choice of 3 party menus.

## The Play Bus

01454 414467, www.theplaybus.com
The Play Bus is a soft play area on wheels for 3-8 year olds. It will come and park outside your house and can accommodate up to 25 people.

## ALSO TRY...

### Castaways

Bourne Chapel, Waters Rd, Kingswood, BS15 8BE
0117 9615115, www.bristolcommunitychurch.org
A friendly party hostess/host will look after you during your visit, and party food, invitations, a photo, party gifts and a present for the Birthday Boy or Girl are all included in the price.

### Playzone at Riverside Leisure Club

Station Rd, Little Stoke, BS34 6HW
01452 413214, www.riversidesports.co.uk
Enjoy exclusive use of the indoor soft play area for 1½ hours.

### Playspace

85 Barrow Road, St Philips, BS5 0AE
0117 9550070, www.playspace.co.uk
Various party options to choose from for all ages. See page 149 for more details

### Tiny Tearawayz Soft Play

Unit 31 Broadwalk Shopping Centre Knowle BS4 2QU www.tinytearawayz.co.uk
Parties include iinvitations, party host, dedicated seating area, VIP Treatment, unlimited Squash, 1 hour 15 mins of play, 45 minutes in the party room and hot and cold buffet with ice cream afterwards.

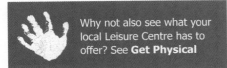

Why not also see what your local Leisure Centre has to offer? See **Get Physical**

# SPORT

## Bristol Dojo

Upper Floor, Middle Unit, 74-78 Avon St, BS2 0PX
07527 031946 or 0800 7566990
www.bristoldojo.com
Offers a range of parties from karate, street dancing, bouncy castles, mini football and more. Parties held on weekend afternoons.

# LOCAL HALLS

There are local halls and churches available for hire all over Bristol. Below and over the page are just a few recommended places.

### All Saints Church Hall

Grove Road, Fishponds, Bristol, BS16 2BW
0117 965 4143

### Elmgrove Centre

Elmgrove Road, Cotham, Bristol, BS6 6AH
0117 924 3377, www.elmgrovecentre.org.uk

### Holy Cross & Southville Social Club

Dean Lane, Southville, Bristol, BS3 1DB
0117 963 1282

### Redland Parish Church

Redland Church Office, Redland Green Road, BS6 7HE
0117 973 7423

### St Christopher's Church Hall

Hampstead Road, Brislington, Bristol, BS4
0117 983 4435

### St George Community Centre

321 Church Road, St. George, Bristol, BS5 8AA
0117 960 6249 / 07757 319 582
www.stgeorgecc.co.uk

# YOGA

## Yoga Stars

Covering Bristol/Bath/South Glos.
07976 350564
www.yoga-stars.co.uk
hello@yoga-stars.co.uk

Children's yoga teacher Sarah Claridge brings the ancient art of yoga as a fun and healthy way for your child to celebrate his/her birthday! Features traditional yoga postures developed into specially themed adventures, yoga games, craft activity and an all-important relaxation time! A special gift to birthday child and each child receives a party certificate! See also **Get Physical**.

# PARTY VENUES OUTSIDE BRISTOL

## Avon Valley Country Park

Pixash Lane, Bath Rd, Keynsham, BS31 1TP
0117 986 4929
www.avonvalleycountrypark.co.uk

Superb venue with animals, play areas (inside and out). Contact for more details. Also see full entry in **Animals and Wildlife**.

## Puxton Park

Puxton Park, Cowslip Lane, W-o-T, BS24 6AH
01934 523500

# PARTY CHILDCARE

A mobile crèche with qualified staff and appropriate equipment can be hired for short periods of time to look after a set number of children during a special occasion such as a wedding or company fun day. Contact the companies below to find out more about what they offer.

## ABC Childcare Crew

46b High Street, Westbury-on-Trym, BS9 3DZ
0117 959 1161
www.abcchildcarecrew.co.uk
info@abcchildcarecrew.co.uk

## Partycrechers

01179 076210 or 07811 373490
www.partycrechers.co.uk

# Eating Out

## Contents

All the places in this section have been recommended to us as they are considered child-friendly. Above everything else, this means that they have a good attitude towards children and, in most cases, the basic equipment to make your visit easier. If you need something specific, please phone in advance to check. And keep recommending great places to eat to us!

We listen to feedback and have highlighted restaurants and cafès that are particularly supportive of breastfeeding mums with the symbol below. Thank you to Bristol NCT and NHS for all the work they do in this area. If you are a business and you would like to take part in this scheme please call 0117 9002274. More places are being added all the time. See www.avon.nhs.uk/kris

We only list recommendations from you. Please let us know what you think of the places listed, and recommend anywhere we have missed.

**BRISTOL**
BREASTFEEDING

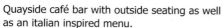

# CENTRAL BRISTOL

## HARBOURSIDE

### Arnolfini

16 Narrow Quay, Bristol BS1 4QA
0117 917 2305, www.arnolfini.org.uk
Daily 10am-11pm (Sun 10.30pm)
Full Menu served: Mon-Wed 10am-10pm,
Thu-Sat 11am-10pm, Sun 11am-10pm

Quayside café bar with outside seating as well
as an italian inspired menu.

### Bordeaux Quay

V-Shed, Canons Way, BS1 5UH
0117 9431200
www.bordeaux-quay.co.uk
Brasserie: Mon-Fri 8am-10.30pm,
Sat 9-1am, 12-10.30pm, & Sun 9am-4pm
Restaurant: Mon-Sat 12-3pm, 6.30-10pm,
Sun 12-4pm

Superb restaurant designed to have a minimal
impact on the environment. The Brasserie is
breastfeeding friendly.

### Ferry Station Café

Narrow Quay, BS1 4QA
0117 3763942, www.ferrystation.co.uk
Mon-Tue 8am-4pm, Wed-Thu 8am-6pm,
Fri 8am-11pm, Sat 10am-11pm, Sun 10am-6pm

Idyllically situated, ethically minded café.

### Firehouse Rotisserie

Anchor Square, Harbourside, BS1 5DB
0117 915 7323
www.firehouserotisserie.co.uk
Mon-Sun 12-2.30pm & 6-11pm
(closed sunday evening Oct-Apr)

California-style cooking served in casual
restaurant next to @Bristol.

### Pizza Express

Unit 1, Harbourside, BS1 5TY
0117 927 3622, www.pizzaexpress.com

Family friendly chain with children's menu
and activities. See also Park Street and Clifton
Village.

### Riverstation

The Grove, Bristol, BS1 4RB
0117 914 4434, 914 9463
www.riverstation.co.uk
Bar-Kitchen: Mon-Weds 9am-11pm,
Thur-Sat 9am-12am, Sun 11am-10.30pm
Restaurant: Mon-Thur 12-2.30pm & 6-10.30pm, Fri-
Sat 12-2.30pm & 6-11pm, Sun 12-3pm & 6-9pm

Environmentally responsible bar and
restaurant in an idylic setting on the
waterfront (children like watching the ducks)
Often has offers where kids eat free.

### Severnshed Restaurant

Grove Harbourside, Bristol, BS1 4RB
0117 925 1212
www.shed-restaurants.com

Mon-Sun 12pm-midnight (2am Fri/Sat)

Buzzing harbourside restaurant with outdoor
seating.

### Watershed Café Bar

1 Canons Rd, Harbourside, BS1 5TX
0117 927 5101
www.watershed.co.uk
Mon 10.30am-11pm, Tue-Thur 9.30am-11pm, Fri
9.30am-12pm, Sat 10am-12am, Sun 10am-10.30pm.

# BROADMEAD & CITY CENTRE

### Bella Italia

8-10 Baldwin St, Bristol, BS1 1SA
0117 929 3278, www.bellaitalia.co.uk

Sun-Thu 9am-11pm, Fri & Sat 9am-11.30pm

Welcomes children and has an appealing
children's menu.

### Bottelino's Restaurant

22 Bond Street, Bristol, BS1 3LU
0117 926 8054, www.bottelinos.net

Mon-Sat 11.30am-2.30pm, 5.30pm-11pm

Nice Italian restaurant with lunchtime fixed
price special offers Mon-Sat on pizza and
pasta. Best to call to reserve a table.

**Please note:** restaurant facilities
are subject to change. Please keep us
up-to-date. **www.titchhikers.co.uk**

## Queen Square Dining Room & Bar

63 Queen Square, Bristol, BS1 4JZ
0117 929 0700, www.queen-square.com
Mon-Fri 9am-11pm, Sat 4-11pm, Sun 10am-4pm
(restaurant closed Mon evenings)

Large, airy and informal place to eat.

## The Commercial Rooms

43 Corn Street, Bristol, BS1 1HT
0117 927 9681
Mon-Sun 8am-9pm

Wetherspoons pub with children's menu.

## The Galleries Food Court

Galleries, 25 Union Gallery, Broadmead, BS1 3XD
0117 929 0569 Gallery Management
www.themall.co.uk
Mon-Sat 8.30am-5.30pm, Thu 8.30am-6.30pm,
Sun 10.30am-4.30pm

Food court including many popular chains.

## The Hole in the Wall

2 The Grove, Queens Sq, Bristol, BS1 4QZ
0117 926 5967, www.beefeater.co.uk
Mon-Sat 12pm-11pm, Sun 12pm-10.30pm

Good pub near waterfront

## Zizzi's

84B Glass House, Cabot Circus, Bristol. BS1 3BX
0117 929 1066
Mon-Sat 12:00pm-11pm & Sun 12pm-10:30pm.

Popular Italian restaurant. Will do children's portions of pizza or pasta as required.

## MORE TO TRY

**Bella Pizza**
Unit 15, Silver St, Broadmead, BS1 2DU
0117 929 8014.

**Café Amore**
14 Nelson Street, Bristol, BS1 2LE

**Caffè Nero**
38 Corn St, Bristol BS1 1HT
0117 927 9758

**Pizza Hut**
23-25 St Augustines Parade, BS1 4UL
0117 925 2755
www.pizzahut.co.uk

## PARK ST & TRIANGLE

### Boston Tea Party

75 Park St, Bristol, BS1 5PF  0117 929 8601
www.thebostonteaparty.co.uk
Mon-Wed 7am-7.30pm, Thu-Sat 7am-10pm,
Sun 9am-7.30pm

Relaxed café with terraced garden.

### Bristol City Museum Café

Queens Road, Clifton, BS8 1RL
0117 922 3571  Daily 10:30am-4:30pm

Children's meal deal available, with choice of 5 different items to put in bag with puzzles.

### Browns Restaurant & Bar

38 Queens Rd, Clifton, Bristol, BS8 1RE
0117 930 4777, www.browns-restaurant.com
Mon-Sat 12pm-11pm, Sun 12pm-10.30pm

Large attractive licensed refectory, very popular with families.

### Krishna's Inn

4, Byron Place, Triangle South, Bristol, BS8 1JT
0117 927 6864
Mon-Thu/Sun 12pm-3pm, 6pm-11pm,
Fri/Sat 12pm-3pm, 6pm-12pm

Specialists in Kerala cuisine very popular with families. No children's menu but happy to adapt any dish.

### Nando's

49 Park Street, Bristol
0117 929 9263, www.nandos.co.uk
Sun-Thur 12pm-11:30pm & Fri-Sat 12pm-12am

Chicken restaurant serving great hot wings and chips! Vegetarian options available.

### Pizza Express

31 Berkeley Square, Bristol, BS8 1HP
0117 926 0300, www.pizzaexpress.com
Mon-Sat 11.30am-11pm, Sun 11.30am-11pm

See entry under Harbourside.

### Zizzi

7 Triangle South, Bristol
0117 929 8700, www.zizzi.co.uk
Mon-Sat 12pm-11pm & Sun 12pm-10:30pm

See entry under Cabot Circus.

# WHITELADIES RD

## Boston Tea Party

97 Whiteladies Rd, Bristol. BS8 2NT
0117 923 9571,
www.thebostonteaparty.co.uk
Mon-Fri 7:30am-6pm, Sat 8am-6pm & Sun 9am-6pm.

Also see Park Street and Clifton Village.

## Caffé Gusto

Unit 3, Clifton Down Shopping Centre,
Whiteladies Road, BS8 2NN
Other local branches: St. Michaels Hill,
Queens Rd Clifton, Clifton Village, Harbouside,
Prince St & Clare St.
Mon-Sun 7am-6pm

Locally owned and run coffee bars.

## Planet Pizza

83 Whiteladies Rd, Bristol, BS8 2NT
0117 907 7112
Mon-Sun 11am-11pm
& 187 Gloucester Rd, Bishopston, BS7 8BF

Pleasant & cosy family run pizza restaurant.
No separate children's menu.

# CLIFTON VILLAGE

## Avon Gorge Hotel

Sion Hill, Bristol, BS8 4LD
0117 973 8955, www.theavongorge.com
Open daily for cakes & coffees from 11am, hot bar
food served from 12-10pm. Ask for children's menu.

Large sun terrace with magnificent views of
the Suspension Bridge.

## Boston Tea Party

1 Princess Victoria Street, BS8 4HR
0117 973 4790
www.thebostonteaparty.co.uk
Mon-Sat 7:30am-6pm & Sun 9am-6pm.

Also see Whiteladies Rd and Clifton Village

## Pizza Express

2-10 Regent St, Bristol, BS8 4HG
0117 974 4259, www.pizzaexpress.com
Mon-Sat 11.30am-11pm, Sun 12-10.30pm

See page 180 for more details.

182

## Primrose Café & Bistro

1 Boyces Avenue, Clifton, Bristol
0117 946 6577, www.primrosecafe.co.uk
Mon-Sat 10am-5pm, Sun 10.30am-3pm

Great place to people watch from their outside
tables. Can get very busy and buggies are
restricted.

## Zizzi

29-33 Princess Victoria Street, Bristol. BS8 4BX
0117 317 9842, www.zizzi.co.uk
Mon-Sat 12pm-11pm & Sun 12pm-10:30pm

Popular Italian restaurant. Will do children's
portions of pizza or pasta as required.

# NORTH BRISTOL

# HENBURY

## Blaise Tea Rooms

Blaise Castle Estate, Henbury Road, Bristol
0117 904 1897
Mon-Sun 8.30am-7pm, closes 4pm winter

Adjacent to children's play area.

# GLOUCESTER RD

## The Annex

Seymour Road, Bishopston, Bristol
0117 949 3931
Mon-Sat 11.30am-3pm, 5pm-7pm, Sun 12-11pm

In summer months, children can play in the
enclosed back garden.

## Café Delight

189 Gloucester Road, Bishopton
0117 944 1133, www.cafedelight.co.uk
Mon-Sat 9am-5.30pm, Sun 9.30am-4pm,
Tue-Sat open evenings

Laid-back licensed café serving good variety
of snacks and Medi-themed home cooking
with great special's board. Has separate
children's menu.

## Halo Restaurant & Bar

141 Gloucester Road, Bristol, BS7 8BA
0117 944 2504
Mon-Fri 12pm-11pm,
Sat 10am-11pm, Sun 12pm-11am

Popular bar, restaurant with large garden.

# ST WERBURGH'S

## St Werburgh's City Farm Café

Watercress Rd, Bristol, BS2 9YJ
0117 923 2563
Wed-Sun 10am-4pm

Lively and unusual tree house café overlooking children's play area.

# THE DOWNS

## Downs Tea Room

Next to the Water Tower, Durdham Downs, Bristol.
BS9 1EL  0117 923 8186 Mon-Sun 8.30am-6pm

Right on the edge of the Downs near the large Water Tower.

# WESTBURY-ON-TRYM & HENLEAZE

## Café Kondi

105 Henleaze Road, Henleaze, Bristol
0117 962 8230
Mon-Fri 8.30am-5pm, Sat 9am-4pm

Very child friendly, serves light meals and snacks, plus great coffees and children's menu.

# CRIBBS CAUSEWAY

## Nando's

Unit 208, Cribbs Causeway Retail Park, BS34 5UR
0117 959 0146
Mon-Fri 11am-9pm, Sat 11am-7pm, Sun 11am-5pm

See description under Park Street.

## TGI Fridays

The Venue, Cribbs Causeway, Bristol. BS10 7UB
0117 959 1987, www.tgifridays.co.uk
1649@crww.com
Mon-Thu 11:30am-10:30pm, Fri & Sat 11:30am-11pm & Sun 11:30am-10:30pm.

Large American-style restaurant popular with children who love all the showmanship of the staff!

## The Lamb & Flag

Harvester Restaurant, Cribbs Causeway, BS10 7TL
0117 950 1490
Mon-Sat 11am-11pm, Sun 11am-10.30pm

Harvester restaurant with garden and imaginative farm-like interior. Active policy to welcome family groups; early bird menus and offers.

## The Mall Food Court

The Mall, Cribbs Causeway, Bristol, BS34 5QU
0117 903 0303 Cribbs Management
www.cribbscauseway.co.uk
Mon-Fri 10am-9pm, Sat 9am-7pm, Sun 11am-5pm

Recently refurbished. There are many fast food outlets situated on the second floor — including Spud U Like, McDonalds, Druckers & more. See Mall website for full restaurant list. Starbucks, Pizza Hut & Nando's have their own seating. Also look for Costa Coffee, near John Lewis or Café Giardino, near M&S.

# NORTH EAST BRISTOL

# EASTON

## Café Maitreya

89 St. Marks Road, Easton, Bristol
0117 951 0100
Fri 11am-3pm, Sat & Sun 11am-3.30pm,
Tue-Sat 7pm-11pm

Good vegetarian food in light airy surroundings. Menus clearly marked to show vegan, wheat/gluten free and dairy free items. Kids' menu.

## STAPLE HILL

### Staple Hill Oak

Staple Hill, BS16 5HN
0117 956 8543
Mon-Sun 9am-9pm

Popular Wetherspoons pub where children are
well catered for — all children's meals include
a drink, meal, fruit and activity pack. Open for
breakfast from 9am.

## EMERSONS GREEN

### The Beefeater Emersons Green

200/202 Westerleigh Rd, Bristol, BS16 7AN
0117 956 4755
Mon-Sat 11am-11pm, Sun 12pm-9pm

Modern pub in village setting with a Beefeater
restaurant.

### The Mill House

The Village, Emersons Green, Bristol, BS16 7AE
0117 970 2023
Mon-Sat 11am-11pm, Sun 12pm-10:30pm.

Popular family pub located on commercial
estate. Open for coffees from 9am weekdays,
food served daily from lunchtime onwards,
good choice including separate children's
menu. Children love Indoor Playpen 'Wacky
Warehouse', where they can play for £2.50,
(under 12 months free).

### Willy Wicket

Badminton Road, Downend, BS16 1DP
0117 956 7308
Mon-Sat 12pm-11pm, Sun 12pm-10.30pm

Popular dining pub near Emersons Green in
a converted nineteenth century farmhouse
offering a small children's menu.

## EAST BRISTOL

## ARNOS VALE

### Bocabar

Paintworks, Bath Rd, Arnos Vale, BS4 3EH
0117 9728838
www.bocabar.co.uk
Open 10am-12am Mon-Thur 10-2am Fri-Sat and
10am-11pm Sun

Well recommended. Tapas and cakes are
served all day, deli sandwiches, pizza
(evenings only), and breakfast (mornings
from 10am).

## KINGSWOOD

### Kingswood Colliers

94-96 Regent Street, Kingswood, BS15 8HP
0117 967 2247
Sun-Thurs 9am-12pm & Fri & Sat 9am-1am.

Part of the Wetherspoons chain.

### The Crown

126 Bath Rd, Longwell Green, Bristol, BS15 6DE
0117 932 2846
Mon-Sat 11am-11pm, Sun 12pm-10.30pm

Harvester restaurant with an imaginative
farm-like interior and a beer garden with play
equipment. Children's menu available.

### Wishing Well

Aspects Leisure Park, Longwell Green,
Kingswood, Bristol. BS15 9LA
0117 947 5341
Mon-Sat 11am-11pm & Sun 11am-10:30pm.
£3 for one hour in 'Fuzzy Eds'.

Good family dining including an all-day family
feast & two-for-one offers. Indoor 'Fuzzy Eds'
fun house located next to pub.

# SOUTH EAST BRISTOL

## KEYNSHAM

### The Brass Mill

Avon Mill Lane, Keynsham, BS31 2UG
0117 986 7280
www.vintageinn.co.uk/thebrassmillkeynsham
Mon-Sat 12am-11pm, Sun 12pm-10.30pm

A Brewers Fare pub tucked away near Keynsham especially designed for families. Scenic location by the river Avon.

# SOUTH BRISTOL

## BEDMINSTER

### Windmill Hill City Farm Café

Philip St, Bedminster, BS3 4EA
0117 963 3233
www.windmillhillcityfarm.org.uk
Tue-Sat 9am-5pm, Sun 10am-4pm.

Nice café serving healthy, organic food, open to all, whether you visit the farm or not.

## SOUTHVILLE

### Oasis Café

Southville Centre, Beauley Rd, BS3 1QG
0117 923 1039, www.southville.org.uk
Mon-Fri 8:30am-5:30pm & Sat 9am-3pm.

Based in the Southville centre, popular, spacious community café serving wholesome inexpensive menu including children's portions. Vegetarian and vegan options available.

### The Riverside Garden Centre Café

Clifthouse Road, Southville, Bristol, BS3 1RX
0117 966 7535
www.riversidegardencentre.com/cafe
Mon-Sat 9.30am-5pm & Sun 11am-4pm

Popular café with homemade food. Small play area for toddlers and young children.

# SOUTH WEST BRISTOL

### The Dovecote

Ashton Road, Bristol, BS41 9LX
01275 392245
Mon-Sat 12pm-11pm, Sun 12pm-10.30pm

Vintage Inn chain restaurant next to Ashton Court. Large garden with open views.

## Why not take a picnic?

The secret of a great picnic is simplicity, plus careful planning and packing.

With potentially fussy children in tow, take a favourite thing of theirs and pack things suitable for both adults and children.

Bear in mind that some food does not travel well. Salad goes soggy when left in a sandwich (so pack separately).

Finger food is a good idea. Pies, drumstick, carrot-sticks, crisps.

Take crunchy veg, spring onions, peppers, celery. Very refreshing. Plus cooked or cured hams.

Take adequate liquid refreshment.

Don't forget the bag for your recycling.

For further advice, hampers and fabbest ingredients, try Pat, Nina or Sylvie at Arch House Deli (Boyce's Ave, BS8)

# Further Afield

This is a selection of the best family eateries worth a hike for.

## Bowl Inn

Church Road, Lower Almondsbury, BS32 4DT
01454 612757, www.theoldbowlinn.co.uk

Traditional village pub, next to the pretty church, with à la carte restaurant and bar menu.

## The Golden Heart

Down Rd, Winterbourne, BS36 1AU
01454 773152
Food served: Mon-Fri 12pm-3pm, 5:30pm-9pm & Sat & Sun 12pm-9pm.

Quaint old pub with restaurant serving a range of home cooked food. Large garden with play equipment.

## Salmon Inn

Wanswell, Berkeley, GL13 9SE
01453 811306
Mon-Sun 12pm-11pm.

Oak-beamed village pub with a few nooks and crannies, bare floorboards and a piano.

## The Dog Inn

Badminton Rd, Chipping Sodbury, BS37 6LZ
01454 312006
Food served Mon-Sat 12pm-2:30pm & 6pm-9:30pm & Sun 12pm-2:30pm & 6pm-9pm.

A busy pub with a large garden with play equipment. Adventurous selection including a fun menu of good food for children.

## Gumstool Inn

Calcot Manor, Nr Tetbury, Glos, GL8 8YJ
01666 890391, www.calcotmanor.co.uk
Sat-Sun 12pm-9pm, Mon-Fri 12pm-2pm & 7pm-9pm
On the B4135 Dursley-Tetbury, at junction with A46

A gastropub that positively welcomes families. Part of the luxury Calcot Manor country hotel (which has a similarly child-friendly reputation), the inn is situated in a former farmhouse set around a courtyard of lime trees, ancient stone barns and stables dating back to the 14th century. (Also see our fantastic reader offer on page 191.)

## The Priory Inn

London Road, Tetbury, GL8 8JJ
01666 502251, www.theprioryinn.co.uk
Mon-Sun 7am-10pm

Friendly hotel/gastropub serving teas, coffees and cakes from 7am. Lunch served from 12pm using local produce cooked in wood-fired oven. Fantastic children's menu available. There are many buggy-friendly walks around Tetbury, or you can while away the afternoon by the fire!

## The Lock Inn Café

48 Frome Rd, Bradford-on-Avon, Wiltshire, BA15 1LE
01225 868068, www.thelockinn.co.uk/cafe
Mon-Sun 8.30am-6pm 7 days & evenings 6:30-9:30pm.

Situated on the popular Kennet & Avon Canal, a great stop-off on your cycle ride. Try the famous Boatman's Breakfast. Also hires out bikes, see Cycle Hire in Transport chapter.

## The Fountain Inn & Boxer's Restaurant

1 St Thomas Street, Wells, BA5 2UU
01749 672317, www.fountaininn.co.uk
Food Mon-Sun 12pm-2pm, 6pm-9.30pm

Award-winning, family friendly gastro-pub.

## Carpenter's Arms

Stanton Wick, Nr Pensford, Somerset, BS39 4BX
01761 490202, www.the-carpenters-arms.co.uk
carpenters@buccaneer.co.uk
Food served Mon-Fri 12pm-2pm, 7pm-10pm
Sun 12pm-2.30pm, 7pm-9pm
Off the A368, about ¾ mile from Jct with A37

17th century miners' cottages overlooking the Chew Valley, this is a great place to relax after visiting the nearby Folly Farm. See p.106.

# Family Holidays & Weekend Aways

## Contents

### Tips:

Much of enjoying a good holiday with your children is about managing your expectations. Making a list of what you can and can't cope with, especially if you have very small children, is a good start. See our checklist over the page. And never be afraid to ask questions; you'll be glad you did.

The accessibility of Europe and North America via Bristol International Airport has kept the South West holiday industry on its toes. The impressive response is family boltholes, cool campsites, and grand mansion hotels within rolling acres meaning you do not have to travel far to 'get away' from it all. Book in confidence knowing the following places have all been recommended.

### Titch Hikers' Offers

See the offers in this chapter for Avalon Beach Hotel in Bournemouth and Calcot Manor near Tetbury.

Got family coming to stay in Bristol?

Visit the excellent Bristol for Families section of the **Visit Bristol** website for places to stay: www.visitbristol.co.uk

# choosing a holiday

Some things to consider:
Your budget!
Do you worry about noise from others?
Do you worry about noise from your child?
Do you want time out - baby sitting, kids club?
Do you want to cook?

The map below will give you an idea of where some of the main listings in this chapter are located.

- Youth Hostel
- Self catering
- Hotel
- Campsite

**Away with the Kids**
0161 282 1980, www.awaywiththekids.co.uk
**Baby Friendly Boltholes**
www.babyfriendlyboltholes.co.uk

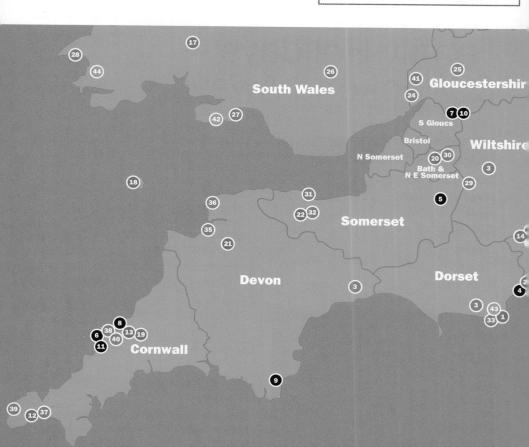

# Something Different

## Yurts 1

Herston Camp Site, Washpond Lane, Swanage, BH19
01929 422932, www.yurtvillage.co.uk

A brilliant family option. Ranging in size from
5 metres across to almost 7 metres, they are
spacious (and you can stand up!) At Herston
Camp Site, the yurts have a double futon
bed and two single futon beds. They also
have wood burning stoves for cooking (and
snuggling up near!)

## Beach Huts 2

01202 315437, www.beach-huts.com
Contact individual properties for pricing.

There are not many ways to get closer to
the beach than hiring your own beach hut.
While there are many beach huts that allow
overnight stays in the UK, Mudeford in Dorset
is just superb for families. A no car area, it is
only accessible by ferry or land train - both
great fun for children. Once you are there,
you can simply have fun on the sand, cycle
to the scenic headland of Hengistbury Head,
or hire a boat for a bit of fun in the shallow
water.

## Feather Down Farms 3

01420 80804
www.featherdownfarms.co.uk
Nearest farms: Moores Farm - Holcombe, Somerset,
Knaveswell Farm - Corfe Castle, Dorset, Belle Vue
Farm - Poulshot, Wiltshire, Aller Farm - Stockland,
Devon.

From about £195 (short break) to £795 pw

There are currently 22 (plus two abroad) of
these small working farms offering a truly
unique experience. Modern paraphanalia
becomes a distant memory as cooking takes
place on a wood-burning stove, you sleep
in a spacious tent complete with everything
you could need, food is readily available to
purchase from the farm shop, and children
revel in their discoveries of working life on a
farm.

## Holiday Equipment Hire

**Baby Equipment Hirers Association**
www.beha.co.uk,

**Holiday Buggies -** (South Devon)
01803 322095, www.holidaybuggies.com

**Little People Direct -** (Hants, Bournemouth)
01202 425142, www.littlepeopledirect.com

**Baby Comes 2 -** (Nationwide)
0208 9898032, www.babycomes2.co.uk

**Little Stars -** (Nationwide)
020 8621 4378 www.littlestars.co.uk

## ASSISTED HOLIDAYS

**Family Holiday Association**
16 Mortimer St, London, W1T 3JL
020 7436 3304, www.fhaonline.org.uk

The Family Holiday Association helps provide
holidays for families in need. Applications are
only accepted from referring agencies (social
workers, health visitors) on behalf of families.
Families must meet certain criteria such as
having a low income, at least one child of
3+yrs and having not had a holiday in the last
four years.

## ON A BUDGET

### NCT Houseswap

ncthouseswap.ning.com
Membership is only £29.99 a year

A list of over 200 UK family homes that you
can holiday in for FREE when you swap with
your own home. To sign up to the House
Swap register send a cheque made payable to
NCT Trading to:

NCT House Swap, Alexandra House, Oldham
Terrace, London, W3 6NH

**Plan your route with: www.theaa.com**

# Hotels

Staying in hotels, though it may not come cheap, has never been better for parents and children. The choice, from basic to luxury, is increasing, the facilities for children improving, and the possibility of rest and relaxation inviting.

If travelling with small children, the following questions may be useful to ask before you set off so as to avoid disappointment on arrival.

- Is there a lift and/or pram access to the room?
- If you want to go downstairs for a meal, is there baby listening or babysitting?
- What are the availability of cots/extra beds?
- Do they offer a children's menu and is there an early sitting?

All the hotels featured here have many facilities that will make your stay more enjoyable. They are truly welcoming of children and there will be lots for your children to do once you are there. As with all types of accommodation, however, if you need something specific for your stay, make sure that you confirm it is available prior to booking.

## Avalon Beach Hotel 4

43 Grand Ave, Southbourne, Bournemouth, BH6 3SY
01202 425370, www.avalon-beach-hotel.co.uk
From £90 double B&B (rooms for up to 6).
Apart Hotel rooms from £120 pn (up to 5 guests)

Patricia and Paul promise to make families feel warmly welcome at their lovely Bournemouth hotel. Children are extremely well catered for with travel cots, high chairs and a baby bath available, baby sitting, board games and books, dvd player and movies, plus a nutricious children's menu. There are even pet rabbits in the secluded garden. Parents can relax in the knowledge that after a busy day exploring the beach or nearby New Forest, pushchairs, dirty wellies, and other paraphenalia can be stored, and wet, muddy or sandy clothes can be washed. There are a choice of modern, light and airy family rooms, or apart-hotel rooms complete with full kitchens or kitchenette.

### 15% discount

Avalon Beach Hotel Guests can enjoy a discount on stays of 3 nights or more outside school holidays on all family rooms.

On booking mention 'Titch hikers' special deal'.

## Babington House 5

Babington, Nr Frome, Somerset, BA11 3RW
01373 812266
www.babingtonhouse.co.uk
From £315 room only (family room).

Babington House is set in vast grounds which include a lake, woods, walks, and croquet pitch. On first arrival it can seem extremely smart and a little daunting if you have young children in tow (and when you see Kevin McCloud of Grand Designs' impeccably well behaved children you may think of turning back). But the staff soon help you to feel welcome and at ease, and on closer inspection, you will see that there are many children climbing the trees and enjoying the indoor and outdoor pools. The house itself is so homely that you could imagine living there. The rooms are sumptuous, the service unbeatable (the staff make it a policy to know exactly who is staying and to know your children's names so it has a sort of extended family feel when you are there), and the facilities are so relaxing that you will go home feeling pampered and refreshed. There are a choice of family rooms and all come with equipment for babies, but you have to be quick as rooms tend to book up fast. There is a children's tea provided in the House Kitchen. There is also a well-equipped 'Little House' with friendly staff. A treat well worth saving up for.

## Bedruthan Steps Hotel    6

Mawgan Porth, Cornwall, TR8 4BU
01637 860860, www.bedruthan.com
Low/Mid/Peak season from £77pp/£101pp/£128pp
double DB&B, discounted rates for children

Wonderfully welcoming to families, set above a beautiful beach, with footpaths in both directions along the stunning North Cornish coast. The hotel has fabulous facilities for children of all ages. There are supervised clubs for children of all ages (some only during school holidays), indoor and outdoor swimming pools as well as play areas with helicopters and trains to ride, ball pools with slides, jumps and ropes, and a soft play area for very young children. For older children, there is a cyber café and a surf school, and also a spa for adults. A fabulous 4 star hotel for all with an environmental conscience.

## St Enodoc Hotel    8

Rock, Cornwall, PL27 6LA
01208 863394, www.enodoc-hotel.co.uk
From £155 family room B&B, £25 extra child (in same room)

St Enodocs is in a lovely location set against Cornwall's rugged north coast overlooking Rock. The views sweep across the Camel estuary towards Padstow. The hotel is bright and modern with 16 double bedrooms and four spacious family suites (these have microwaves and fridges). Children of all ages are welcomed, and facilities include a children's play room and an outdoor swimming pool. Children's tea is provided and baby listening is available.

## Calcot Manor   7

Near Tetbury, Gloucestershire, GL8 8YJ
01666 890391, www.calcotmanor.co.uk
Family rooms from £330 per room pn B&B, children's supplements apply

Calcot Manor is a country house set in 220 acres of grounds - perfect for exploring by foot or bike. Children are warmly welcomed at the hotel, and there are many features especially for them. The indoor Playzone is a restored barn with play equipment and areas to suit all ages of children from 0-16. Children can play there with their parents or they can be booked in and looked after by Nannies from the Ofsted regulated creche. Children can swim in the indoor and outdoor pools at certain times. During the Summer months they can also enjoy Maize maze. The family bedrooms are in the converted barn and courtyard in front of the main house, and have been beautifully designed with families in mind - choose from a deluxe room through to a duplex suite depending on the needs of your family. The rooms are connected to reception via a dedicated baby-listening service. And all family rooms come equipped with a changing mat, nappy bags, washing-up liquid and bottle washing and preparing equipment. Extremely appetising menus for both parents and children.

## Fingals Hotel 9

Dittishaw, Dartmouth, TQ6 0JA
01803 722 398, www.fingals.co.uk
Mid season/peak season from £110/£120 double BB,
£15 extra child (same room)

This is a fabulous, individual, quirky hotel run with much energy and imagination by Richard and Sheila. Richard has restored the original run-down farmhouse into an informal yet stylish hotel. This is particularly suitable for older children with a range of activities including swimming, snooker and tennis, and even houses a mini-cinema. The hotel also has a self-catering family barn available for hire which is perfect for a family of four. A barn is attached to the hotel and all hotel facilities are available for use.

## The Priory Inn 10

London Rd, Tetbury, Glos, GL8 8JJ
01666 502251, www.theprioryinn.co.uk
Four interconnecting rooms and family suite. Children under 12 stay free if share parent's room. From £139 B&B (family of 4). Call for prices

An extremely family friendly hotel, parts of which date back to the 16th century. Among the 14 rooms are four sets of interconnecting rooms and one large family suite, all recently refurbished. The owners, Tanya and Dave, make sure that there are thoughtful touches for making children feel welcome, such as baskets of toys, books, puzzles, or a babyccino in the coffee bar. The food at the Inn all comes from within a 30 mile radius, is home-made, and freshly cooked. There is an appetising children's menu including the invitation for them to make their own pizzas. And if you want a meal just the two of you, most listening devices will work in the restaurant or you can book a qualified babysitter (but you will need to give some notice for this).

Why not save space in the car and packing time by hiring your holiday equipment? See **Equipment Hire** p.189

## Watergate Bay Hotel 11

On The Beach, Watergate Bay, Cornwall, TR8 4AA
0 1637 860543, www.watergatebay.co.uk
From £210 low season, £259 mid season, £323 high season (family suite B&B, up to 5 people)

The location of Watergate Bay makes this an ideal holiday for busy toddlers and young children. With two miles of sandy beach right outside the front door, they can enjoy sandcastle building and rock pooling to their heart's content. Back at the hotel there is a safe, soft play area for babies, an activity room with games and toys for older children (3-7 years), and a quiet area for reading during the day and stories and a film during the evening supervision session (between 6.30-9.30pm). There is also an outdoor pirate ship. Family suites include a king-size bedroom, bathroom and separate bunk room for the children. Also see The Coach House (below) for more economical accommodation.

## Luxury Family Hotels

www.luxuryfamilyhotels.com

This small chain of country house hotels really do everything they say on the tin. They offer clean, luxurious rooms, often with antiques, but amazingly unspoilable! There's plenty going on for children of all ages from onsite swimming pools, games rooms, ofsted registered childcare, fun on the lawns, to early sittings for mealtimes (no junk here, children get fantastic home cooked, interesting food). (Changing mats, cots, are all provided).

### Moonfleet Manor

Fleet, Nr Weymouth, Dorset, DT3 4ED
01305 786948 (From £160 double, B&B. Rooms for between 3-7 guests)
**Overlooks Chesil Beach and Fleet lagoon.**

### Woolley Grange

Woolley Green, Bradford on Avon, BA15 1TX
01225 864705 (From £90 double, B&B. Rooms for between 2-6 guests). Outdoor heated pool.
**Jacobean Manor House set in open countryside.**

### Fowey Hall

Hanson Drive, Fowey, Cornwall, PL23 1ET
01726 833866 (From £140 double, B&B. Rooms for between 3-6 guests)
**Impressive views over the charming port.**

Many hotels can be a little on the pricey side for most of us. However, most do great last minute offers. Check out their websites.

## MORE FOR THE ADULT

### The Well House

St Keyne, Liskeard, PL14 4RN
01579 342001, www.wellhouse.co.uk
One Family Suite - sleeping 4 - £255 p/n DBB. Cots £7.50 p/n. Children aged 5 -14 sharing a room or on a z-bed £35.00 p/n B&B, £70 DB&B. Children eating from the evening dinner menu will be charged at the normal tariff.

The Well House has one of the top five restaurants in the whole of Cornwall (it has been awarded 3 AA Rosettes over 22 consecutive years), and so is a fine dining hotel for those families that take food seriously. The privately owned country house does not necessarily specialise in families with young children, but the owners have one family suite available to enable parents to experience its delights. There is a superb menu for children, as well as three acres of terraces, lawns, ponds and gardens, an outdoor heated pool and an all weather 'club' size tennis court.

### useful websites

www.arewethere.co.uk
Travel games and travel ideas

www.travellingwithchildren.co.uk
Excellent online travel and holiday shop.

www.holidaynanny.org
Provides holiday nannies.

## MORE OF THE BEST

### Driftwood Hotel

Rosevine, Nr Portcatho, S Cornwall, TR2 5EW
01872 580644, www.driftwoodhotel.co.uk
From £175 double B&B, children's rates
**Relaxing and peaceful retreat.**

### The Coach House @ Watergate Bay

On The Beach, Watergate Bay, Cornwall, TR8 4AA
0 1637 860543, www.watergatebay.co.uk
From £78 double BB, children's rates
**Budget accommodation near the main Hotel.**

### The Sandbanks Hotel

Sandbanks, Poole, BH13 7PS
0845 337 1550, www.sandbankshotel.co.uk
From £95 B&B pppn, children's rates

**Family hotel on this blue flag beach.**

### The Cottage Hotel

Hope Cove, Kingsbridge, South Devon, TQ7 3HJ
01548 561555, www.hopecove.com
From £47.80pppn DB&B, children's rates

**Traditional family hotel, by the cove.**

### Thurlestone Hotel

Thurlestone, Nr Kingsbridge, Devon, TQ7 3NN
01548 560382, www.thurlestone.co.uk
From £92pppn B&B, discounted children's rates.
**On a blue flag beach.**

### Woolacombe Bay Hotel

Woolacombe, Devon, EX34 7BN
01271 870388, www.woolacombe-bay-hotel.co.uk
From £80pp double B&B, children's rates.
**Luxurious Victorian hotel overlooking stunning beach.**

### Knoll House Hotel

Studland Bay, Dorset, BH19 3AH
01929 450450, www.knollhouse.co.uk
From £98pp double, DB&B, children's rates.
**On the edge of the Jurassic Coast.**

### Saunton Sands Hotel

Braunton, Devon, EX33 1LQ
01271 892001, www.sauntonsands.co.uk
From £90 pppn, children's rates. Call or look online for special offers
**Family run hotel with lots for children.**

### Treffedian Hotel

Aberdyfi, Wales, LL35 0SB
01654 767 213, www.trefwales.com
From £196 2nights, children's rates. Call or look online for special offers
**Traditional, family run, coastal hotel.**

# Self-catering

Self-catering arguably offers the most home-from-home holiday option, and is good if you are sticking to a budget or want more privacy. There is an abundance of choice in this country and the quality and family friendliness of properties just keeps getting better. We've listed some of our favourites below but do check out the holiday companies suggested at the end of the chapter.

N.B. The places we list are child friendly and so should have high chairs, cots etc. But please do check when booking.

## CORNWALL

### The Cove                           12

Lamorna, Nr Penzance, Cornwall, TR19 6XH
01736 731411, www.thecovecornwall.com
From about £700/£1100 off peak/peak pw

Want to come back from a busy day at the beach to find a meal prepared for you in your own apartment? At the Cove you can. Stay in stylish flats (or a yurt!). There is a heated pool, therapy room, children's high tea and play area.

### The Olde House Cottages          13

Chapel Ample, Wadebridge, Cornwall, PL27 6EN
0844 7700420, www.theoldehouse.co.uk
Contact for prices

Lovingly restored and new farm cottages made of Cornish stone with slate roofs and comfortably furnished. Attractions for families include the farm trail as well as the beaches of Daymer Bay (perfect for young children) and Polzeath nearby. The leisure centre has an adventure playground, tennis courts, indoor pets corner, snooker table, play barn, heated indoor swimming pool and jacuzzi.

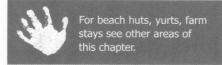

For beach huts, yurts, farm stays see other areas of this chapter.

## NEW FOREST

### Robin's Nest                       14

Minstead, Hampshire
Contact New Forest Living: 0845 680 0173
www.newforestliving.co.uk
From about £900 pw. Part week & w/e options.
Sleeps 8 (2 doubles, 2 twins).

Stylish and peaceful property with spacious and enclosed lawned gardens. This family friendly house is good for crawlers and toddlers as it is almost all on one level. The owners also provide a welcoming box of toys, DVDs, books, bath toys and toddler ride ones. Plus all the essentials for babies and toddlers such as a travel cot, high chair, baby bath, as well as a steriliser.

### Tom's Lane Cottage                 15

Minstead, Hampshire
Contact New Forest Living: 0845 680 0173
www.newforestliving.co.uk
From about £600 pw. Part week & w/e options.
Sleeps 4 (1 double, 1 twin) plus cots.
Welcome hamper.

This lovely cottage is set within the grounds of an Arts & Crafts country house. It is a comfortable and stylish property, yet still very child friendly with its large, private garden complete with garden toys, and all the equipment provided by the owners to cater for little ones (cot, highchair, bed guard, stairgates, plug covers, booster seat, bath toys, books, DVDs, and more). Children will marvel at the ponies happily wondering in the lane, as well as Poppet the Shetland pony. And the whole family will love the ease of the direct access to miles of open forest. The pretty village of Lyndhurst is nearby.

Visit nearby Furzey Gardens where your children will love the African style round houses, tree house, swings, crawl tunnel, and the boat and picnic area. Or Longdown Farm (www.longdownfarm.co.uk) in nearby Ashurst.

## Twin Cottage 16

Twin Cottage, Bisterne Close, Burley, BH24 4BA
07515 887725, www.twincottage.com
£1275 pw, offers often available. Sleeps 4 (1 double,
1 twin/double) plus cots. Welcome hamper.

This cosy, well-equipped, luxurious, semi-detached cottage is situated right in the heart of the forest where ponies wonder freely past the gate. The owner, Amanda, really has thought of everything for babies through to older children, so you can afford to pack lightly. Groceries can be ordered and delivered for your arrival.

# WALES

## Clydey Cottages 17

Penrallt, Lancych, Boncath, Pembrokeshire, SA370LW
01239 698619, www.clydeycottages.co.uk
From £300/400/600 for 1/2/3 bed cottage

These sympathetically and attractively restored 18th century cottages are set in 20 acres of grounds, featuring meadows, woodlands and a small river. The child-friendly facilities include an indoor heated swimming pool, outdoor play area with swings, a sandpit, slide and ride-on toys, animal feeding, plus oodles more. All necessary baby equipment is provided, there is babysitting available, and your groceries can be ordered and delivered for your arrival. There are also beauty treatments and massage available in your cottage.

# LUNDY ISLAND

## Lundy Island 18

Bristol Channel, North Devon, EX39 2LY
01271 863636, www.lundyisland.co.uk
Contact Lundy Island Shore Office for prices.

Lundy lies off the coast of North Devon, where the Atlantic ocean meets the Bristol Channel, with nothing between it and America. At three and a half miles long and half a mile wide, it is an oasis of peace and tranquilty. Arrive by boat and stay in one of a wide range of buildings, including a castle, lighthouse or a 'gentleman's villa'.

Why not order your groceries online and get them delivered to your holiday cottage?

# FARM COTTAGES

## Higher Lank Farm 19

St Breward, Bodmin, Cornwall, PL30 4NB
01208 850716, www.higherlankfarm.co.uk
From £700 a week (4 night options) B&B

A special place to stay for pre-school children, where everything is provided. It's a working farm with animal feeding after breakfast. There is a wonderful outdoor play area and a selection of indoor toys. Good choice of accommodation. Bookings are only taken from families with at least one child under 5 years.

## Pitcot Farm Cottages 20

Pitcot Lane, Stratton on Fosse, Bath, BA3 4SX
01761 233108, www.pitcotfarm.co.uk
From £350/450 pw. Sleep 4 and 6/8.

Two self-catering farm cottages, created from one single story barn, in the quiet of open farmland. Tennis court housed in a large barn

## Torridge House Cottages 21

Little Torrington, North Devon, EX38 8PS
01805 622542, www.torridgehouse.co.uk
From about £340-1400 pw

Family farm holidays, U7's especially welcome. Help feed the animals on the farm - pigs, lambs, chickens, rabbits, and ducklings - and enjoy the outdoor heated pool and many other facilities. Ten lovely cottages sleeping between 4 and 11, all truly child-friendly. Babysitting available.

## Westermill Farm Cottages 22

Exford, Exmoor, Somerset, TA24 7NJ
01643 831238, www.westermill.com
From £170 pw.

Six Scandinavian style cottages on a 500 acre working sheep and beef farm in the heart of the Exmoor National Park. Also see Camping.

## ON THE BEACH

### The Black House                    23

Hengistbury Head, Bournemouth, BH6 4EW
07855 280191, www.theblackhouse.co.uk
From £300-1230 pw. 1/2/3 bed apartments.

This smuggler's cottage, dating back 200
years, sits right at the end of the Mudeford
Spit in Bournemouth. The fabulous location
means that you are literally surrounded by
water; the harbour to one side, and the sea to
the other. The four apartments are fairly basic
but perfectly equipped and easy to clean.
Mudeford spit is car-free and so your journey
to the cottage is magical for young children,
whether you choose to arrive by the 'noddy'
(land) train or by the short ferry ride from
Mudeford Quay. A rowing boat is included
in the price and so the more adventurous
family can take this into the shallow water of
Christchurch Harbour. Bikes are recommended
as there are some lovely rides through the
trees over the National Trust protected
Hengistbury Head. There is a barbeque
provided, plastic 'crockery' and cutlery, a high
chair, and travel cot. We cannot recommend
these apartments enough.

## HOLIDAY PARKS

### Butlins

Minehead, Somerset, TA24 5SH
0845 070 4734, www.butlins.com

### Center Parcs

Longleat Forest, Warminster, Wiltshire, BA12 7PU
08448 267723, www.centerparcs.co.uk

### Hoburn Holiday Park Cotswolds

Broadway Lane, South Cerney, Glos, GL7 5UQ
01285 860216  www.hoburne.com

### Ruda Holiday Park

Croyde Bay, North Devon, EX33 1NY
0871 641 0410, www.parkdeanholidays.co.uk

### Pontins

Brean Sands, Somerset
0844 576 5943, www.pontins.com

## SEARCH OTHER LOCATIONS...

**Away with the Kids**
0161 282 1980, www.awaywiththekids.co.uk

**Baby Friendly Boltholes**
www.babyfriendlyboltholes.co.uk

**Child Friendly Cottages**
www.childfriendlycottages.co.uk

**Polruan Cottages**
01726 870 582, www.polruancottages.co.uk

**Salcombe Holiday Homes**
01548 843485, www.salcombe.com

# Camping

Camping with children of all ages can be enormous fun and an affordable way to get away from it all. Camping no longer needs to equate to roughing it either as many campsites have excellent facilities (should you want them!) The many benefits include lots of freedom for children to run around. Possible disadvantages include no babysitting services, noise of other campers, worries about the noise of your children, and of course... the rain! All the following sites have showers and toilets unless indicated.

**Recommended websites:**

www.forestholidays.co.uk

## WALES

### Pencelli Caravan and Camping 26

Pencelli, Brecon, Powys, Wales, LD3 7LX
01874 665451, www.pencelli-castle.co.uk
Tents (from £8 pn adult, £4.50 child) & caravans (from £16 pn 2 people sharing). U5's free

In the heart of the Brecon Beacons National Park, this family-friendly, well-run camping and caravan site is one for those families who like a site with a good range of facilities. It has also won the award for 'loo of the year' for many years running!

### Llanmadoc Caravan & Campsite 27

Llagadranta Farm, Gower, Swansea, SA3 1DE
01792 386202, www.gowercampsite.co.uk
Tents & caravans. Contact for prices. Opens May

This is a great campsite located on one of the Gower's beautiful beaches. The site is basic but very peaceful. Plenty of walking and stunning views. 50 pitches available. Families and couples only. Small shop.

### Porthclais Farm 28

St Davids, Pembrokeshire, Wales, SA62 6RR
01437 720 256, www.porthclais-farm-campsite.co.uk
Tents & caravans - £6 adult, £3 child, U5's free.
Open Easter-end Oct

Set within the Pembrokeshire National Park, right on the sea-front, Porthclais Farm is a small, family-run campsite, with acres of space. Caerfai (very safe for small children and toddlers with shallow rock pools for paddling and shrimping), Porthsele and Whitesands beaches are nearby, as is St David's, the smallest city in the UK. A new toilet/shower block was built in 2008.

## GLOUCESTERSHIRE

### Christchurch Caravan & Camping Site 24

Bracelands Drive, Christchurch, Coleford, GL16 7NN
01594 837258, www.forestholidays.co.uk
Tents & caravans. From £8 per pitch pn. Opens end Mar

This site is on a gentle slope high above the beautiful Wye Valley, with waymarked walking routes down to the river through the surrounding woodland. Nearby are the Clearwell Caves ancient iron mines. Lots of onsite facilities including hot showers, shop, laundry facilities and children's play area.

### Croft Farm Leisure & Waterpark 25

Bredons Hardwick, Tewkesbury, Glos, GL20 7EE
01684 772321, www.croftfarmleisure.co.uk
Tents & caravans - from £14 (w/e bookings minimum stay 2 nights). Open Mar-Jan

Lakeside camping and caravan park with sailing, windsurfing and canoeing (tuition and equipment hire available). Children's play area and plenty of space for cycling. Laundry facilities are also available.

## WILTSHIRE

### Brokerswood Country Park    29

Brokerswood, Westbury, Wiltshire, BA13 4EH
01373 822238, www.brokerswood.co.uk
Tents & caravans - from £10 pn. Open all year

A Gold Conservation Award winning site, Brokerswood is well located for visiting Bath, Salisbury, Stonehenge, Longleat and beyond. The site offers generous size pitches on a flat, open field. There is a centrally-heated shower block ensuring a comfortable stay all year round, laundry, and a café offering breakfast, picnics and lunches, also open for evening meals and take-aways. There is no additional charge for awnings or showers. Pitch prices include access into the Country Park.

## SOMERSET

### Newton Mill Camping    30

Newton Road, Bath, BA2 9JF
01225 333909, www.newtonmillpark.co.uk
Tents & caravans. Contact for pricing.

Newton Mill Camping is located in a hidden valley close to the centre of Bath. There is a children's playground, free fishing, nearby café, bar and restaurant, hot showers/water, and laundry facilities. There is also the level, traffic-free Bath-Bristol cycle path and frequent bus services.

### Pool Bridge Campsite    31

Nr Porlock, Somerset, TA24 8JS
01643 862521, www.porlock.co.uk
Tents & caravans. £5 pppn, £2.50 child, U5's free.
Opens Easter-Oct

A Somerset gem within easy reach of great beaches and Exmoor National Park. Very sheltered and level ground.

## Westermill 32

Exford, Exmoor, Somerset, TA24 7NJ
01643 831238, www.westermill.com
Tents & caravans - £5 adult, £3 child pn. Contact for opening dates

This is a picturesque, secluded, quiet valley site set in 15 acres of mown meadows in the Centre of Exmoor National Park. Camping is beside the River Exe where you can also swim and fish (there is one field fenced off from the river). There is a small shop selling locally sourced food. BBQ's are allowed as long as they are placed off the ground.

# DORSET

## Tom's Field Camping 33

Tom's Field Rd, Langton Matravers, Swanage
01929 427110, www.tomsfieldcamping.co.uk
Tents & motorvans, NO caravans. From £12 for family pitch.

Tom's Field is a lovely, peaceful campsite. It is right in the middle of the beautiful Dorset coastline, ideal for walking, climbing and family holidays, and near Swanage, with its lovely sandy beach. Token operated showers, large toilets for mum plus children, baby bathing and changing facilities in one drying room which is generally heated, clothes washing sinks, shop. Tom's Field also has a Walkers Barn, available all year with three bunk rooms, bathroom and kitchenette, and a Stone Room - a sort of stone tent with a futon and basic facilities - no toilet!.

# HAMPSHIRE

## Roundhill Campsite 34

Beaulieu Road, Brockenhurst, Hampshire, SO42 7QL
0845 130 8224 (bookings), 01590 624344 (site)
www.forestholidays.co.uk
Tents & caravans - from £9 per pitch (family discounts available). Opens end Mar-end Sep

A spacious heathland site. Roundhill has plenty of room to let you enjoy the freedom of the forest, and an on-site lake for fishing. Recently refurbished shower/toilet blocks. No shop but near Beaulieu and Brockenhurst.

# DEVON

## Stoke Barton Farm 35

Stoke, Hartland, Bideford, Devon, EX39 6DU
01237 441 238 , www.westcountry-camping.co.uk
Tents & caravans. From £5 adult, £3 child, £1 U5.
Opens Easter - end Sep

Stoke Farm is a working livestock and arable farm, in a beautiful spot on the North Devon coast, with wonderful views down to Hartland Quay. There is ample space for camping and for children to run around safely. There is a play area for children with swings and a giant trampoline. Also a laundry Room with washing machine and tumble drier. Dogs are allowed.

*"Stoke Barton farm is quite simply a wonderful, peaceful place to stay. A welcome change from busy, commercial campsites."*
*Titch Hikers' reader.*

## Little Meadow Campsite 36

Watermouth, Ilfracombe, North Devon, EX34 9SJ
01271 866862, www.littlemeadow.co.uk
Tents & caravans. From £11 (car plus 2 people)
Opens Easter - end Sep. Booking recommended.

A small (50 generous sized pitches), extremely tranquil, uncommercial site on a 100 acre working organic farm, with wonderful views. There is a wooded, traffic-free play area for children (must be supervised), and a shop providing papers and good quality groceries. Footpath from site to Watermouth Harbour, beach, South West coastal path, Castle and pub. There are also 3 individually sited holiday caravans available to rent. This site promotes environmentally friendly practices and waste recycling is compulsory.

*Why not visit Lundy Island from Ilfracombe?*
*See: www.lundyisland.co.uk*

**More campsites over the page.**

# Family Camping the Cool way
## by Sophie Dawson, Cool Camping

**Q. What inspired you to do a 'Cool Camping Kids'?**
**A.** Kids absolutely adore camping, it's probably their favourite type of holiday. It's an excuse for them to forgo baths and run around freely outside, a chance for imaginations to go wild and an opportunity to try new, exciting things like cooking over a campfire and sleeping beneath the stars. All the while they're breathing in lung-gulps of fresh air, getting rosey-cheeked and having more fun than they ever thought possible away from Cbeebies and the Wii. The Cool Camping philosophy is to get outdoors and enjoy some quality time with Mother Nature, so we thought it was about time we brought out a book encouraging families to do just that, together.

**Q. The whole book is fantastic, but is there anything that you are particularly proud of?**
**A.** We're particularly proud of the features in Cool Camping: Kids (Residential Camps, Campfire Cooking, Family Festivals, Camping Games and Clover Stroud's fantastic Mum's Guide to Camping). They add colour and fun to the book as well as offering great advice and recommendations on how to make the very best out of your camping trip.

**Q. What tips would you give families with very young children (0-5's) who are a bit nervous about embracing their tent legs?**
**A.** Choosing a campsite not too far away from home eases some of the anxiety that comes hand-in-hand with taking a little one off camping for the first time. If you need to, you can just pack everything and everyone back in the car and get home quickly. As your tent legs grow so can the distance from home. We'd also recommend finding out what sort of facilities are available there beforehand – do they have baby changing facilities and a plentiful supply of hot water? Is there a playground, or any other onsite fun? Always try to arrive at your site while there are still a few hours of daylight left so you have time to pitch the tent, take a look around, have a bite to eat and generally ease into the camping experience.

**Q. What sites in the South West are 'must-go' places for families with children 0-5's? And why?**
**A.** 3 'Must-go' places for families with under 5s in the south / south west:

*Arthur's Field, Treloan Lane, Nr Portscatho, Cornwall* is a cracking site for young 'uns. Every morning, Debbie the owner rings a bell, Pied Piper-like, and children run to help her collect eggs from the hens and feed the rabbits. There's private access to 3 secluded beaches for splashing about, rock-pooling and sand castle building.

*Rocks East Woodland, Ashwicke, nr Bath, Somerset* has loads of space for kids to run around safely, especially in the huge (vehicle free) 100 acre woodland. You can choose your own spot to plonk the tent before heading off to relax by campfires, swinging in hammocks. There's a fantastic teddy-bear trail for tots, as well as a sculpture trail; and Bath, with all its family friendly entertainment, shops & eateries is nearby.

*Abbey Home Farm, Burford Road, Cirencester, Gloucestershire* has a wonderful ethos. There are brightly coloured totem poles to play around, woodland fun to be had and it has its very own, solely organic shop that's just a wander through the woods away. The yurts are well equipped and the site's a safe distance away from roads too, so parents can relax by a fire knowing the kids can play hide and seek or roam around the fields without worrying.

Punk Publishing: £12.99

# CORNWALL

## Lower Treave Caravan Park    37

Crows-An-Wra, Penzance, Cornwall, TR19 6HZ
01736 810 559, www.lowertreave.demon.co.uk
Tents & caravans, £3 pitch fee, from £4.50 per adult,
£2.25 per child, U4's free. Static caravans from £210
p/w. Open Apr-end Oct

Lower Treave is a very well run campsite
close to the beautiful beaches of Sennen and
Porthcurno. The site covers 4½ acres and has
been well landscaped to provide 80 spacious
touring pitches on 4 terraced levels with views
across the surrounding countryside. Shop,
laundry room and Wi-Fi access. 5 caravans
are also available for private hire.

## Old MacDonald's Farm    38

Porthcothan Bay, Padstow, Cornwall, PL28 8LW
01841 540829, www.oldmacdonalds.co.uk
Tents & caravans, from £5 per adult, £2 per child,
U2's free. Open all year but farm park closed Winter.
B&B rooms from £35 pppn (Easter-Sep)

A small family campsite with trampolines,
slides and other play equipment as well as
a whole farm of animals where children are
encouraged to hold and feed rabbits, lambs,
calves and ponies. Pony and train rides. 5mins
walk from Porthcothan Bay. Café and small
games room on site. There are also three bed
and breakfast rooms available.

## Trevedra Farm Caravan &    39
## Campsite

Sennen, Penzance, Cornwall, TR19 7BE
0 1736 871835 before 9pm,
01736 871818 (summer). Please do not call
Sundays.
www.cornwall-online.co.uk/trevedra
Tents & caravans. From £5 adult, £2 child. Opens
Easter - end Sep. Booking essential.

Run by the same family for 65yrs. A working
farm where you can watch cows being milked.
Located close to the beautiful Sennen Cove
and coastal footpath. There is a separate
camping field with its own toilet/shower
facilities. The shop has daily deliveries,
bread, cakes, take-away breakfast, lunch and
evening meals in peak season. Launderette &
utility room. Booking essential in peak season.

## Treyarnon Bay Campsite    40

Treyarnon Bay, Padstow, Cornwall, PL28 8JR
01841 520681, www.treyarnonbay.co.uk
Tents (from £7), caravans (from £9). Static caravans
from £175 p/w. Open Apr-end Sep

Sea views from site, only 200yrds from a
family beach and cliff walks. The site has
toilet blocks, shower, laundry room, shop,
and families have their own separate area.
The hotel next door with bar and evening
entertainment welcomes campers.

# HEREFORDSHIRE

## Doward Park Campsite    41

Great Doward, Symonds Yat, Ross-on-Wye, HR9 6BP
01600 890438, www.dowardpark.co.uk
Tents & motorcaravans only. Pitch from £12.50 (2
people, 1 car). Extra adult £2.50, child £2, U4's free.
Open all year.

This site is situated in an area of outstanding
natural beauty. The river, the forest and
Symonds Yat are all within walking distance,
and a short stroll from the site takes you to
the Seven Sisters Rocks, and King Arthur's
Cave, where the bones of mammoths and
other prehistoric creatures have been found.
Visit Yat Rock - with its fantastic view. Or
cross the Biblins bridge (this is an amazing
wire suspension bridge, popular with children
for its wobbliness but not for pushchairs)
and walk along the river to Symonds Yat
East (where you may see Peregrine Falcons).
Alternatively, take either of the two rope
ferries across the river that are run by the
Saracen's Head and the Olde Ferrie Inne.
Should you wish to cycle, there is a cyclepath
from Symonds Yat East to Monmouth along
the track of the old Wye Valley Railway. You
can get to this from the track running past
the campsite down to the Biblins suspension
bridge. Back at the campsite, let the children
run free in Bluebell Woods, a fenced children's
play area (no dogs). If you fancy trying a local
pub you can take a shortish walk downhill
but the shortest walks are not suitable for
pushchairs. Shop and laundry facilities. Also
see **Walks, Woods & Nature Reserves.**

Camper Vans

## Experience Life in the slow lane

As the new owners of **The Bristol Camper Company** we are delighted to carry on the tradition that the previous owners set. We want to offer families a new way of holidaying here in the UK. We will deliver an outstanding holiday experience with little of the stress and strain that accompanies vacationing abroad, and at the end of the day you can be assured you will have had a holiday the whole family will remember forever. We have increased the number of VW campers to 3, and due to the demands for a larger type of camper, we are delighted to introduce our brand new Autoroller 700; this is a modern 7-berth campervan with, most importantly, six seat belts. The Roller, which we have named Ronny, is full of luxuries including central heating, double glazing, shower and flush toilet, and would be ideal to explore in when the weather becomes cooler, as it is fully winterised. You can rest assured that whatever your choice, the Campers are serviced and maintained to the highest order. They also come with our complimentary welcome gifts of wine and organic bread, tea, coffee, and chocolate. If you are hiring a van for a birthday or anniversary, we will also sneak a bottle of bubbly into the fridge.

Our chosen charities are Sustrans and the make a wish foundation; we will donate £10 from every hire to the chosen charity.

**Terry Rich, Bristol Camper Company**

Also see Advert on page 199.

*The absolute best bit for me was the giddy freedom to go wherever the fancy took us at a moment's notice – no timetables, planned routes or pitching tents, everything we needed neatly tucked into Betty's snug but surprisingly spacious interior. A thoroughly enjoyable experience that we aim to repeat as soon as we can!*
*Nicola McCarthy - in Bristol Blue (otherwise known as Betty), November 2008*

**Look out for the Titch Hikers' Guide to Family Travel. Coming soon...**

# Youth Hostelling

www.yha.org.uk

Think youth hostelling is only for young, free and single travellers? Think again. One of the leading budget accommodation providers in the UK, there is a lot going on for families of all ages. It is no longer necessary to be a member of the YHA, however members always pay less (annual family membership is just £22.95). All listed properties have cots and other facilities for children unless stated.

## FAMILY FAVOURITES

### Poppit Sands                                    42

Seaview, Poppit, Pembrokeshire, SA43 3LP
0845 371 9037. Adult £9.95, child £7.50
A charming hostel that was formerly an inn. Poppit Sands sits in 5 acres of grounds with lots of outdoor space for children. The grounds reach down to the sea and overlook a blue flag sandy beach. Although the hostel welcomes children under three, it should be noted that there are steps down from the car park. Self-catering only.

### Swanage                                    43

Swanage, Dorset, BH19 2BS
0845 371 9346  (Closed week days in term-time).
Adult £15.95, child £11.95 (B&B)

This is a large elegant Victorian manor house just a few minutes walk from the town centre of Swanage and its safe, sandy beaches. The hostel welcomes families of all ages, from babies to teenagers. TV, games room and washing machine.

### Broadhaven                                    44

Haverfordwest, Pembrokeshire, SA62 3JH
0845 371 9008
Adult £19.95, child £14.95

Spacious, modern, single storey building, set in its own grounds just 100m from the stunning Blue Flag beaches of St Brides Bay.

Lots of activities for children of all ages. The Pembrokeshire Coastal Footpath runs past the property and boat trips to nearby islands are available. There is a full meals service with a wide range of locally sourced, home made dishes so you can relax at the end of the day in the licensed, conservatory style dining room overlooking the bay. There is also a new cafe/bar with indoor and outdoor seating offering home made soups, cakes, paninis and other snacks during the day. Open weekends and school holidays from Easter until end October. Fresh fish and barbeques are a speciality.

### Okehampton

Klondyke Rd, Oakhampton, Dartmoor, EX20 1EW
0845 371 9651, adult £13.95 child £10
**Fantastic for family-based activity holidays.**

### Brecon

Groesffordd, Brecon, Powys, LD3 7SW
0845 371 9506, adult £13.95 child £10.50
**Ideal for exploring the Brecon Beacons.**

### Port Eynon

Old lifeboat house, Port Eynon, Swansea, SA3 1NN
0845 371 9135, adult £15.95 child £11.95
**Superb base for exploring the Gower Coast.**

### Minehead

Alcombe Combe, Minehead, Somerset, TA24 6EW
0845 371 9033, adult £11.95 child £8.95
**Near some family friendly sandy beaches.**

### Beer

Towns End, Bovey Combe, Beer, EX12 3LL
0845 371 9502, adult £13.95 child £10.50
**A beautiful fishing village.**

### Golant

Penguite House, Golant, Nr Fowey, PL23 1LA
0845 371 9019, adult £15.95 child £11.95
**Overlooks the lovely Fowey estuary.**

### Lizard

Lizard Point, TR12 7NT
0845 371 9550, adult £15.95 child £11.95
**This has stunning views of Lizard Point.**

**If we haven't listed your favourite place, suggest it to us today...**

# Childcare

## Contents

The kind of childcare you choose will depend on many things, including availability – which means planning ahead in as much (or as little) time as you have! This chapter takes parents and carers through the options. It contains details of the main childcare providers and guidance on how to make a choice that is right for you.

## Tips

Seek recommendations from parents you know and trust as to what has worked for them. And, no matter how last minute your childcare arrangements have to be, it's always advisable to ask prospective carers lots of questions and, if applicable, get references.

### 1Big Database **1BIG** Database

This is an on-line directory of services, organisations and groups for children and young people aged 0 to 19 and their parents and carers in Bath and North East Somerset (B&NES), Bristol and South Gloucestershire.

**www.1bigdatabase.org.uk**

**Got older children?**
Check out the holiday and after school playschemes on www.childcarelink.gov.uk

# Childcare choices?

## Childminders

Childminders use their own homes to look after children from birth onwards. They're popular with parents because children spend time in a homely environment with the same carer every day, and at £3/5 per hour/per child, it's relatively inexpensive. The crunch comes in trying to find one that has space to accommodate your child. Try the agencies listed over the page or ChildcareLink (see previous page). Registered by Social Services (who inspect their homes and do Criminal Records checks), they're also inspected by Ofsted - but as always, get references. Hours, fees and food costs also need to be set out in a contract.

## Nannies

Nannies care for your child in your own home, at times that suit you. They will do everything for your little one including laundry, cooking, and cleaning. Nannies can be an expensive option at £6.50 - £9 per hour full-time, but are more cost effective if you have two or more children, or nanny share with other parents. You usually employ them directly, so you're responsible for tax and N.I. (see Nanny Tax on page 208) – but there are companies who'll arrange this for you. Most nannies hold set qualifications and are registered or police checked, but it is very important to take up references. All the agencies listed over the page can also provide nannies on a temporary or emergency basis (see also Useful Contacts at the end of this chapter). Nannies can also be sought to go away on holiday with your family, or to look after children and the house (Proxy Parenting) if you have to go away.

## Mother's Helps

Mother's Helps will be experienced with children although they are not normally childcare trained, so shouldn't be left in sole charge of small children. They offer a helping hand with childcare and light housework, and at £5-£7.50/hr they can work full or part-time. They are a good part-time option when children are at school or as relief over holidays, and you'll find them through the listed nanny agencies.

### City of Bristol College
0117 312 5278

Childcare students are often looking for placements with families who have a baby under a year old. Students must be supervised, and families need public liability insurance. Police checks will be carried out.

## Au Pairs

Au pairs are foreign students who live with you in return for helping with housework and childcare. They're not qualified, so can't be left in sole charge of young children, but should help out for up to 5hrs a day over five days for an allowance (c.£50 pw) plus two evenings of babysitting. While it's useful to have flexible help on hand, particularly over the summer, you may have to enrol them in a class and/or pay for their study, and English language skills can be variable. And you'll need a spare room!

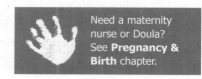

Need a maternity nurse or Doula?
See **Pregnancy & Birth** chapter.

206

# Day Nurseries

Open all year round, Monday to Friday, day nurseries provide full-time day care for children from as young as six weeks old up to five years old. They are inspected by Ofsted and must meet national daycare standards and adhere to specific staff-to-child ratios and numbers of qualified staff.

When visiting, find out what a typical day entails and how many other children will be in the room with your child. Also ask what the carer to child ratio is.

Some of the benefits of nurseries are that your child will mix with peers and learn social skills; they will learn to cope with being looked after by different carers with a variety of personalities; they will have access to a wide variety of equipment.

Many day nurseries take children on a part-time basis, some for just a morning a week, which may be useful for those of you looking for some time to yourself. Friday is often a day that part-time working parents don't use their nursery. So you may find a space then. Also see **Pre-schools and Early Education** if your child is over 2.

# Child Share

Childcare can be expensive, and although some parents can rely on relatives for help, many don't have this luxury. So what else can you do? Well, you could try sharing childcare with other parents.

A more formal way of doing this might be through a LETS – Local Exchange Trading Scheme. These are networks of people who exchange goods and services with each other for free. People earn community credits by providing a service – such as gardening – and then spend the credits on services offered by others in the scheme – such as childcare. See www.letslinkuk.net for local schemes.

Everyone needs to pull their weight: you'll need parents who are both reliable and trustworthy, and you all need to be organised about who's doing what and when.

# Babysitters

Having time to yourself in the evenings is important, but it can be difficult finding someone you can trust to look after your children. Expect to pay from £5 per hour for their services. Ideally a babysitter should be over 15yrs old and you should check what experience they have with children, or if they have any childcare training. Also check references. The agencies below and over the page can help, or try advertising at local colleges for student nannies or local nurseries for nursery nurses.

### Bristol Babysitting Agency

68 Oakleaze Rd, Thornbury, BS35 2LW, 01454 851960, www.bristolbabysitting.co.uk

# Creches

Crèches are available all over the region in shopping centres, colleges and leisure centres. See **Shopping** and the Leisure Centre tables in **Get Physical** to find a crèche near you. Most will require you to be on the premises. Also see Parties for mobile crèches.

# Carer's Respite

Chances for carer's of children who are disabled to have some respite are essential. Small, local charities, like **Time2Share** in Bristol, support disabled children and their families in Bristol, Bath and North East Somerset. They do this mainly through a volunteer befriending service and social groups. In the Bristol area, they are funded to support 25 children and young people and they are usually full to capacity, so are unable to accept many new referrals.

If you would like to find out more about **Time2Share**, or become a befriender, you can email info@ time2share.org.uk, phone 0117 941 5868, or look at our website www.time2share.org.uk

# CHILDCARE AGENCIES

## Alphabet Childcare

184a Henleaze Rd, Henleaze, BS9 4NE
0117 962 5588, www.alphabet-childcare.co.uk
alphabet@btconnect.com

Long-established and much recommended agency with a register of nannies, mother's helps, housekeepers, proxy parents and babysitters - both permanent and for a temporary basis. See **Adverts** in this section, Courses for Parents, and Pregnancy and Birth chapters.

## Childcare Solutions

Lower Wick Farm Estate Offices, Dursley, GL11 6DD
01453 707 483, www.childcaresolutions-sw.co.uk

Offers temporary, permanent and emergency nannies, mother's helps, maternity nurses, proxy parents and babysitters. Normally able to offer childcare with as little as 24 hrs notice. All childcarers have childcare experience and are CRB checked.

## Nannies and Childcare

3 Clare Avenue, Bishopston, BS7 8JF
0117 944 2893
www.nanniesandchildcare.co.uk

New, Bristol-based agency which aims to take away the stress of finding the right type of childcare for your family. Mother's helps, au pairs, nannies, childminders, and babysitters on a permanent or temporary basis. See **Adverts** on inside front cover and in this section.

## Tinies Childcare

31 Penn Street, Broadmead, Bristol, BS1 3UA
0117 9297254 / 07913 744545
www.tinieschildcare.co.uk

National organisation with a regional Bristol office. Temporary and permanent childcare offered.

# Nanny Tax

Aaarrgghh... you've got the most amazing nanny in the world but you are spending ages working out how to pay her tax which sort of defeats the object. Luckily, help is at hand.

## Nannytax

PO Box 988, Brighton, BN1 1NT
0845 2262203
www.nannytax.co.uk

Nannytax is the original and inexpensive countrywide payroll service, designed to look after your nanny's tax and national insurance contributions.

## The Alphabet Childcare Tax & NI

184a Henleaze Rd, Henleaze, BS9 4NE
0117 962 5588, www.alphabet-childcare.co.uk
alphabet@btconnect.com

Free advice to nannies, service can also set up pay and deduction records for employers for an annual fee. See more about Alphabet Childcare above.

# Nurseries

These are listed under their locations:
Central Bristol, North West Bristol, North Bristol, North East Bristol, East, South East, and South West. You can find out more about Nursery Education on page 207.

## CENTRAL BRISTOL NURSERIES

### BEDMINSTER

#### Little Friends Nursery

City of Bristol College, Marksbury Rd, Bedminster, Bristol. BS3 5JL
0117 312 5425

Mon-Fri: 8am-5.30pm

Children aged 18mths-5yrs. 30 places.

#### South Street Family Unit

British Road, Bedminster, Bristol. BS3 3AU
0117 903 9941

south.street.family.unit@bristol.gov.uk

Part of social services facilities, all children are referred by health visitors.

### CITY CENTRE

#### Buffer Bear Nursery

Clock Tower Yard, Temple Meads, BS1 6QH
0117 907 9935, www.bufferbear.co.uk

Mon-Fri: 8am-6pm

Underneath building formerly the British Empire Museum.

Friendly nursery providing care and education for children aged 3mths-5yrs. Can offer a short 'school day' from 9.30am-3.30pm and term time only places on a limited basis. 72 places available.

### Redcliffe Early Years Centre

Spencer House, Ship Lane, Redcliffe, BS1 6RR
0117 903 0334, redcliffe.n@bristol.gov.uk

Mon-Fri: 8am-6pm

Designated Children's Centre operating a neighbourhood nursery. Children 6mths-4yrs. 64 places. Call for application form.

### CLIFTON

#### Amberley Hall

21 Richmond Dale, Clifton, BS8 2UB
0117 974 1550

Mon-Fri: 8am-6pm

Accepts children aged 3mths-5yrs. Qualified teacher, plus teachers for dancing. 50 places.

#### Clifton Tots

8 St Paul's Road, Clifton, Bristol, BS8 1LT
0117 923 7416

Mon-Fri: 8am-6pm

Children aged 3mths up to school age.

#### Mornington House Day Nursery

Mornington Road, Clifton, BS8 2UU
0117 973 3414, www.bristolchildcare.co.uk

Mon-Fri: 8am-6pm

Key focus on "children learn through play". Provides places for 9 under two's and 19 over two's. Accepts children aged 6wks-5yrs. Nursery is part of 'Bristol Childcare Business', which is a family run business incorporating 3 day nurseries located throughout Bristol.

#### Mama Bear's Day Nursery

17 Oakfield Road, Clifton, Bristol. BS8 2AW
0117 974 2929, www.mamabear.co.uk

Mon-Fri: 7:30am-7pm

Based in 19th century building. Offers care for up to 57 children, aged 6 mths-5yrs.

## COTHAM

### Archfield House Nursery

2 Archfield Road, Cotham, BS6 6BE
0117 942 2120, www.archfieldhousenursery.co.uk

Mon-Fri: 8am-6pm

Cares for children from birth-5yrs. Situated in a large homely Victorian house. Wonderful large garden with pets and summer house. Qualified teacher and visiting French teacher.

## ST JUDES

### Rosemary Nursery School & Family Unit

Haviland House, Great Ann St, St Judes, BS2 9DT
0117 377 3297

Mon-Fri.

Local authority nursery school. Provides care for up to 12 children aged 2-5 years.

## KINGSDOWN

### Bristol University Day Nursery

34 St Michael's Park, Kingsdown, Bristol, BS2 8BW
0117 927 6077, www.bristol.ac.uk/nursery

Mon-Fri: 8.30am-5.30pm

Nursery occupies 2 sunny Victorian houses, situated behind University library. Has 4 groups; baby-room (3 mths-1yr), toddler room (1-2yr olds) and 2 spacious rooms for the 'Cubs' (2-3yr olds) and 'Lions' (3-4yr olds).

Priority given to University students/staff.

## ST PAULS

### St Pauls Day Nursery

Little Bishop St, St Pauls, BS2 9JF
0117 377 2278
st.pauls.day.n@bristol.gov.uk

Mon-Thu: 9.30am-4pm

State nursery providing sessional daycare for 2-5yr olds. Children referred to a panel through health visitors or social worker.

## SOUTHVILLE

### First Steps Day Nursery

Southville Centre, Beaulieu Road, BS3 1QG
0117 953 3043, www.southvillecentre.org.uk

Mon-Fri: 8am-6pm

Small, friendly relaxed nursery based in a
large room at the Southville Centre, with a
private outside play area. Flexible session
times offered for 1-5yr olds. Fully accessible
to children with special needs. 41 places.

### Magic Roundabout

141 Coronation Road, Southville, BS3 1RE
0117 963 9800

Mon-Fri: 7:30am-6pm.

Provides care for up to 92 children, aged 0-5
years.

# NORTH WEST BRISTOL NURSERIES

## CLEVEDON

### Folly Farm Day Nursery

Clevedon Road, Tickenham, BS21 6RY
01275 854597

Mon-Fri: 8am-6pm

Quality care and pre-school education for
2-5yr olds in a rural setting. Provision for
special needs. 23 places.

## PORTISHEAD

### Leapfrog Day Nursery

Serbert Rd, Portishead, Bristol. BS20 7GF
01275 847275, www.leapfrogdaynurseries.co.uk

Mon-Fri: 7:30am-6pm.

Purpose built single storey nursery. Caters for
up to 91 children.

## LAWRENCE WESTON

### Step Ahead Day Nursery

City of Bristol College, Broadlands Drive, Bristol.
BS11 0NT
0117 914 8494

Mon-Thu: 8am-5.00pm, Fri: 8-4.30pm

Takes children aged 2-5yrs from parents
attending college or in local community.

### Sansway House Day Nursery

89A Saltmarsh Drive, Lawrence Weston, BS11 0NL
0117 982 9609, www.sanswaydaynursery.co.uk
enquiries@sanswaydaynursery.co.uk

Mon-Fri: 8am-6pm

Affordable and flexible childcare. Can offer
full-time and even occasional care for
children, aged 3mths-8yrs. Separate rooms for
different ages, plus an out-of-school room for
older children. Large garden and indoor soft
play room.

## SHIREHAMPTON

### Mama Bear's Day Nursery

112-116 Grove Leaze, Shirehampton, BS11 9QU
0117 982 3345, www.mamabear.co.uk
shirehampton@mamabear.co.uk

Mon-Fri: 7.30am-7pm
Near M5 junction 18 & A4 Portway, near Park & Ride

Cares for children aged 3mths-5yrs in a fun,
friendly and safe environment where children
enjoy learning and make new friends. Pre-
school rooms for 3-5year olds.

# NORTH BRISTOL NURSERIES

## ASHLEY DOWN

### Ashgrove Park Day Nursery

60 Ashgrove Rd, Ashley Down, BS7 9LQ
0117 951 3123

Mon-Fri: 8.15am-5.45pm

Open for children aged 6wks-5yrs. Been established since Jan 1990.

Students on low income or benefits with children aged 3mths-5yrs can apply to the Learner Support Fund. Nursery also has an after school collection from Sefton Park and runs a playscheme in the holidays.

## BISHOPSTON

### Clyde House Day Nursery

1 Nevil Rd, Bishopston, BS7 9EG
0117 924 7488

Mon-Fri: 8.15am-5.45pm

Accepts children aged 6wks-5yrs. Established 1988. 31 places.

## FILTON

### Abbeywood Tots Day Nursery

97 Station Rd, Filton, Bristol, BS34 7JT
0117 969 3990, www.abbeywoodtots.com

Mon-Fri: 7.45am-6pm

Accepts children aged 0-5yrs. Facility also provides before and after school care and offers holiday play schemes.

### Abbeywood Tots (Filton College)

Filton College Campus, North Site, Filton Avenue, Filton, Bristol, BS34 7AT
0117 969 9712

Mon-Fri: 7am-6pm.
Cares for up to 32 children aged 0-5 years.

### Abbeywood Tots Day Nursery

1 College Way, Filton, Bristol. BS34 7BH
0117 969 3990, www.abbeywoodtots.com
info@abbeywoodtots.com
Mon-Fri: 7:45am-6pm

Cares for up to 108 children 0-5 yrs. Also provides before and after-school care and holiday play scheme.

### Priory Day Nursery

99 Gloucester Rd North, Bristol, BS34 7PT
0117 969 2503, thepriory@bristolchildcare.co.uk
Mon-Fri: 7.30am-6pm

Friendly, safe nursery with caring staff offering learning through play. Takes children aged 6wks-5yrs. Strong focus on "children learn through play".

## HENLEAZE

### Toybox

11 The Drive, Henleaze, Bristol, BS9 4LD
0117 962 3010

Mon-Fri: 8am-6pm

Homely environment, caring for children aged 3mths-5yrs.

## REDLAND

### Art Raft Piglets Nursery

St Saviours Hall, Woodfield Rd, Redland, BS6 6JQ
0117 904 6358, www.artraft.com
office@artraft.com
Mon-Fri: 8-6pm

Self-contained day nursery with a strong arts focus for children aged 12mths-5yrs. Foundation education for 3-5year olds.

### Pooh Corner Day Nursery

46 Lower Redland Rd, Redland, BS6 6ST
0117 946 6178, www.poohcornernursery.co.uk
Mon-Fri: 8am-6pm

Friendly caring environment for 3 mths-5yr olds. Situated in large Victorian house. Separate floors for under and over 2s. Excellent facilities. See advert on p 215.

## The Rocking Horse Day Nursery

34 Northumberland Rd, Redland, BS6 7BD
0117 924 0431, www.rockinghorsebristol.co.uk
redland@rockinghorse-bristol.co.uk

Mon-Fri: 8am-6pm

Cares for babies of 6 wks up to 5yrs. All
qualified staff. 30 places. Located in an
Edwardian semi-detached house, with sn
enclosed walled garden.

## Tin Drum Nursery

32 Redland Grove, Redland, Bristol, BS6 6PR
0117 924 7175

Mon-Fri: 8am-6pm

Warm, caring and happy environment for
0-4yr olds, with separate rooms and activities
for different age groups. Situated in a
large Victorian house. Helpful staff keen to
stimulate and care for the children. Frequent
outings.

## Torwood Lodge Nursery

27-29 Durdham Park, Redland, BS6 6XE
0117 973 5620, www.torwoodhouse.bristol.sch.uk

Mon-Fri: 8am-6pm

Caring and efficient nursery providing a
stimulating environment for children from
birth to 2yrs. Older children may continue
their care at the adjoining Torwood House
School Nursery.

# ST ANDREWS

## The Green Door Day Nursery

35 Belvoir Rd, St Andrews, BS6 5DQ
0117 985 3267, www.greendoornursery.co.uk
Mon-Fri: 8am-5.45pm.

Accepts from birth to 5yrs. Children learn
through guided play sessions.

## Zebedees Day Nursery

26-28 Walsingham Road, St Andrews, BS6 5BT
0117 985 3389, www.zebedees.net
Mon-Fri: 8am-6pm

Friendly nursery open 52 weeks of the year
for 3mths-4yr olds, with excellent facilities
including soft play and a security system.
Nursery nurses and early years' teacher
employed.

# HORFIELD

## Filton Avenue Nursery School & Children's Centre

Balkeney Road, Horfield, BS7 0DL
0117 377 2680, www.filtonavenuenursery.ik.org
Mon-Fri: 8am-5:45pm.
Funded by Bristol City Council. Provides free
high quality early years education and care for
children aged 3 & 4. Part-time and full-time
sessions offered. Nursery also provides paid
childcare for babies and children 0-5 years.

## Peter Pan Nursery

1 Churchways Crescent, Horfield, BS7 8SW
0117 935 5410

Mon-Fri: 8am-6pm

Experienced staff with years of service offering full-time care for children from birth-5 yrs.

## The Honeytree Day Nursery

c/o Monks Park School, Filton Rd, Horfield, BS7 0XZ
0117 931 4650

Mon-Fri: 8am-6pm

Accepts children from 6wks-5yrs. 4 main
play rooms and rooms for sleeping and other
activities. 2 separate gardens.

Also see **Parent & Baby/ Toddler** for a list of the Children's Centres in Bristol.

## We Care For Children
## Aged 3 Months - 5 Years
## 8am - 6pm
## Monday to Friday

For more information please telephone:

Mary Regan or Sarah Bradley
46 Lower Redland Road, Bristol

## 0117 946 6178
## www.poohcornernursery.co.uk

---

# SOUTHMEAD

## Southmead Children's Centre

Doncaster Road, Southmead, Bristol, BS10 5PW
0117 377 2343

Mon-Thurs: 8am-4pm Fri: 8am-1pm

Cares for children aged 6mths-4yrs. 55 places.

# WESTBURY-ON-TRYM

## Acorns Nursery

Henbury Hill House, College Park Dr, W-o-T,
BS10 7AN
0117 950 5885, www.acornsnurseries.co.uk

Mon-Fri 8am-6pm

Full and part-time care offered for children,
aged 6wks-5yrs. Located in large house, U1's
are upstairs, while U2's rotate between six
different rooms downstairs.

## Lake House Day Nursery

2 Lake Road, Westbury-on-Trym, BS10 5DL
0117 962 2948

Mon-Fri: 8am-5.45pm

Offers full-time care from birth to 5yrs, with
Montessori practical life section, French and
pre-school group.

## Little Bears at St Ursula's

St Ursula's High School, Brecon Rd, Westbury on
Trym, BS9 4DT
0117 962 2616, www.st-ursulas.bristol.sch.uk
office@st-ursulas.bristol.sch.uk

Mon-Fri: 8am-6pm

State of the art centre offering pre-school
education for children aged 3-4yrs, offering a
wide range of actitivities, plus a separate art
and design area. Enclosed garden and outside
play area.

215

## Manor House Day Nursery

145 Southmead Rd, Westbury on Trym, BS10 5DW
0117 962 9620, www.themanorhousenursery.co.uk

Mon-Fri: 8am-6pm

Housed in a large manor house with lots of space, it aims to meet needs of individual children. Facilities include sensory garden and separate craft rooms. Cares for 0-5 yr olds.

## Once Upon a Time Day Nursery

2&4 Downs Cote Drive, Westbury-on-Trym, BS9 3TP
0117 962 5203

Mon-Fri: 8am-6pm

Cares from 6wks to 5yrs in a home environment with separate room for babies. Each child has their own key worker who stays with them during all activities. 30 places.

# WESTBURY PARK

## Daisychain Children's Day Nursery

Vining Hall, Etloe Road, Westbury Park, BS6 7PB
0117 970 6828, www.daisychainnursery.co.uk
enquiries@daisychainnursery.co.uk
Mon-Fri: 8am-5:50pm

For children aged 2-5yrs offering a bright, cheerful and well-equipped nursery close to Durdham Downs. Friendly, dedicated, qualified staff with full-time qualified teacher.

## Downs Park Day Nursery

46 Downs Park West, Westbury Park, BS6 7QL
0117 962 8526

Mon-Fri: 8.00am-5.45pm.

Cares from birth to 5yrs.

## The Red House Children's Centre

1 Cossins Rd, Westbury Park, BS6 7LY
0117 942 8293, www.redhousechildrenscentre.org
info@redhousechildrenscentre.org

Mon-Fri: 8am-6pm

Friendly and welcoming. Cares for children aged 2-5yrs.

# NORTH EAST BRISTOL NURSERIES

## DOWNEND

## Mama Bear's Day Nursery

The Old Vicarage, 63 Downend Road, Downend, Bristol. BS16 5UF.
0117 330 5300, www.mamabear.co.uk

Mon-Fri: 7:30am-7pm.

Housed in a converted Victorian Vicarage. Cares for children aged 3 mths-5 yrs.

## FISHPONDS

## Fledglings Day Nursery

25 Oldbury Court Rd, Fishponds, BS16 2HH
0117 939 3398

Mon-Fri: 8am-5.30pm

Accepts children from birth-5yrs. Places for 34 children.

## Stepping Stones Day Nursery

1 Hawkesbury Rd, Fishponds, BS16 2AP
0117 965 7269

Mon-Fri: 8am-6pm

Est. 1975 for children 2-7yrs. Stimulating and very cosy environment.

## UWE Students' Union Halley Nursery

St Matthias Campus, College Rd, Fishponds, BS16 2JP
0117 975 0413/0117 328 4452, nursery@uwe.ac.uk

Mon-Fri: 8.30am-5.30pm

Accepts children from 6mths-5yrs. Priority given to students of UWE, can accept children from the community.

# HAMBROOK

## Barn Owl Nursery

Old Gloucester Rd, Hambrook, BS16 1RS
0117 956 2222

Mon-Fri: 8am-6pm

Small village nursery, with experienced staff, catering for children aged 2-5yrs.

# STAPLE HILL

## Hillside Day Nursery

23 Gladstone Street, Staple Hill, Bristol. BS16 4RF
0117 904 7106, www.hillsidedaynursery.co.uk
Mon-Fri: 8am-6pm

Provides care for up to 20 children aged 0-5 years. Children grouped in 4 separate peer groups.

# EAST BRISTOL NURSERIES

# EASTON

## Easton Community Children's Centre

Russell Town Ave, Bristol, BS5 9JF
0117 939 2550
easton_childrens_centre@yahoo.co.uk
Mon-Fri: 8am-6pm

Centre offers day care facility for children 6mths-5yrs.

## Little Haven Day Nursery

261 Crews Hole Rd, St George, Bristol, BS5 8BE
0117 941 4484

Mon- Fri: 8am-6pm

Friendly pre-school nursery with baby unit. Excellent facilities with full-day and half-day sessions.

## Redroofs Nursery

227 Kingsway, St George, BS5 8AH
0117 949 2600

Mon-Fri: 8am-5.30pm

Day nursery for children aged 0-5 years. During summer months children have access to swimming pool.

# EMERSONS GREEN

## Leapfrog Day Nursery

St Lukes Close, Emersons Green, BS16 7AL
0117 956 8222, www.leapfrogdaynurseries.co.uk
bristol.emersonsgreen@busybees.com

Mon-Fri: 7am-6pm

Purpose built 2 storey nursery with individual outdoor play areas. Accepts children aged 0-5yrs and caters for up to 105 children.

# HANHAM

## Tiny Tots Day Nursery

130 High St, Hanham, BS15 3EJ
0117 947 5436

Mon-Fri: 7.30am-6pm

Full and part-time day care for 0-8yr olds, including holiday club and before and after school care.

# KINGSWOOD

## Hillside Day Nursery

Potterswood, Britannia Rd,
Kingswood, BS15 8DB
0117 960 4330, www.hillsidedaynursery.co.uk

Mon-Fri: 8am-5:30pm

Family-run nursery for up to 33 children, caring for 0-5yrs. 10% discount for siblings.

### Kingswood Foundation Nursery

43 Britannia Rd, Kingswood, Bristol, BS15 8DB
0117 935 2222, www.kfdn.co.uk, info@kfdn.co.uk
Mon-Fri: 8am-5.30pm (6pm on request)

Day nursery accepts children aged 6wks-5yrs. Part of Kingswood Gymnastics and Trampolining Centre, giving children access to all facilities. Staff will also take children on walks or swimming lessons (over 3's), with parental authority.

## SPEEDWELL

### Speedwell Nursery School,

Speedwell Road, Speedwell, Bristol. BS5 7SY
0117 903 032, www.speedwellnurseryschool.com
Mon-Fri

An outstanding nursery school where children thrive and do especially well in both their academic and personal development.

## STOKE GIFFORD

### Leapfrog Day Nursery

Hunts Ground Rd, Stoke Gifford, BS34 8HN
0117 979 9977, www.leapfrogdaynurseries.co.uk
Mon-Fri: 7.30am-6pm

Accepts children aged 3mths-5yrs. Purpose built single storey nursery, with individual outdoor play areas.

### Acorns Nursery

Axa Centre, Brierly Furlong, Stoke Gifford, BS34 8SW
0117 989 9000 ext: 3034
Mon-Fri: 8am-6pm.

Provides care for up to 30 children, aged 0-5yrs.

## WARMLEY

### Redroofs Nursery

24 Poplar Rd, North Common, Warmley, BS30 5JU
0117 949 2700
Mon-Fri: 8am-5.30pm

Accepts children from 0-5yrs. During summer months, children can enjoy swimming lessons.

### The Rocking Horse Day Nursery

Grange School, Tower Rd North, Warmley, BS30 8XQ
0117 947 6218
www.rockinghorsebristol.co.uk
warmley@rockinghorse-bristol.co.uk
Mon-Fri: 7.30am-6pm.

Cares for children aged 6wks-5yrs. All qualified staff.

# SOUTH EAST BRISTOL NURSERIES

## BRISLINGTON

### Abacus Day Nursery

6-8 Emery Rd, Brislington, BS4 5PF
0117 977 2868
Mon-Fri: 8am-6pm

Accepts children aged 6wks-8yrs. Cares for up to 82 children.

### Mama Bear's Day Nursery

216 Allison Rd, Brislington, BS4 4NZ
0117 972 8234, www.mamabear.co.uk
brislington@mambear.co.uk
Mon-Fri: 7.30am-7.00pm

Cares for children aged 3 mths-5yrs in a fun, friendly and safe environment where children enjoy learning and make new friends. Nursery school available for 3-4yr olds. Open plan setting and extensive gardens overlooking south Bristol.

## KNOWLE

### Busy Bee Day Nursery

268 Wells Rd, Knowle, BS4 2PN
0117 977 5357

Mon-Fri: 8am-5.30pm

Accepts children aged 6mths-5yrs, with a separate pre-school section. Access to pets, creative activities, plus visits to library and themed activities.

### Court House Day Nursery

270/272 Wells Rd, Knowle, BS4 2PU
0117 977 2210, www.bristolchildcare.co.uk

Mon-Fri: 7.30am-6pm

Cheerful nursery for 6wks-5yrs with a high staff ratio & well planned curriculum. Strong focus on "children learn through play".

### Knowle West Early Years Centre

Leinster Avenue, Knowle, Bristol, BS4 1NN
0117 903 0214
www.knowlewest-ey.bristol.sch.uk
knowleweyc@bristol-city.gov.uk

Day care offered by referral for children, aged 2-3yrs.

## SOUTH BRISTOL NURSERIES

### Four Acres Children's Centre

c/o Four Acres Primary School, Withywood, BS13
0117 903 0460, fouracresdayn@bristol.gov.uk
Mon-Fri: 8am-6pm

Full day care facilities for children from birth to 4yrs. Provides both day care and referred child places from social care.

### Hartcliffe Early Years Centre

Hareclive Road, Hartcliffe, Bristol. BS13 0JW
0117 903 8633, hartcliffeearly.years@bristol.gov.uk
Mon-Fri: 8:15am-5:30pm

Provides care for children 2-5 years. Places for up to 140 children.

### Mama Bear's Day Nursery

Hengrove Community Arts College, Petherton Rd, Hengrove, BS14 9BU
01275 891 316, www.mamabear.co.uk
hengrove@mamabear.co.uk
Mon-Fri: 7.30am-7pm

Cares for children aged 3mths-5yrs in a fun, friendly and safe environment where children enjoy learning and make new friends. Pre-school available for 3-4yr olds.

### Abbeywood Tots Day Nursery

Stockwood Lane, Stockwood, Bristol. BS14 8SJ
0117 969 3990
www.abbeywoodtots.com
Mon-Fri: 7am-6pm

Provides care for up to 51 children aged 0-2 yrs. Also offer before and after-school care and holiday playscheme.

## SOUTH WEST BRISTOL

### Asquith Court Nursery

C/O David Lloyd Tennis Club, Ashton Rd, BS3 2HB
0117 953 2830
Mon-Fri: 8am-6pm

Full day care offered for children aged 3mths-5yrs in a safe, stimulating environment. Also able to offer a pre-school curriculum. Children enjoy frequent walks and picnics to nearby Ashton Court Estate.

### Teddies Nursery

Clanage Road, Bower Ashton, Bristol, BS3 2JX
0117 953 1246
www.teddiesnurseries.bupa.co.uk
Mon-Fri: 8am-6pm

Part of the BUPA Group, Teddies accepts children from 3mths-5yrs, offering nurtured play and learning activities to help develop confidence and social skills.

Not listed a nursery close to you? Try the following Government website:
**www.childcarelink.gov.uk**

## Local Council Websites

An extremely useful place to start your childcare search is with your local Council website:

### Bristol Children & Young People's Services
0845 129 7217
www.bristol-cyps.org.uk; askcyps@bristol.gov.uk

### Bath & North East Somerset Family Information Service
Keynsham Town Hall, BS31 1NL
0800 0731214
www.bathnes.gov.uk/fis; fis@bathnes.gov.uk

### North Somerset Childcare Service
Children and Young People's Services, Town Hall, Walliscote Grove Rd, Weston-super-Mare, BS23 1UJ
01275 888 778
www.n-somerset.gov.uk; cis@n-somerset.gov.uk

### South Gloucestershire Children & Young People Information Service
Riverside Court, Bowling Hill, Chipping Sodbury, BS37 6JX
01454 868 008
www.southglos.gov.uk; cis@southglos.gov.uk

Please recommend your local nursery or childcare facility if we have missed it out of this book.

**Go to www.titchhikers.co.uk**

Remember, we only list recommendations.

## USEFUL CONTACTS

### Daycare Trust
www.daycaretrust.org.uk
Charity website includes helpful information on choosing the right childcare, and paying for childcare.

### Parents Centre
www.parentscentre.gov.uk
Information and support for parents about children's learning and childcare options.

### HM Revenue & Customs
www.hmrc.gov.uk
Information on Tax Credits and Child Benefits.

### Office for Standards in Education (Ofsted)
www.ofsted.gov.uk
0845 601 4772, Early Years Regional Centre

All childcare comes under the jurisdiction of Ofsted who register and inspect facilities, as well as investigating complaints. Recent reports can be downloaded from their website, although for security, childminders' names and addresses are withheld, so you will need to ask them for their unique reference. Alternatively contact your local Council's Children's Service or your Ofsted Early Years Regional Centre.

### Emergency Childcare
www.emergencychildcare.co.uk, 0870 774 7898
Offers childcare solutions to working parents who have experienced a breakdown of their regular childcare. Parents can search and book local nursery and childminder places or an emergency nanny, on a flexible, ad hoc or daily basis.

# Pre-schools & Early Education

## Contents

We list many recommended preschools but you may find the following Government website helpful if we do not list a preschool in your area: **www.childcarelink.gov.uk**

Attending pre-school is the first real step on your child's formal education path. It is a great way for your child to meet other children and adults and to develop socially, as well as learning many other skills.

### Useful websites:

**Bristol Family Information Service**
0845 129 7217, www.bristol-cyps.org.uk

**Bath & North East Somerset Family Information Service**
Keynsham Town Hall, BS31 1NL
0800 0731214, www.bathnes.gov.uk/fis

**North Somerset Childcare Service**
Children and Young People's Services, Town Hall, Walliscote Grove Rd, Weston-super-Mare, BS23 1UJ
01275 888 778, www.n-somerset.gov.uk

**South Gloucestershire Children & Young People Information Service**
Riverside Court, Bowling Hill, Chipping Sodbury, BS37 6JX
01454 868 008, www.southglos.gov.uk

# EARLY EDUCATION IN BRISTOL

## What is pre-school education?

The period from age three to the end of the reception year is described as the foundation stage. Children work through this initial stage of the national curriculum at a pre-school, playgroup or in a nursery class attached to a primary school, nursery school or day nursery. Most children transfer to the reception year in a primary school in the September following their fourth birthday.

This pre-school learning is a distinct stage and important both in its own right and in preparing children for later schooling. The early learning goals set out six areas of learning which form the basis of the foundation stage curriculum. These areas are:

- Personal, social and emotional development

- Communication, language and literacy

- Mathematical development

- Knowledge and understanding of the world

- Physical development

- Creative development

## Choosing the right pre-school facility

Only you as a parent can decide what is best for your child so we recommend that you visit as many places as you need to. There are many pre-school groups held in Church Halls often called playgroups, whilst some primary schools also offer pre-school education in a nursery class. There are also pre-schools that follow a particular method, such as Montessori or Steiner pre-school. Whatever you choose, your child will normally spend a morning or afternoon on their own there for about 2½ hours up to five times a week. Most will follow the same term dates as a school.

All pre-schools, playgroups and nurseries, where children attend sessions of less than four hours, are now inspected by Ofsted (Office for Standards in Education) to ensure that they meet national standards. When visiting, you can request a copy of their Ofsted report, or call your Ofsted Early Years Regional centre on 0845 601 4771.

For a comprehensive list of pre-schools, within your area, contact:

**Bristol Family Information Service**
0845 129 7217, www.bristol-cyps.org.uk

**ChildcareLink**
www.childcarelink.gov.uk

**Pre-school Learning Alliance**
0117 907 7073, www.pre-school.org.uk

## Nursery education grants

All parents are entitled to claim assistance for the cost of pre-school education for their children once their child has reached 3yrs, providing they attend a registered provider. This applies to children at nursery schools, playgroups, pre-schools, day nurseries, and children's centres.

3 and 4 year olds in England are entitled to a minimum of 12.5 hours free learning per week for 38 weeks of the year. This will rise to 15 hours a week from 2010, delivered flexibly over a minimum of 3 days.

Grants are claimed in the term following the child's third birthday up until the child reaches five years old. To access the grant parents will be asked by the provider to sign a Parental Registration form so that the preschool can claim back the money and deduct it from the termly cost. In cases where the grant does not cover the entire cost of the pre-school session, parents will need to top up the fee.

For further information on nursery grants, see: **www.direct.gov.uk**

The following two subchapters separate those pre-school establishments that are funded i.e. Local Authority Nursery Schools and those that are fee paying (although nursery education grants may apply).

# NURSERY SCHOOLS

The Local Education Authority funds a number of early education places to allow children to spend a year in nursery provision before starting school. Places are available at some infant schools which have a nursery class attached to the school or at council run nursery schools. If parents have applied for a nursery education grant, they cannot get a free early education place.

Parents who wish to apply for a place should contact the school directly. Attending the nursery attached to a primary school does not guarantee your child a place at the school. To find out if there is an LEA nursery class or school in your area contact your local Family Information Service (details at the start of the chapter).

## CENTRAL BRISTOL

### Redcliffe Early Years Centre

Spencer House, Ship Lane, Redcliffe, BS1 6RR
Mrs FM Blight: 0117 903 0334
Mon-Fri 9am-11.30am & 12pm-3pm

Foundation stage offered for 3-4yr olds living within the catchment area. Parents must call for an application form. Also Breakfast Club 8am-9am and Tea Club 3pm-6pm.

### Rosemary Nursery School & Family Unit

Haviland House, St Jude's Flats, Bristol, BS2 0DT
Mrs Sarah Burns: 0117 903 1467
Mon-Fri 9am-3pm

Local authority nursery school for children aged 3-4yrs.

### St Pauls Nursery School & Children's Centre

Little Bishop Street, St Paul's, Bristol, BS2 9JF
Ms L Driver: 0117 903 0337
Mon-Fri, term time only, 9am-3pm.

Full and part-time education places available for 0-4yr olds.

### St Phillip's Marsh Nursery School

Albert Crescent, St Phillip's Marsh, Bristol, BS2 0SU
Mrs P S Willmott: 0117 977 6171
www.stphilipsmarshnursery.co.uk
st.philips.marsh.n@bristol.gov.uk
Mon-Fri 9am-3pm (9am-11:30am or 12:30pm-3pm).

Accepts children aged 3-4yrs, providing a range of activities to promote and encourage children's independence and learning.

### St Werburgh's Park Nursery School

Glenfrome Road, St Werburgh's Park, BS2 9UX
Mrs E Jenkins: 0117 903 0323
www.stwerburghsparknursery.bristol.sch.uk
stwerburghsn@bristol.gov.uk
Mon-Fri 9am-3pm (9am-11:30am or 12:30pm-3pm).

Maintained nursery school offering nursery education and care. Breakfast club 8am-9am.

## NORTH WEST BRISTOL

### Bluebell Valley Nursery School

Long Cross, Lawrence Weston, Bristol, BS11 0LP
Mrs Christine Menzies: 0117 903 1472
bluebell.valley.n@bristol.gov.uk

Early education for children 3-5yrs old. In addition, the school has inclusive places for children aged 3-7yrs who have complex and severe learning difficulties. Contact the school for further information.

### Henbury Court Primary School

Trevelyan Walk, Henbury, Bristol, BS10 7NY
Mr Tingle: 0117 377 2196
www.henburycourt.bristol.sch.uk
henbury.court.p@bristol.gov.uk
Mon-Fri 8.50am-11.30am, 12.40pm-3.20pm

Nursery class for 3yr olds, part-time and full-time places, phone for application procedure.

# NORTH BRISTOL

## Filton Avenue Nursery School and Children's Centre

Blakeney Road, Horfield, Bristol, BS7 0DL
Mrs Rachel Edwards: 0117 377 2680
filtonavenuen@bristol.gov.uk
Mon-Fri 9am-11.30am, or 12.45pm-3.15pm (term time only).

Free pre-school education, from 3yrs for families in the North Bristol City Council area. Waiting list places for those attending either five mornings or five afternoons a week.

# NORTH EAST BRISTOL

## Blaise Primary School

Clavel Road, Henbury, Bristol, BS10 7EJ
Mrs Yvonne Roberts: 0117 377 2424
www.blaise.bristol.sch.uk
Mon-Fri 8.55am-11.30am, 1pm-3.30pm

Nursery class attached to the school offering pre-school education for those rising 4yrs, ideal for those wishing to go to the school.

## Little Hayes Nursery School

Symington Road, Fishponds, Bristol, BS16 2LL
Mrs S Rolfe: 0117 903 0405
www.littlehayes.ik.org
littlehayesn@bristol.gov.uk
Mon-Fri 9am-11.30am, 12.30pm-3pm

LEA run pre-school for 3-5yr olds, please phone for a place.

# EAST BRISTOL

## Speedwell Nursery School

Speedwell Road, Speedwell, Bristol, BS5 7SY
Mrs Gillian Lowe: 0117 903 0329
www.speedwellnurseryschool.com
speedwell.n@bristol.gov.uk
Mon-Fri 9.30am-12pm, 1pm-3.30pm

Local authority nursery school for children aged 3-4yrs.

# SOUTH EAST BRISTOL

## Burnbush Primary School

Whittock Road, Stockwood, Bristol, BS14 8DQ
0117 353 3506, www.burnbush.bristol.sch.uk
burnbush.p@bristol.gov.uk
Mon-Fri 9am-11.30am, 12.45pm-3.15pm

LEA-funded nursery class attached to the school with pre-school places for 3-4yr olds.

## Waycroft Primary School

Selden Road, Stockwood, Bristol, BS14 8PS
Simon Rowe: 0117 377 2198
Mon-Fri 9am-11.30am, 12.45am-3.10pm

LEA-funded nursery school, attached to the school, offers pre-school education for 3-5yr olds.

# SOUTH BRISTOL

## Cheddar Grove Primary School

Cheddar Grove, Bedminster Down, Bristol, BS13 7EN
Miss Abbott: 0117 903 0418
www.cheddargrove.bristol.sch.uk
Mon-Fri 9am-11.30am, 12.45pm-3.15pm

LEA-funded nursery class for 3-5yr olds. Morning or afternoon sessions available.

## Fairfurlong Primary School

Vowell Close, Withywood, Bristol, BS13 9HX
Peter Overton: 0117 377 2182
www.fairfurlong.bristol.sch.uk
fair.furlong.p@bristol.gov.uk
Mon-Fri 9am-11.15am, 1pm-3.15pm

Nursery class attached to the school offering pre-school education for 3-5yr olds.

## Four Acres Children's Centre

Four Acres Primary School, Four Acres, Withywood, BS13 8RB
Dawn Butler: 0117 903 0460
www.fouracreschildrenscentre.co.uk
fouracresdayn@bristol.gov.uk
Mon/Thu/Fri 9.30am-12pm, Wed 12.30pm-3pm

Free pre-school education from 2½-4yrs olds, registered with Sure Start.

## Gay Elms Primary School

Withywood Road, Withywood, Bristol, BS13 9AX
Annette Osbourne: 0117 903 0311
gay.elms.p@bristol.gov.uk
Mon-Fri 9am-11.30am, 12.40pm-3.10pm

Pre-school education offered for 3-5yr olds.
Attached to the school.

## Highridge Infant School

Ellfield Close, Bishopworth, Bristol, BS13 8EF
Jill Spiteri: 0117 377 2366
highridge.i@bristol.gov.uk
Mon-Fri 8.45am-11am, 12.45am-3.15pm

Nursery class for children rising 3yrs.

## Bridge Learning Campus Primary

Bishport Avenue, Hartcliffe, Bristol.
Mr G Grimshaw: 0117 903 0356
www.teyfant.bristol.sch.uk
Mon-Fri 8.30am-11.30am, 12.30pm-3pm

LEA-funded pre-school for 3-5yr olds.
Attached to primary school.

# SOUTH WEST BRISTOL

## Ashton Gate Primary School

Ashton Gate Road, Ashton Gate, Bristol, BS3 1SZ
Mrs S Willson: 0117 903 0236
www.ashtongate.bristol.sch.uk
ashtongatep@bristol.gov.uk
Mon-Fri 9am-11.30am, 1pm-3.30pm

LEA-funded pre-school for 3-5yr olds.
Attached to school. Must be 3yrs old by 31
August. Please call to apply for a place.

# FEE PAYING PRE-SCHOOLS, NURSERIES AND PLAYGROUPS

Most pre-school groups are privately run, non-profit making organisations providing a fun learning environment through play, for children 2½-5yrs. Under the Ofsted guidelines, they must adhere to correct adult to child ratios, have a first aider on site and all members must be police checked. Sessions last 2-3hrs, costing £5-£10. Each child normally attends 2-5 sessions a week. Popular pre-schools have waiting lists, so get your child's name down at least a year before they are due to start. Opportunity Playgroups are set up for children with special needs, usually with trained staff. If your child has special needs, a Statement of Needs is required; your local education authority should be able to help you obtain this and advise you of local groups.

**Advantages:**

- Good first step encouraging your child's learning and independence
- Local therefore your child will meet peers going on to the same school.

**Disadvantages:**

- Term time, short sessions, therefore usually not suitable for working parents.

# CENTRAL BRISTOL

## Christ Church Clifton Pre-school

The Crypt, Christ Church, Clifton, BS8 3BN
0117 9733750
www.christchurchclifton.org.uk
Mornings only during term time - 9.15am - 11.45am
£8.05 per morning session

Lively and fun pre-school run in the crypt of Christ Church. Takes children from aged 2½-4 years 11mths. Children are eligible for the nursery grant for the term after their 3rd birthday.

## Clifton High School Nursery Department

1 Clifton Park, Clifton, BS8 3BS
Heather Thomas: 0117 973 0201
www.cliftonhigh.bristol.sch.uk
8.30am-12pm mornings, 8.30am-3.30pm all day
3.30pm-6pm after school club for lower school

Happy, lively and informal atmosphere for children rising 3yrs. Stimulating curriculum offered in a spacious building and gardens.

# NORTH BRISTOL

## Bluebells Pre-School

Shield Road School, Shields Av, Northville, BS7 0RR
Jacquline Thinnock: 01454 867 189
bluebells@googlemail.com
Mon-Fri 9am-11.30pm, 9am-12.15pm or 9am-3pm
Full day £12.50, afternoon £5.50, morning if stay for lunch £7 (bring packed lunch)

Pre-school education offered for children aged 2½-5yrs.

## Busy Bees Pre-School

St Peters Church Hall, The Drive, Henleaze, BS9 4LT
Sian Jones: 07949 225350
sian-busy-bees@blueyonder.co.uk
Mon & Fri 12:30pm-3pm & Tues, Wed & Thurs
9:15am-11:45am. £8.60 per session.

Warm, caring and happy environment for 2½-5yr olds, "where each child feels valued".

## Fallodon Playgroup

44th White Tree Scout Hut, Fallodon Way, Henleaze, BS9 4HR
Jenny Aulds: 07717 615070 mobile
Mon-Fri 9.15am-12pm. £6 a session, max 24 children

Privately-run playgroup, Ofsted inspected. Children, aged 2½-5yrs, enjoy supervised free play in a large hall and outside, weather permitting.

## Harcourt Pre-School

Wells Room, St Albans Church, Bayswater Ave, BS6 7NS
Mrs Christine Williams: 0117 923 7421
Mon-Fri 9am-3:15pm

£3.30 per hour.

Established in 1956, for children aged 2½-5yrs. It is a happy, caring environment ensuring children build up confidence.

## Horfield Methodist Playgroup

Horfield Methodist Church, Churchways Ave, BS7 8SN
Cherry Arnal: 07977 348850
Mon-Fri 9am-11.30am

£3.50 a session

Church sponsored pre-school, offering foundation stage education for 2½-5yr olds.

## Horfield Welly Pre-School Playgroup

Wellington Hill West, Horfield, Bristol, BS7 8GT
Mrs L Seymour: 07837 133 925
Tue-Fri 9.30am-12pm

£8.10 per session

Following Early Years guidelines, for children aged 2½-4yrs.

## Jack and Jill Pre-School

Northcote, Great Brockeridge, Westbury on Trym, Bristol, BS9 3TY
Julie Claridge: 0117 962 2888
www.jackandjillpre-school.co.uk
Mon-Fri 9am-12pm, 1pm-3pm

Established 25 yrs ago. This small, friendly pre-school in a quiet location, accepts children from 2½yrs for afternoon sessions. Children 3+yrs stay five mornings a week.

## Little Bears at St Ursula's

St Ursula's School, Brecon Road, Westbury-on-Trym
Helen Glynn: 0117 962 2616
www.st-ursulas.bristol.sch.uk
Mon-Fri 8am-6pm

State of the art centre offering pre-school education for children aged 3-4yrs. Offers a wide range of actitivities, plus a separate art and design area. Can provide care from 8am until 6pm if required.

## Magic Dragon Pre-school

Church of the Good Shepherd Hall, Bishop Road,
Bishopston, BS7 8NA
Miriam Lord: 0117 924 3446
Mon-Thu 9.30am-11.45am, term time

£7 a session or nursery grant if applicable

Children aged 3-5yrs looked after in a friendly
atmosphere, with stimulating activities and
resources.

## Noah's Ark Pre-School

Cairns Rd Baptist Church, Cairns Road, Westbury
Park, BS6 7TH
Carol de Beger: 0117 944 6229
www.noahsarkps.org.uk
www.cairnsroad.org (Please click on to see various
other child groups offered at church).
carol@noahsarkps.org.uk
Mon-Fri 9.15am-11.45am, or 12.45pm-3.15pm

£8.50 a session or £20 per day.

Open to children of all faiths aged 2½-5yrs.
Christianity taught. Also an optional lunch club
Mon-Fri 11.45-12.45, so that children can stay
an extra hour or all day if desired.

## Pied Piper Playgroup

Bishopston Methodist Church, 245 Gloucester Rd,
Bristol, BS7 8NY
Mrs Jenny McCaren: 0117 942 5104
Mon/Tue/Wed/Fri 9.15am-12pm

£7.50 a session

Playgroup for children aged 2yrs/10mths-5yrs,
parent participation required twice a term.

## Redland High Nursery Class

1 Grove Park, Bristol, BS6 6PP
Judith Ashill: 0117 924 4404
www.redland.bristol.sch.uk
Mon-Fri 8.45am-3.45pm

Accepts girls aged 3-5yrs. Also offers after
school facilities until 6pm and a holiday club
for 3-11yr olds.

## Redland Pre-school

Friends Meeting House, 126 Hampton Road,
Redland, Bristol, BS6 6JE
Louise Douglas: 0117 908 0455
Mon-Fri 9.15am-1.15pm, term time

Well-established friendly pre-school run by
an elected committee of parents. Places for

children aged 2yrs 10 mths-5yrs. Also offers
lunchtime sessions for older ones at an
additional cost.

## Silverhill School Nursery

Swan Lane, Winterbourne, BS36 1RL
Ian Philipson-Masters: 01454 772 156
www.silverhillschool.co.uk
Mon-Fri 8am-6pm

Independent nursery and prep school for
children aged 2½-11yrs. Holiday scheme
available to pupils.

## St Bonaventures Pre-School

Greyfriars Hall, Friary Lane, Bishopston, BS7 8HN
Louise Stutt: 07840 796 993
Mon-Fri 9am-1pm.

Very friendly atmosphere. For children from
3-4 yr olds. Awarded 'outstanding' by a recent
Ofsted report.

## St Matthews Church Playgroup

Clare Road, Cotham, Bristol, BS6 5TB
Sue Last: 0117 944 1598 or 0117 973 5664
www.stmatthews-bristol.org.uk
playgroup@stmatthews-bristol.org.uk
Mon, Wed, Thurs & Fri sessions available between
9:15am-3pm.

£7.75 a session

Community playgroup offering pre-school fun
for 2½-4yr olds in a caring, supportive and
lively learning environment. Phone for a place.

## The Lantern Playschool

Redland Parish Hall, Redland Green Road, BS6 7HE
0117 946 4699, www.lantern.org.uk
info@lantern.org.uk
Mon/Tue/Thurs/Fri 9:15am-12:15pm.
Lunchtime club 12:15pm-1:15pm.

A Christian school aimed at 3-5yr olds,
offering a high quality pre-school education.

## The Red House Children's Centre

1 Cossins Rd, Westbury Park, BS6 7LY
Jo Kirby: 0117 942 8293

Converted Redland house provides a home-
from-home atmosphere for this friendly
pre-school, taking children aged 2-5yrs, with a
variety of sessions between 8am-6pm.

### Torwood House School

27-29 Durdham Park, Redland, BS6 6XE
Samantha Packer: 0117 973 5620
www.torwoodhouse.bristol.sch.uk

Mon-Fri 8am-6pm, continues through holidays

Friendly, independent nursery and preparatory school from 2-11yrs. Great location next to the Downs. Runs popular holiday club.

### Westbury Baptist Pre-school

Reedley Road, Westbury on Trym, Bristol, BS9 3TD
Mary Hughes: 0117 962 9990
www.westburybaptist.org.uk
pre-school@westburybaptist.co.uk
Mon-Fri 9am-1pm (term-time).
£5.75 per hour or £12 per session

Caring pre-school run with a Christian ethos.

### White Tree Pre-school

Westbury Park Methodist Church Hall, 4 North View, Westbury Park, Bristol, BS6 7QB
0117 924 9894, 07980 426 9289
www.whitetreepreschool.ik.org

Mon-Fri 9.15am-12pm, Thu 12.30pm -3pm

Pre-school education for 2½-5yr olds, within the context of the Christian faith. Warm, caring environment. Variety of activities provided in a large, airy, carpeted hall encouraging all areas of child development. Close to the Downs for walks.

## NORTH EAST BRISTOL

### Bristol Children's Playhouse

Berkeley Green Rd, Eastville, BS5 6LU
Jackie Cutmore: 0117 951 0037
bristolchildrensplayhouse@yahoo.co.uk
Mon-Fri 9am-12.45pm term time

Small fee to be introduced

Pre-school nursery for children aged 2½-5yrs. Parent support required.

### St Josephs Pre-School

St Josephs Church Hall, Forest Rd, Fishponds, BS16 3QT
Cathy Williamson: 0117 914 7173
Mon-Fri 9am-12pm, Tues/Wed/Thur/Fri 1pm-4pm

From 2yrs/10mths-4½yrs. Community-based group encouraging parent participation.

### Sticky Fish Pre-School

Fishponds Baptist Church, Downend Rd, BS16 5AS
Rachel Betts: 0117 904 2768
Mon-Fri 9.30am-1pm

£8 per session

Preparation for school, learning through play. Takes children aged 2½-5yrs.

## EAST BRISTOL

### Barton Hill Family Playcentre - Extended Day Playgroup

Barton Hill Settlement, 43 Ducie Rd, BS5 0AX
Vadna Chauhan: 0117 955 6971
www.bartonhillsettlement.org.uk
fpc@bartonhillsettlement.org.uk
Nursery open 8am-6pm.

£2 a session (term-time).

Two's Group has a stimulating and social environment, for children 2-3yrs. Preparing them for the pre-school group.

### Barton Hill Family Playcentre Pre-school

Barton Hill Settlement, 43 Ducie Rd, BS5 0AX
Vadna Chauhan: 0117 955 6971
www.bartonhillsettlement.org.uk
fpc@bartonhillsettlement.org.uk
Mon 12.30pm-3pm,

Tue/Wed/Fri 9.15am-11.45am, term time

Pre-school runs four times a week for 2½-5yr olds.

### Crossways Pre-School

Methodist Church, Windsor Place, Mangotsfield, BS16 9DE
0117 957 3923
Mon-Fri 9.30am-2.30pm

£8.70 per session.

Sessional or full day care for children aged 2½-5yrs. Very friendly, well-established school with qualified staff.

## Fishponds Pre-School

St Johns Church, Lodge Causeway, Fishponds,
Bristol, BS16 3QG
07947 231 086
Tue-Fri 9am-11.30am, Tues 1pm-3.30pm, term time
£5 a session.

Charity pre-school run by a committee of
parents and friends, for children aged
3-5yrs. One large hall divided up for
different activities.

## Kingswood Methodist Church Playgroup

Grantham Rd, Kingswood, BS15 1JR
Laura Wood: 0117 961 3488
www.kingswoodmethodist.org.uk
kmc@kingswoodmethodist.org.uk
Mon/Tue/Wed & Fri 9.30am-12pm &
Thu 12.30pm-3.00pm

Offers a safe, stimulating environment for
2½-5yr olds with trained staff.

## St George Pre-school Group

The Baptist Church, Cherry Orchard Lane, BS5 8HG
Mrs Sharon Carstairs: 0117 935 4534 or 0845 129
7217 or 0771 967 2137
sharoncarstairs@tiscali.co.uk
Mon-Fri 9am-11.30am

Accepts children aged 2½-4yrs.

## Tiny Happy People Nursery

Easton Christian Family Centre, Beaufort St, BS5 0SQ
Modupa Kefentse: 0117 955 5877
Mon-Fri 9.30am-12pm, 12.30pm-3pm, term time

A stimulating learning enviroment where
children are supported to discover and learn
through the foundation stage. Both inside and
outside classrooms and lunches available.

# SOUTH EAST BRISTOL

## Christ Church Playgroup

Church Hall, Petherton Road, Hengrove, BS14 9BP
Heather Wayborn: 0117 975 4616
Mon/Tue/Thu 9am-11.30am. Also, at busy times Mon
& Thu 12.30pm-3pm

Pre-school for children aged 2yrs/10mths-
5yrs. Occasional parent participation required.

## Counterslip Baptist Church

648 Wells Road, Whitchurch, Bristol, BS14 9HT
Jane Wood: 01275 833377
worship@counterslip.co.uk
Mon-Fri 9.30am-12pm, Tues 12.30pm-2.45pm
£5 a session (nursery ed. grant from 3+yrs)

Pre-school for children aged 3-5yrs with a
wide range of foundation stage activities.

## Hamilton Playgroup

Holymead Junior School Annexe, Wick Rd,
Brislington, BS4 4HP
0117 914 4471
hamiltonpre-school@hotmail.co.uk
Mon-Fri 9am-11.30am, 12.30pm-3pm
£5.50 per session (term-time)

Friendly atmosphere with stimulating
activities.

## Sunshine Under Fives Pre-school

St Gerard Majella Church Hall, Buller Road, BS4 2LN
Karon Nichol: 0117 977 4170
sunshinepreschool@hotmail.co.uk
Mon-Fri 9.15am-11.45am or 12.15pm-3pm
£5 a session

A friendly, well-organised group with lots of
activities for children aged 2yrs/10mths-5yrs.
Members of Pre-school Learning Alliance.

## Queen's Road Methodist Church Pre-School

Queen's Road Methodist Church, Queen's Rd,
Keynsham, BS31 2NN
Ginny Ireland: 0117 987 7753
grps@internet.com
Mon-Fri 9.30am-12pm,
Mon-Fri (excl Tue) 12.30pm-3pm
£5 a session

Accepts children aged 2yrs/9mths-5yrs,
offering quality care and education.

## Sydenham Road Under Fives Playgroup

Totterdown Baptist Church, Sydenham Rd, BS4 3DF
Mrs Maria Hulme: 0117 377 8665
srufbs4@yahoo.co.uk
www.sydenhamroadunderfives.org
Mon-Fri 9.45am-11.30am

Stimulating, community-based group for
3-5yr olds. Lots of craft activities. Bikes used

indoors and out (weather permitting). Run by voluntary committee.

## The Village Pre-school

St Lukes Church Hall, Church Parade, Brislington, Bristol. BS4 5AZ
07798 501770
Mon-Fri 9.15am-11.45am

£4 a session

Friendly, caring environment for 3-4yr olds. Very good Ofsted inspection. Long-serving experienced staff.

## Waycroft Primary School

Seldon Road, Stockwood, Bristol, BS14 8PS
Simon Rowe: 0117 377 2198
waycroft_p@bristol-city.gov.uk
Mon & Wed 9:15am-10:45am

£3 a session

Play to Learn session held at the school with qualified play leader for 2-3yr olds. Must book into a morning or afternoon session.

# SOUTH WEST BRISTOL

## Ashton Vale Pre-school

Ashton Vale Church, Risdale Rd, Ashton Vale, BS3 2QY
Lynne Branson: 07980 065 799
Mon-Fri 9am-11.30am for nursery age or
Mon-Fri 12.30pm-3pm for pre-nursery age

Nursery age free, pre-nursery age £3.75 a session

Pre-school focusing on early learning goals of foundation stage, for children aged 3-5yrs.

## Windmill Hill Children & Family Centre

Philip Street, Bedminster, Bristol, BS3 4EA
Mary Radley: 0117 963 3299
www.windmillhillcityfarm.org.uk/children-family/apple-blossom.html
info@windmillhillcityfarm.org.uk

Mon-Fri 8am-6pm

Nursery sessions for children aged 3mths-5yrs.

# MONTESSORI NURSERY SCHOOLS

Dr Maria Montessori's aim was to help children attain their maximum learning potential while becoming well balanced individuals in the pressures of today's life. Within a Montessori school, children work through core material, (such as Language and Literacy, and Practical Life) at their own pace. Independence, self-discipline, social manners and behaviour, physical co-ordination, and creativity, are among the skills that are nurtured. Find out more at: www.montessori.uk.com

## Clevedon Montessori School

34 Albert Road, Clevedon, BS21 7RR
Maureen Burgoyne: 01275 877743
clevedonmontessorischool@cableinet.co.uk
Mon-Fri 9am-3pm, term time

Accepts children aged 2½-5yrs. In their first year, children do a minimum of three mornings, pre-schoolers do three full days.

## The Clifton Children's House

2 York Gardens, Clifton, BS8 4LL
Mrs Rosamund Payne: 0117 923 7578
www.bristolmontessori.co.uk
rjp@ygardens.demon.co.uk
Mon-Fri 9.15am-12pm or 1:15pm-3.15pm Mon & Wed, (term time).

The Clifton Children's House Montessori Nursery School was established in 1989 and is registered for 24 children. It is situated in a Victorian House not far from the Clifton Suspension Bridge. It accepts children aged 2½-4½yrs. Younger children start in afternoons, in a small group, progressing to mornings in their pre-school year. We cannot recommend this wonderful pre-school enough.

## Stoke Bishop Montessori School

70 Parrys Lane, Stoke Bishop, Bristol. BS9 1AQ
Sandra Harris: 0117 968 6960
www.stokebishopmontessori.co.uk
info@stokebishopmontessori.co.uk
Mon-Fri 8am-6.15pm

Full and part-time places for 2-5yr olds.

# STEINER EDUCATION NURSERY SCHOOLS

## Bristol Steiner Waldorf School

Rudolf Steiner Education, Redhill House, Redland Hill, Redland, BS6 6UX
0117 933 9990
www.steiner.bristol.sch.uk
kindergarten@bristolsteinerschool.org
Mon-Fri 8.55am-3.30pm various sessions available for early years.

Provides alternative, quality education for 3-14yr olds.

## The Rowan Tree Kindergarten

Bristol Steiner School, 12d Cotham Rd, Cotham, BS6 6DR
0117 973 4399
www.steiner.bristol.sch.uk
9am-12.15pm, 12.45-3.15pm

Children from 3½-6yrs can learn in a homely environment and develop at their own pace.

# DIFFERENT LANGUAGE GROUPS

## Clwb y Ddraig Goch (Welsh Club)

50 Richmond Street, Totterdown, Bristol, BS3 4TJ
Sioned Alexander: 0117 971 6478
sioned@alexanderthomas.co.uk

Structured sessions for 0-9yr olds on the Welsh language and culture using games and songs. Meeting places vary. Phone for details.

## Deutsche Spielgruppe

The Church Hall, St Matthews Church, Clove Rd, Cotham, BS6 5TB
Nadya Webster: 0117 902 1509
www.spielgruppe-bristol.org
Mon 3.30pm-5.30pm

£3 a session or £25 for 10 sessions.

Group for German-speaking parents and their pre-school children. Lots of toys, craft activities and songs. Meets at St Matthews throughout the year except during the summer holidays when there are informal meetings at local parks.

## Ecole Française de Bristol

PO BOX 275, Henbury Village Hall, Church Lane, Bristol, BS10 7WZ
0117 959 3311, www.ecolefrancaisebristol.co.uk
info@efb1.fsnet.co.uk
Mon-Fri 8am-5.30pm

Where learning French is friendly and fun. Stimulating immersion classes open to French and English speaking children from 2 ½ years old. Also available are beginners after-school classes for primary school children. Very caring native qualified teachers and assistants. Small class sizes.

# Early Years Education

Full-time education is compulsory for all children between 5 and 18 years of age. The overwhelming majority of children will begin the full time experience at the age of 4, in September when the formal academic year commences. The choice of education is a matter for parents. Most children will attend a state school. The majority of those who do not will attend a fee-paying 'independent' school. A small (but growing) minority of children are home schooled. In Bristol, there is quite a strong tradition of innovative, diverse education options, and the choice is accordingly wide.

## State Education

There are over a hundred state primary-age schools in the greater Bristol area, including those on the fringes of Bristol in the South Gloucester and North Somerset local education authority boundaries. All state schools operate within a framework of central and local government supervision. Despite this, they are self-managing, and each has its individual character and ethos. Some (voluntary-aided state schools) promote a particular religious denomination. All work in partnership with other state schools and the relevant local education authority(ies). Each follows the National Curriculum.

For further information on your local state primary schools, see **www.bristol-cyps.org.uk**.

State schools do not charge fees, and certain additional services are free to the user (for example, a carton of milk is provided for children under five, and in some schools this extends to children aged five and above). School meals are free only to people on certain statutory benefits. Free transport is provided by the council in certain exceptional circumstances. Additional costs which parents and carers bear include school uniforms (where appropriate), and school trips.

## Independent (fee paying) schools

Fee-paying schools are independent of local education authority supervision, and are not required to follow the National Curriculum. Many do follow the curriculum largely. Most admit students on a first-come-first-serve basis, at least until senior school, when an entrance exam of one kind or another can be expected. Fees increase with the age or your child. Expect to pay about £2000 per term for a five year old. For this you will typically have school lunches included, but other costs (uniforms etc) will usually be borne by the parent or carer. Scholarships covering part of the fees are available for students who can demonstrate academic and/or sporting excellence.

For further information, see **www.bristolindependentschools.co.uk**

## Home schooling

For the option of home schooling, see the Education Otherwise website: **www.educationotherwise.org.uk**, or that of the Home Education Advisory Service: **www.heas.org.uk**.

# Family Health

## Contents

For practitioners who only work with pregnancy and birth, **see Pregnancy & Birth**

We are very fortunate to have many healthcare services available to us in and around Bristol but sometimes, when there is so much choice, it can be hard to know where to turn. This section is here to give an outline of who is who in the health world, which is especially important when it comes to seeking help in an emergency. It also lists recommended clinics and practitioners, as well as giving an overview of general childhood health needs and where to seek help and advice. More specific information for certain aspects of healthcare is found in **Advice & Support**, and **Pregnancy & Birth**.

### NHS Direct

0845 46 47, www.nhsdirect.nhs.uk

Confidential advice line, staffed by nurses, offering healthcare advice 24 hours a day. They will assess your needs and either give advice or refer you to your out of hours GP or hospital. They also give information about local NHS services, such as GPs and dentists.

# General Health

## USEFUL CONTACTS

## HEALTHCARE SERVICES

**Avonweb** www.avon.nhs.uk

Online site redirecting you to information about NHS services, such as GPs, dentists, hospitals and opticians, in Bristol, Bath, North East and North Somerset, and South Gloucestershire. Or see your specific Primary Care Trust (PCT) below.

## TRANSLATION

**Maternity & Health Links**
Charlotte Keel Health Centre, Seymour Rd, Easton
0117 9027100

Information videos, bilingual scripts, interpreting and advocacy service.

## PRIMARY CARE TRUSTS (PCTS)

**Bath and North East Somerset PCT**
01225 831800, www.banes-pct.nhs.uk

**Bristol PCT**
0117 9766600, www.bristolpct.nhs.uk

**North Somerset PCT**
01275 546 770, www.northsomerset.nhs.uk

**South Gloucestershire PCT**
0117 330 2400, www.sglos-pct.nhs.uk

## GPs & NURSES

### Family Doctor (GP)

If you or a member of your family have any health concerns, your first point of contact will probably be your family doctor (GP). If your problem occurs out of surgery hours, you can contact NHS Direct (08454647). If you are not registered with a GP, you can find the telephone number of the nearest surgery in the yellow pages, from NHS Direct, Avonweb or your local PCT.

### Practice Nurses

Registered nurses, usually based in health centres or surgeries, work closely with GPs and often run clinics in specialised areas, such as family planning, diabetes and asthma.

## WALK-IN CENTRES

NHS walk-in centres provide treatment for minor injuries and illnesses seven days a week. You don't need an appointment and will be seen by an experienced NHS nurse.

See www.nhs.uk

**Bristol City NHS Walk-in Centre**
35 Broad Street, BS1 2EZ
0117 906 9610
Mon-Sat 8am-8pm, Sun, B/H 10am-6pm

**South Bristol NHS Walk-in Centre**
5 Knowle West Health Park, Downton Road, Knowle West, BS4 1WH
0117 903 0000
Daily 9am-9pm

## HOSPITALS & MENTAL HEALTH

### A&Es

The following hospitals all have accident and emergency departments.

**Frenchay Hospital**
Frenchay Park Road, BS16 1LE
0117 970 1212

**The Bristol Royal Hospital for Children**
Upper Maudlin Street, BS2 8BJ
0117 9342 8460

**The Bristol Royal Infirmary**
Marlborough Street, BS2 8HW
0117 923 0000

**Royal United Hospital**
Combe Park, Bath, BS1 3NG
01225 428331

**Weston General Hospital**
Grange Road, Uphill, Weston-Super-Mare, North Somerset, BS23 4TQ
01934 636 363

**Gloucestershire Royal Hospital**
Great Western Road, Gloucester, GL1 3NN
08454 222222

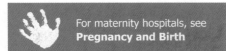
For maternity hospitals, see
**Pregnancy and Birth**

## Minor Injuries Units

### Southmead Hospital
Southmead Rd, Westbury-on-trym, Bristol, BS10 5NB
0117 9595100

### Clevedon Cottage Hospital
Old Street, Clevedon, North Somerset, BS21 6BS
01275 872212

### Paulton Hospital
Salisbury Road, Paulton, Bristol, BS39 7SB
01761 412315

## Bristol Eye Hospital

Lower Maudlin Street, Bristol, Avon, BS1 2LX
0117 923 0060 (Trust Switchboard)
0117 928 4613 (A&E)

A&E onsite.

## Bristol Dental Hospital

Lower Maudlin Street, Bristol, Avon, BS1 2LY
0117 928 4383

In emergencies: if you already see a dentist, contact your own dental practice for emergency advice or possible treatment. If you do not currently have a dentist and you require emergency treatment during the daytime or information on accessing NHS dental care, call the Single Point of Access line on: 08451 206 680 Mon-Fri, 9am-6pm

## Mental Health Emergencies

0117 942 9224 or outside office hours 01454 615165

If it is not an emergency, your doctor is the first person to contact. (Call NHS Direct if you do not have a doctor - 08454647). You can also contact Adult Care Services for help and advice - 0117 922 2700. See **Advice & Support** for more on Mental Health.

# LATE NIGHT PHARMACIES

In all chemist shops (or pharmacies) there is a pharmacist on duty who is able to give advice on the treatment of many health problems. There will always be a pharmacy in your area open outside normal shop hours. A list of these is published daily in the Bristol Evening Post or can be obtained by telephoning NHS Direct. More details in **Shopping and Services**.

# ADVICE & COMPLAINTS

## Complaints

If you are not happy with the care that you have received from any aspect of the NHS, you have every right to complain. For information about how to make a complaint, see www.nhs.uk or contact your local PCT, see above.

## Patient Advice & Liaison Service

For information about the NHS and any other health related enquiry:

### University Hospitals Bristol
(Includes St Michael's, the Children's Hospital, the BRI, Eye and Dental Hospitals)
0117 342 3705, www.uhbristol.nhs.uk

### North Bristol NHS Trust:
www.nbt.nhs.uk
Frenchay Hospital
0117 340 6646
Southmead Hospital
0117 323 6285

# Complementary Healthcare

This section puts several branches of western medicine under the same umbrella as those medicines which are traditionally thought of as complementary. Some of these services can be received within the NHS but many are private. Some offer reduced rates.

Most of the clinics and practitioners listed below offer their services to non-specific age groups or clients. See Child Health at the end of this chapter or **Pregnancy & Birth** if your needs are more specific.

### Institute of Complementary Medicine

Can-Mezzanine, 32-36 Loman Street, SE1 0EH
0207 922 7980, www.icmedicine.co.uk

Charity providing information on the safe and best practice of Complementary Medicine.

## GENERAL CLINICS

### Bristol Natural Health Service

407 Gloucester Rd, Horfield, BS7 8TS
0117 944 4448
www.bristol-natural-health-service.co.uk

Wide range of treatments including psychotherapy, acupuncture and homeopathy.

### Chiron Centre

130 Westbury Road, Westbury-on-Trym, BS9 3AL
0117 962 0008, www.chironcentre.co.uk

Acupuncture, craniosacral therapy, and more.

### Clover House Children's Complementary Therapy Centre

447 Bath Road, Saltford, Bristol, BS31 3AZ
01225 344047, www.cloverhouse.org

Charity set up to relieve sickness and suffering of children (from aged 3) and young people through the provision of complementary care. Appointment includes seeing 3 therapists covering aromatherapy, nutrition & imagery. £35 a session (3 sessions are recommended). Bursary fund for families on low income.

### Kingswood Natural Health Centre

355-359 Two Mile Hill Rd, Kingswood, BS15 1Af
0117 914 5590, www.kingswoodnaturalhealth.co.uk

Range of complementary & holistic therapies in a professional and relaxing environment.

### Natural Health Clinic

39 Cotham Hill, Cotham, BS6 6JY
0117 974 1199, www.thenaturalhealthclinic.com

Wide selection of practitioners including psychotherapy, osteopathy and nutrition. Initial 30 min consultation to help decide most appropriate therapy.

### Neal's Yard Therapy Rooms

126 Whiteladies Road (above Neal's Yard Remedies),
0117 946 6035, www.nealsyardremedies.com

Offers a wide range of therapies including pregnancy and postnatal reflexology, baby massage, and pregnancy and postnatal shiatsu. No access for buggies.

### The Centre for Whole Health

12 Victoria Place, Bedminster, BS3 3BP
0117 923 1138, www.lamrim.org.uk

Offers complementary medicine and courses in Massage, Shiatsu, Tai-Chi, Yoga and more.

### The Chandos Clinic

21 Chandos Rd, Redland, BS6 6PG
0117 974 5084, www.chandosclinic.co.uk

Offers many therapies including homeopathy, reflexology, shiatsu, allergy therapy, and osteopathy for babies and growing children.

### The Clifton Practice

8-10 Whiteladies Rd, Clifton, BS8 1PD
0117 946 6070, www.thecliftonpractice.co.uk

Offers all the main complementary and alternative therapies.

### The Medical

1a Christmas Steps, Bristol, BS1 5BS
0117 376 37 32, www.themedicalbristol.co.uk

Wide range of services and clinics.

# A-Z of therapies

## and names of well recommended practitioners

---

## ACUPUNCTURE

Used in traditional Chinese medicine for around 4,000 years. It involves the painless insertion of fine needles into specific points on the body. Treatment is sometimes available on the NHS. Many of the clinics featured left offer acupuncture. See also **Chinese Medicine** on right.

### British Acupuncture Council

0208 735 0400, www.acupuncture.org.uk

Free information and lists of local practitioners. Look for letters such as MBAcC, after a practitioner's name.

---

### Jill Glover (MBAcC)

Alma Vale Centre, 30 Alma Vale Road, Clifton
0117 377 1186

Acupuncture and Chinese herbs for pregnancy, childbirth, postnatal depression, exhaustion, fertility issues, and menstrual difficulties.

---

## AROMATHERAPY

Aromatherapy is the holistic application of essential oils, often involving massage. Aromatherapy can be used on small children and can be beneficial during pregnancy, labour and postnatally.

### The International Federation of Aromatherapists

020 8567 2243, www.ifaroma.org

Provides lists of local practitioners. Look out for MIFA after a practitioner's name.

### The Register of Qualified Aromatherapists

PO Box 3431, Danbury, Chelmsford, Essex
01245 227 957

Professional association of aromatherapy practitioners who have undergone training of the highest standards. Write with SAE or phone to find an aromatherapist in your area.

For listings of aromatherapists and those qualified to do baby massage, see **Pregnancy & Birth** and **Courses for Parents.**

---

## Anne Badger (MGCP)

0117 963 6557 or 07706 094686
annebadger@madasafish.com

Anne offers aromatherapy and massage (see next page) in pregnancy, labour and postnatally. She also offers aromatherapy blends of essential oils which are safe to use in pregnancy, and which can help with headaches, insomnia, IBS and more. Anne also offers baby massage (see **Courses for Parents**), baby shiatsu classes and 1:1 sessions.

---

## Victoria Kubiak (APNT)

01275 876688
Clinics in Sneyd Park, Queen Charlotte St, and Clevedon.

Clinical Aromatherapy to relieve a wide range of physical and stress related conditions.

---

## CHINESE MEDICINE

Traditional Chinese medicine, also known as TCM, includes a range of traditional medical practices originating in China. TCM practices include such treatments as herbal medicine, acupuncture, dietary therapy, and both Tui na and Shiatsu massage.

### Association of Traditional Chinese Medicine (UK)

020 8951 3030, www.atcm.co.uk

Main UK regulatory body for the practice of acupuncture, Chinese herbal medicine, and tuina (Chinese therapeutic massage).

---

## AcuMedic Chinese Medical Centre

Manvers Chambers, Manvers Street, Bath, BA1 1PE
01225 483 393, www.acumedic.com

Treatments for babies from (6+mths) and children with skin conditions such as eczema and psoriasis. Infertility clinic. Staff help with buggies over the steps at entrance.

**Back pain?**
**Also see Back in Action on page 28.**

## Chinese Medicine & Skin Centre

51 Sandy Park Rd, Brislington, Bristol, BS4 3PG
0117 972 4716

Qualified and registered consultant of Herbal Medicine and Acupuncture. Treatments offered can help most common and chronic disorders including baby and children's eczema, impetigo, scabies, flu, coughs, poor appetite and constipation.

## Oriental Medicine Practice

35 North View, Westbury Park, BS6 7PY
0117 907 8890, www.orientalmedicine.co.uk

Offers acupuncture, shiatsu, Chinese herbs, nutritional consultation and allergy testing for babies and children. Has practitioners who will support women in pregnancy and during labour, both in hospital and for home births.

# CHIROPRACTORS

Chiropractors diagnose and treat conditions rising from the mechanical dysfunction of the joints and their effects on the nervous system. Chiropractors use their hands to adjust the joints of your spine and extremities where signs of restriction in movement are found. They can help with pains experienced throughout pregnancy, including pelvic girdle pain. They can also help postnatally.

Common issues that they help with in babies include prolonged crying, difficulties with feeding and sleeping, and frequent infections. These may be the result of constraint within the womb or a difficult delivery that has caused stress to the bones of the baby's head and neck. With children, asthma, bedwetting and hyperactivity may be helped. See also Cranial Osteopaths opposite.

### The British Chiropractic Association

Blagrave House, 17 Blagrave St, Reading, RG1 1QB
0118 950 5950, www.chiropractic-uk.co.uk

Make sure your pracitioner is registered with the General Chiropractic Council (GCC).

## Vital Health Chiropractic & Physiotherapy Clinic

8 North View, Westbury Park, BS6 7QB
0117 973 0878

Chiropractors and osteopaths with a particular interest in treating women pre-conceptually and throughout pregnancy. They also treat babies and children for infantile colic, growing pains and headaches.

## Christine Andrew - Whole Person Clinic

9 Dongola Road, Bishopston, BS7 9HQ
0117 973 0878, www.wholepersonchiropractic.fw.nu

Christine is truly amazing. She is a trained midwife and has a special interest in pelvic girdle pain in pregnancy and women's health.

## ALSO TRY

**Clifton Chiropractic**
123 Pembroke Road, Clifton BS8 3EU
0117 974 4217, www.cliftonchiropractic.co.uk

**Hands on Health Clinics**
**Keynsham Clinic:**
2 Temple Court, Keynsham, Bristol BS31 1HA
0117 986 6578
**Frenchay & Downend Clinic:**
17 Cleeve Wood Road, Downend, Bristol BS16 2SF
0117 956 7300
**Kingswood Clinic:**
Orchard Medical Centre, McDonald Walk, BS15 8NJ
0117 961 2060

**The Medical**
1a Christmas Steps, Bristol, BS1 5BS
0117 376 37 32, www.themedicalbristol.co.uk

## Hydrotherapy Pool

Hydrotherapy is exercise or physiotherapy treatment in a warm-water pool. The water temperature is usually 34-37ºC - warmer than normal swimming pools. The temperature of the water allows your muscles to relax and eases pain in your joints. Contact Purely Active, 07847 786866, www.purelyactive.com   or see entry in **Pregnancy and Birth** chapter.

# CRANIAL OSTEOPATHS

Cranial osteopathy is a delicate form of manipulation to the skull and facial bones. Treatment can be helpful in pregnancy and for babies and young children with feeding difficulties, colic, sleep disturbances, behavioural problems, learning difficulties, asthma and ear infections. It can be available on the NHS. Also see Osteopaths below.

## International Cranial Association
478 Baker St, Enfield, Middlesex, EN1 3QS
0208 367 5561

Publishes a directory of practitioners.

## The Craniosacral Therapy Association of the UK
Monomark House, 27 Old Gloucester St, WC1N 3XX
07000 784735, www.craniosacral.co.uk

Practitioner listing and information on craniosacral therapy.

## Bristol Centre for Craniosacral Therapy
26 Cairns Rd, Bristol, BS6 7TY
0117 942 8647, www.bristolcraniosacral.co.uk

Craniosacral therapy for pregnancy, babies and children. A very gentle whole body therapy addressing structural problems and restrictions, arising from the birth process. Also helpful with colic, digestive, respiratory, anxiety and stress difficulties, hyperactivity, and cerebral palsy. Mums encouraged to take sessions too.

## Bristol Children's Clinic
The Family Pracice, 116 Gloucester Rd, BS7 8NL
0117 944 6968, www.bristolchildrensclinic.com

## Bristol Children's Osteopathic Clinic
Chandos Clinic, 21 Chandos Road, Redland, BS6 6PG
0117 974 5084, www.chandosclinic.co.uk

## Vital Health Chiropractic & Physiotherapy Clinic
8 North View, Westbury Park, BS6 7QB
0117 973 0878

# HOMEOPATHY

Homeopathic medicines are derived from a variety of plants, animal materials and minerals. Ask your GP first as you may be able to be referred on the NHS.

## The British Homeopathic Association
01582 408675, www.trusthomeopathy.org

Details of medically qualified homeopaths. Look for the letters MF Hom, FF Hom.

## The Society of Homeopaths
0845 4506611, www.homeopathy-soh.org

Information about homeopathy, and register of qualified homeopaths in your area.

## Individual Practitioners

### Gordon Adam, DSH RSHom
St Andrews
0117 9080494

### Maddhu Anhes, DSH PCH RSHom
St Andrews and Totterdown.
0117 977 8737

### Lesley Harris, DSH RSHom
30 Thingwall Park, Fishponds, BS16 2AE
0117 902 8484

### Jo Morgan, RSHom PCH BA
Bristol Natural Health Service,
407 Gloucester Road, Horfield, Bristol BS7 8TS
0117 944 4448, jomorgan.rshom@blueyonder.co.uk
Runs clinics specifically for babies & children.

### Diane Murray, RSHom
The Chiron Centre, 130 Westbury Rd,
Westbury-on-Trym, BS9 3AL
0117 962 0008

### Penny Stirling, DSH RSHom
The Centre for Whole Health, 12 Victoria Place,
Bedminster, BS3 3BP
0117 923 1138

### Chris Wilkinson DSH RSHom
24 Dunkerry Rd, Windmill Hill, Bristol
0117 963 2306

# MASSAGE

### Anne Badger, MGCP
0117 963 6557, annebadger@madasafish.com

See full entry on page 237.

## OSTEOPATHY

Osteopathy treats faults which occur in the musculo-skeletal system due to stress, injury and sometimes disease. It can be beneficial during pregnancy and for small children. Osteopathy can be available on the NHS.

### General Osteopathic Council

Osteopathy House, 176 Tower Bridge Rd, London, SE1 3LU
0207 357 6655, www.osteopathy.org.uk

List of registered osteopaths and fact sheets. Under the Osteopaths Act 1993, all qualified Osteopaths have to be listed with the General Osteopathic Council.

### The Family Practice

116 Gloucester Road, Bishopston, BS7 8NL
0117 944 6968, www.thefamilypractice.tv

Osteopathy for all including cranial osteopathy for babies and children.

### The Fishponds Practice

834 Fishponds Rd, Fishponds, Bristol, BS16 3XA
0117 949 1290, www.fishpondspractice.co.uk

Offers osteopathy for pregnancy, children and babies. It is also home to a range of other therapies offered by a team of qualified and accredited practitioners.

### Sneyd Park Osteopaths

4 Rockleaze Rd, Sneyd Park, Bristol, BS9 1NF
0117 968 5107
www.bristolosteopaths.com

Treats a range of complaints from aches and pains, to headaches and period pains to name but a few. Specialising in mechanical, visceral and cranial approaches.

## REFLEXOLOGY

Working on reflex points on the feet to treat imbalances in the whole body. It is drug free and can be used to treat many conditions. It can be beneficial during pregnancy, aiding sleep and reducing aches and pains. Some women find it makes labour shorter and less painful. It can also help with fertility problems.

### Association of Reflexologists

5 Fore Street, Taunton, Somerset, TA1 1HX
01823 351010, www.aor.org.uk

Lists of registered reflexologists.

### British Reflexology Association

Monks Orchard, Whitbourne, Worcester, WR6 5RB
01886 821 207, www.britreflex.co.uk

Lists registered reflexologists.

### Alison Burlingham MAR

01275 394493

Alison holds the practioners certificate in reflexology and is a full member of the AOR. One of her specialisations is antenatal and postnatal reflexology.

### Jenny Coles Mobile Reflexology

0117 9076896 Mob: 07779161268
jennycoles@msn.com
£30 per session

Jenny is a fully qualified Reflexologist and a full member of the Association of Reflexologists (AoR).

### Claire Collins BA (Hons) Dip Reflex MIFR

Chiron Centre, 130 Westbury Rd, W-O-T, BS9 3AL
0117 962 0008, www.chironcentre.co.uk
Neal's Yard Remedies, 126 Whiteladies Rd, BS8 2RP
0117 946 6034, www.nealsyardremedies.com
0798 964 7775, www.clairecollins-reflexology.co.uk

Claire is a friendly and skilled reflexologist. She has a diploma in reflexology and is a member of the International Federation of Reflexologists (MIFR). She also has a qualification in Maternity Reflexology which covers working with pregnant women, babies, and post-natal women.

### Henrietta Gibbs Dip BSR VRT MIFR

0117 942 2769 mob. 07812 187730
henriettagibbs@onetel.com

Runs clinics in Redland and Westbury Park. Treats adults and children with various conditions, many hormonal. Works to leave the body healed, balanced and healthy.

### Ruth Bolgar MIFR

0117 924 1252

Offers reflexology for pregnancy and for mums at any time. Ring for a friendly and confidential chat. Ruth sees people in a peaceful treatment room in her own home. Reflexology can encourage labour if you are past your due date and want to avoid being induced.

## SHIATSU

Practitioners use fingers, palms, elbows, knees and feet to apply pressure to the energy lines, to stimulate the body's energy flow. Treatment can be particularly helpful to pregnant women and children.

### The Shiatsu Society UK

Eastlands Court, St Peters Road, Rugby, CV21 3QP
0845 130 4560, www.shiatsu.org

The governing body for all Shiatsu practioners. Look for the letters MRSS after the name. Provides practitioner listings.

### Bristol School of Shiatsu

0844 335 0573
www.shiatsubristol.co.uk

Contact for details of practitioners in the area, registered with the Shiatsu Society UK.

See Anne Badger for baby shiatsu. For yoga see **Pregnancy & Birth**, for Baby Massage see **Courses for Parents**.

## Counselling & Hypnotherapy

## COUNSELLING

### The British Association of Counselling and Psychotherapy

01455 883300, www.bacp.co.uk

Lists of local therapists are available. Look for BACP, UKCP, UKRCP, BCPC after a counsellor's name.

Also see **Advice & Support** where counsellors and psychotherapists are listed under their specialisms.

### Avon Counselling and Psychotherapy Service

11 Orchard Street Bristol BS1 5EH
0117 930 4447, www.acps-bristol.org.uk

This is a charity, established 20 years ago to provide confidential help to individuals and couples over 18 in the wider Bristol and Bath area. All of the counsellors and psychotherapists are professionally trained, registered and accredited by the British Association of Counsellors and Psychotherapists, the UK Council for Psychotherapy or the British Psychoanalytic Council.

## HYPNOTHERAPY

### Braybrooke Hypnotherapy

0117 939 3999, www.braybrookehypnosis.co.uk

Richard is a qualified and experienced clinical hypnotherapist, a qualified counsellor, a certified NLP practitioner and an experienced life coach. Helpful for natural childbirth, stress, anxiety, depression and more.

## Bristol Hypnotherapy Clinic

The Courtyard, 11A Canford Lane, BS9 3DE
0117 968 6886, www.childbirth-bristol.co.uk

Using hypnosis in childbirth can allow you to be in control of your mind and body, reducing fear, anxiety and discomfort. During pregnancy, back pain, nausea, hypertension can be reduced. Phobias, ante and postnatal depression are specialities.

## LIFE COACHING

### Anne Miller

www.annemiller-lifecoach.co.uk
annemiller@blueyonder.co.uk

It is often difficult for a parent to work out their own needs and goals when life contains many conflicts of interest, whether these involve work, family life, or exploring personal goals. Life coaching can help you make more confident decisions that feel right for you. For more information, see our article about Life Coaching with Anne Miller on page 249.

### Braybrooke Hypnotherapy

0117 939 3999, www.braybrookehypnosis.co.uk
See full entry under Hypnotherapy.

# Child Health

The following section gives a little more information about children's potential needs and what is available to them in the Bristol area, as well as national helplines and charities that are commonly used. It should be used in conjunction with the rest of the **Family Health** chapter, and **Advice and Support**. For any queries not addressed here, please consult your GP or health visitor.

## DEVELOPMENT

For the first five years of your child's life, developmental reviews are held at your local clinic. They focus on your child's growth and development, checking their vision, hearing, speech and movement.

You will be given a Personal Child Health Record, which contains charts used to monitor your child's progress and information about immunisations. This record should be taken to all your child's clinic and hospital visits.

## EYES

Eye checks are carried out during your child's developmental reviews. If there are any problems, they may be referred to an optician or a hospital clinic. Children are eligible for free eye tests at an optician from the ages of 1-16yrs. A list of opticians can be found in the Yellow Pages, from Avonweb or your local PCT (see the start of this chapter).

### Bristol Eye Hospital

Lower Maudlin Street, BS1 2LY
0117 923 0060 (Trust Switchboard)
0117 928 4613 (A&E), www.uhbristol.nhs.uk

## TEETH

Dentists advise that you should begin brushing your child's teeth as soon as they come through and you should also take them to the dentist regularly for check-ups. All children are entitled to free dental treatment at any NHS dentist, a list can be found in the Yellow Pages (listed under Dental Surgeons), from NHS Choices (www.nhs.uk) or your local

PCT. If you are having difficulty in obtaining NHS dental services in your area please call 0845 120 6680.

**Dental Emergencies:** You should call your own dentist if you need emergency dental care, as they should have an out-of-hours service. If you do not have a dentist, call NHS Direct on 0845 46 47 or see page 235.

**British Dental Association**
www.bda-dentistry.org.uk

**Dental Helpline**
0845 063 1188 (local rate call in the UK) between 9-5 Monday to Friday

# ACCIDENTS

Accidents are the most common cause of death in children. There are many ways to prevent accidents and you can discuss these with your health visitor, or see our list of contacts below.

**Child Accident Prevention Trust**
Canterbury Court (1.09), 1-3 Brixton Rd
London, SW9 6DE
020 7608 3828, www.capt.org.uk

This is a national charity committed to reducing the number of children and young people killed, disabled and seriously injured as a result of accidents.

**St. John's Ambulance**
The Harry Crook Centre, Raleigh Road, Bedminster, Bristol, BS3 1AP
0117 953 3880, www.avon.sja.org.uk

St John Ambulance run baby and small children first aid courses, for groups of 6 to 12 people. They can be run in your own home, place of work or other suitable venue.

Also see **Courses for Parents**.

**The Royal Society for the Prevention of Accidents**
Birmingham, B5 7ST
0121 248 2000, www.rospa.co.uk

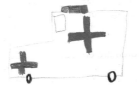

# CHILDREN'S WARDS

If your child needs to go into hospital, they will be admitted to a separate children's ward where they will be looked after by specially trained nurses, doctors and support staff in bright and friendly surroundings. You will be encouraged to stay with your child and take an active part in his or her care and if you wish, to sleep overnight with them.

Each of the hospitals also has play specialists who help to make hospital life as normal as possible, by encouraging children to play as they would at home. They also have specific toys and games, designed to help children understand the treatments they are being given and distractions for some of the more unpleasant procedures that may be carried out such as blood taking.

Older children, who are staying in hospital for long periods, may be disappointed to learn that the hospitals also have school teachers to help them with their studies!

**Bristol Royal Hospital For Children**
Upper Maudlin Street, BS2 8HW
0117 923 0000

**Frenchay Hospital**
Frenchay, BS16 1LE
0117 970 1212

**Southmead Hospital**
Westbury-on-Trym, BS10 5NB
0117 950 5050

## AILMENTS & CONDITIONS

There are many agencies offering information and support on medical conditions, see **Advice & Support**.

## COT DEATH & MENINGITIS

See **Advice & Support** for information on both these conditions.

## IMMUNISATION

Immunisation may protect your child against dangerous infectious diseases. They are given at your local clinic. Full details of which immunisations are given and when are written in your Personal Child Health Record. If you have any questions about immunisations, you can discuss them with your health visitor.

## COMPLEMENTARY HEALTHCARE

There are many complementary therapies available to babies and children. See the **Complementary Healthcare** section at the beginning of this chapter.

## ALLERGY THERAPY

Allergy therapy looks specifically at food and chemicals in relation to health and the development of disease and symptoms. It can help to control and sometimes cure a very large range of common allergic ailments. A few examples include asthma and hyperactivity in children.

## Allergy UK

3 White Oak Sq, London Rd, Swanley, BR8 7AG
Helpline 01322 619 898, www.allergyuk.org
Mon-Fri 9am-5pm

Aims to increase understanding and awareness of allergy. Information, advice and support helping sufferers manage allergies.

## Victoria Kubiak APNT Di ONC

164 Old Church Rd, Clevedon, BS21 7TU
01275 876688

A qualified allergy therapist and nutritional counsellor. Works from Sneyd Park Osteopaths, see page 240.

## EMOTIONAL PROBLEMS

There are many agencies offering information and support for a wide variety of emotional problems that may be experienced by your child. See the practitioners and services below. Also See **Advice & Support** for more information.

## The Bridge Foundation

12 Sydenham Road, Cotham, BS6 5SH
0117 9424510, www.bridgefoundation.org.uk
info@bridgefoundation.org.uk

Offers treatment to children and young people with emotional difficulties. Treatment involves talking and thinking about the root of the difficulties which caused the child to need help. Payment on a sliding scale.

## Parent Support Service

0117 924 4860, www.parentsupportservice.co.uk

Victoria Samuel is a Chartered Clinical Psychologist and comes very well recommended. She provides practical, professional guidance for parents, and sensitive, solution-focused child & adolescent therapy.

Also See **Advice & Support** for more information.

# New Opportunities

## Contents

It is likely that sooner or later after the birth of your child, you will have to or want to think about work. If you do not already have a job to return to, you may be thinking of a radical change of direction or using your skills in new ways. There are lots of opportunities for mums and the main carer to work flexibly. This chapter is intended to give you ideas and inspiration. At the end of the chapter we list other sources of information should you wish to explore further.

### Tip

Travel around this book and see what other parents and carers are up to in Bristol. You are sure to be amazed and inspired.

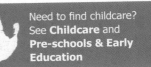

Need to find childcare?
See **Childcare** and **Pre-schools & Early Education**

# DEVELOPING SKILLS

Below are just some ideas of places throughout Bristol where adults can gain a new qualification or learn new skills. Most have creches available.

## ADULT EDUCATION

### City of Bristol College

College Green Centre, St George Rd, BS1 5UA
0117 312 5000, www.cityofbristol.ac.uk

Over 1000 vocational, leisure and accredited courses in various locations across Bristol.

### Filton College

Filton Avenue, Filton, BS34 7AT
0117 9092255, www.filton.ac.uk

Offers GCSEs plus many practical courses e.g. hairdressing, childcare, horticulture. Also has its own nursery, see **Childcare**.

### University of Bristol

Senate House, Tyndall Avenue, Bristol, BS8 1TH
0117 928 9000, www.bristol.ac.uk

Range of under/post graduate courses, evening courses and short courses. Has a nursery.

### University of the West of England

Frenchay Campus, Coldharbour Lane, BS16 1QY
0117 9656261, www.uwe.ac.uk

UWE offers a wide range of under/post graduate courses, and short courses. Many are part-time. Has its own nursery, see **Childcare**.

See Advert at the beginning of the book.

**Know what course you are interested in and want to see if it is available in your area?**

See: www.careersadvice.direct.gov.uk

## Other Sources

### Barton Hill Workshop

43 Ducie Road, Barton Hill, Bristol BS5 0AX
0117 955 6971, www.bartonhillsettlement.org.uk

Courses in computing, basic skills learning, health and wellbeing, languages, and arts and crafts. Also volunteering opportunities.

### Folk House Adult Education Centre

40a Park Street, Bristol, BS1 5JG
01179262987, www.bristolfolkhouse.co.uk

Wide variety of courses from pottery and writing, to fitness and languages.

### Silai For Skills

176 Easton Road, Easton, Bristol, BS5 0HH
0117 941 5180, www.silai.org.uk

Courses in creative textiles for women. Also aims to help build women's talents, & confidence. Affiliated to City of Bristol College.

### St Paul's Learning & Family Centre

94 Grosvenor Rd, St Pauls, Bristol, BS2 8XJ
0117 914 5470, www.bristol.gov.uk

IT, basic skills, English as a second language, crafts, leisure courses and more.

### Workers Educational Association

020 7426 3450, www.wea.org.uk

The UK's largest voluntary sector provider of adult learning. Provides many interesting courses in your local area including creative writing, painting, and organic gardening.

## Distance Learning

### Learn Direct

0800 101 901, www.learndirect.co.uk
Offer online courses in basic English and Maths, as well as courses in IT and Business and Management. Courses can lead to qualifications from Certificates in Adult Literacy and Numeracy (Maths and English), to NVQs, Degrees and Masters Degrees.

### Open University

PO Box 197, Milton Keynes, MK7 6BJ
0845 300 60 90, www.open.ac.uk

Lots of under/post graduate courses including the option of an Open degree where you choose the content of your own degree.

# VOLUNTARY WORK

If you are ready to dip your toe back in the workplace but are not ready for the paid work, volunteering can be a good option. From the Titch Hikers' readers who have experience of volunteering, feedback includes: "it helped me gain skills that I then used for my future paid work", and "it let me try out an area of work that I thought I might like but wasn't sure".

Aspects to consider with voluntary work are:

**Time** - How much do you really have to give? And for how long?

**Finance** - What is the full cost of your time?

**Gains** - What are you hoping to get from it? (Skills, friends, cv material, satisfaction.)

**Environment** - Where are you comfortable being based - face-to-face work, telephone work, online work etc.

**Research** - find out about an organisation before you offer to volunteer, just as you would a paid job.

# VOLUNTARY WORK SOURCES

## National Childbirth Trust

Alexandra House, Oldham Terrace, W3 6NH
www.nctpregnancyandbabycare.com
Local website: www.bristolnct.org.uk

The NCT offers the chance to help other new parents and parents to be. There are roles for everyone, no matter how much time you have to offer or what your skills are.

Roles available include:
Branch Chair (this role could be shared), Branch Vice-Chair, Pregnancy Support Volunteer, Fundraising Volunteers, Valley Cushion & Breast Pump Agents, Breastfeeding Counsellors, Bra Fitters, Nearly New Sale Helpers, Newsletter Editors, Writers and Advertising Sales, and more!

## Netmums

Alexandra House, Oldham Terrace, W3 6NH
www.netmums.com

Superb list of local volunteering opportunities.

"Volunteering with the NCT has been a really positive experience. As a stay-at-home-mum it has been great to have a little something else to think about other than housework and children. And a wonderful way to meet new friends too."
Bobby Spry, NCT volunteer.

## Other Local Volunteering Ideas

### Barton Hill Workshop

43 Ducie Road, Barton Hill, Bristol BS5 0AX
Telephone Lyn Sharry, 954 8887
www.bartonhillsettlement.org.uk

Lots of varied volunteering opportunities.

### Could you be a breastfeeding counsellor for the NCT?

There are only 2 qualifications –

You have breastfed (or will breastfeed) for 6 months; and you would like to help other mothers through problems so they can carry on feeding for as long as they want to.

Most of the training is by way of monthly tutorials with a tutor in Yatton. There is some written work involved, but nothing too daunting. Training takes about 2 years, and leads to a Diploma-level qualification. (Looks good on the CV!) Once qualified, you would do only what you could cope with – as with all NCT 'work', the family always comes first.

"Training to be a Breastfeeding Counsellor has been one of the most interesting, enjoyable and rewarding things that I've ever undertaken.....the course puts considerable emphasis on counselling skills, group work and the importance of self awareness and self evaluation.....the tutorials are great fun and the friendships which are made support you through the training process."

If you think you could be interested in undertaking this very worthwhile training, contact Andrea Peel (the tutor) on 01275 851463 or at:
aep@nsomerset4.freeserve.co.uk

## PAID WORK

If you do not already have a job to return to, or are not sure that your old job fits in with family life, you may be thinking of a radical change of direction or using your skills in new ways. There are lots of opportunities for mums or dads as the main carer to work flexibly, and with every new edition of Titch Hikers' comes a new set of people all over Bristol who have decided to do just this. Whether that is to open up a shop, sell greeting cards, or buy a franchise. Below are some ideas and pointers.

## DIRECT SELLING

This is one of the most flexible options for earning extra money. Your products are supplied for you by the company and then it is up to you to work out your own sales and marketing plan, investing as much or as little time as you like into it. Definitely for the more sociable person. For a list of local selling opportunities see: www.netmums.com

## FRANCHISING OPPORTUNITIES

Buying a franchise is a great way of running a business but with all the support and methods already put in place by the franchisor.

Examples of fantastic local franchising opportunities can be found on:

www.mumandworking.co.uk and www.netmums.com

For more information about buying a franchise, also see these websites: www.british-franchise.org and www.whichfranchise.com

## FREELANCE WORK

Another way for skilled individuals to put their talents to good use, whether these are in photography, journalism, marketing, or many other areas. Can be hard to break into and work can be unreliable.

www.freelanceuk.com and www.peopleperhour.com are well recommended websites.

> "Working for yourself can be daunting and time consuming but pays off when you can rearrange work to fit in with your children's special assemblies and the like! ... My kids also get to understand what work is all about!"
>
> Paula Brown, Tatty Bumpkin Franchisee

## SETTING UP A BUSINESS

New businesses are launching over Bristol and the West all the time. Owning and running your own business is hard work and often there is little distinction between home and work. However, it can be extremely satisfying knowing it's your own idea and your own hard work.

www.businesslink.gov.uk is a really useful site for new businesses to consult. As is www.mumandworking.co.uk

### Work for Titch Hikers'

We are often looking for parents & carers to help with various aspects of the books. We all work on a not for profit basis so you will not earn a fortune but you could gain some excellent skills or keep your CV up to date. Contact us at:

**mail@titchhikers.co.uk**

# Life Coaching with Anne Miller

**Titch Hikers' Editor, Elspeth Pontin, recently tried an hour life coaching session with Anne Miller and was pleasantly surprised with the results.**

I love the work that I do. I also love being a Mum to four young children. But, like the pressures of many parents, at certain points I find juggling the house work, children, being a wife, and managing my job (especially like now when a deadline is looming), pretty stressful and almost impossible.

I'm not keen to give up any of the things that I do. So, my main question for Anne Miller, Life Coach, was whether she could help me find a way to manage the tasks more successfully without having to abandon any of them.

The first task that Anne had sent me to do was a wheel of life where I plotted my satisfaction with various aspects of my life. This was really illuminating, demonstrating how the things that gave me the most satisfaction in life were also the things that I seemed to struggle to fit in on a daily basis. I could just not see how anyone could help me find more hours in the day, which seemed to me to be the only answer.

On meeting Anne it was clear that we were going to get straight down to business. Given the nature of my visit, I found this no nonsense approach relaxed me and I was keen to 'work'. Anne was very easy to talk to. We had decided to do a values exercise based on what it is important for me to be. All the work for the session comes from you with Anne facilitating the process but being careful not to influence it. The idea is that if it all comes from you, without any judgement from Anne, the results are likely to be more honest, therefore less likely to jar, and more likely to be implemented.

The exercise itself is based on a common sense procedure, not frightening at all. It encouraged me to think clearly and to start to order my complex life, and the results were quite surprising. What's more, I discovered areas in my day that made little sense, yet took up a good deal of my time at the expense of other things. I came away from the session feeling energised where I had felt drained. My time with Anne was very well spent.

## Need to knows:

**Life coaching is not the same as counselling.**
**Life coaching is solution based or goal orientated. You are therefore encouraged to look forward rather than back.**

Anne has free handouts with Top Tips for Parents, and Top Tips for Women Returning to Work which you can request at www.annemiller-lifecoach.co.uk

Relaxed Birth and Parenting trains women to run 'Active Birth' and 'Relaxed Birth and Parenting' workshops, yoga-based active birth classes, and to work as a Doula. Check our web-site for details or call Dominique Sakoilsky on 07969204763 or www.relaxedbirthandparenting.com

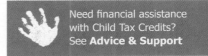

Need financial assistance with Child Tax Credits? See **Advice & Support**

## USEFUL SOURCES OF FURTHER INFORMATION

The following places provide lots of useful information on various aspects of returning to work.

### Careers Advice
www.careersadvice.direct.gov.uk
**For advice on careers and learning.**

### Directgov
www.direct.gov.uk
**Find out about flexible working, maternity and paternity rights, money, tax and benefits.**

### Jobs 4 Mothers
11 Sherborne Gardens, London W13 8AS
0208 537 3319 , www.jobs4mothers.com
**An online jobs board with flexible employment opportunities for parents.**

### Mum and Working
11 Sherborne Gardens, London W13 8AS
0208 537 3319 , www.mumandworking.co.uk
**Fantastic site with lots of information about returning to work, as well as job listings (both flexible and set working hours).**

"I was inspired to set up Mum and Working after talking to other parents who really wanted to find a flexible part-time job that they could do from home. I knew the jobs were out there but that noone had a brought them all together in one comprehensive, easy to use, site... and www.mumandworking was my answer!

Joslyn Bellamy, Director of Mum and Working

### Trades Union Congress
Congress House, Great Russell Street, WC1B 3LS
020 7636 4030, www.tuc.org.uk
**Information about work-life balance.**

### Working Families
1-3 Berry Street, London, EC1V 0AA
020 7253 7243, www.workingfamilies.org.uk
**Charity that aims to help children, working parents/carers and their employers find a better balance between responsibilities at home and work.**

# Advice & Support

## Contents

Family life does not always run smoothly. At times of trouble, we often find it difficult to know where to turn. Whatever your concerns, there is help out there. There is an incredible network of charities and support agencies in the UK, offering a huge range of services both regionally and nationally. In this chapter, we have created a directory which lists many organisations and charities that can either help you or advise you on where to find help. It's by no means exhaustive, but we cover most bases and it should point you in the right direction.

N.B. Contact details frequently change and new support services are starting up all the time. Please let us know any updates via our website.

Also see **Family Health** and for pregnancy related issues, see **Pregnancy & Birth.**

# FOR PARENTS & FAMILIES

## GENERAL SUPPORT

### Bristol City Council

Social Services and Health Department, Amelia Court
PO Box 30, Bristol, BS99 7NB
0117 922 2000, www.bristol.gov.uk
Mon-Fri 8.30am-5pm (until 4.30pm on Fri)
Emergency out of hours: 01454 615 165

Services include: social workers, family support workers, special needs provision, respite care, adoption and fostering, child protection, services and support for disabled children and their families.

### Bristol Children & Young People's Information Service

0845 129 7217, www.bristol-cyps.org.uk
askcyps@bristol.gov.uk

Provides free, impartial and confidential information and/or guidance on a full range of childcare, children's services and resources in Bristol. See also:

www.1bigdatabase.org.uk

### CRY-SIS

BM Cry-sis, London, WC1N 3XX
www.cry-sis.org.uk, info@cry-sis.org.uk
Helpline 08451 228669
9am-10pm

A helpline that gives emotional and practical support to parents whose babies cry excessively. Helpline gives local contacts available out of hours.

### Fulford Family Centre

237-239 Gatehouse Ave, Withywood, BS13 9AQ
0117 9782441
Provides help, support and advice to families with young children who live in Hartcliffe, Withywood and Highridge. Family centre organises and is base for various groups, including Monday drop-in group for parents/carers of children under 5, Friday drop

-in group, women's craft group, children's group, dads group etc. Also provides individual and family counselling, play therapy, welfare rights advice, holidays and outings.

See Also: Children's Centres in **Parent & Baby/Toddler** chapter.

### Home-Start Bristol

Unit 11, The Greenway Business Centre, Doncaster Road, Southmead, Bristol. BS10 5PY
0117 950 1170 (0800 068 6368 Free Info Line)
www.home-start.org.uk

Provides befriending home visits to families with pre-school children under stress. Befrienders are all parents themselves.

### Multiple Births

#### Twins and Multiple Births Association (TAMBA)

2 The Willows, Gardner Road, Guildford, GU1 4PG
www.tamba.org.uk, enquiries@tamba.org.uk
01483 304442                              Mon-Fri 9.30am-5pm
Twinline: 0800 138 0509           Daily 10am-1pm
& 7pm-10pm

Information and mutual support network for families of twins, triplets and more and the professionals involved in their care. Details of local groups can be obtained from the helpline.

### Parentline Plus

0808 800 2222, www.parentlineplus.org.uk

Recently merged with Parent Network and the National Step-Family Association. Call centres run by parents, offering a confidential, anonymous listening ear and practical help. The lines are often busy so keep trying!

#### Totterdown office

104-107 Wells Rd, Bristol, BS4 2SS
0117 971 4831 - Safiyyah cooper
safiyyahcooper.safiyyah@btconnect.com

Offers a range of parenting courses for parents and carers.

### Working Families

See **New Opportunities** chapter.

# FOR BABIES & CHILDREN

## Bristol City Council Child Protection

0117 945 4320, www.bristol-city.gov.uk

The telephone directory provides a list of all local Child Protection offices.

## ChildLine

www.childline.org.uk
Children's correspondence address:
Childline, Freepost, NATN1111, London, E1 6BR
Helpline: 0800 1111
Help & Advice for children: 0808 800 5000
For children living away from home:
0800 884444          Mon-Fri 3.30pm-9.30pm
                              Sat-Sun 2pm-8pm
Textphone 0800 400222   Mon-Fri 9.30am-9.30pm
                              Sat-Sun 9.30am-8pm

Free helpline for children and young people. It provides a confidential telephone counselling service for any child with any problem, 24/7. It comforts, advises and protects.

## Childtime

The Old Treasury, 30A College Green, BS1 5TB
www.childtime.org.uk, info@childtime.org.uk
0117 929 1533 answerphone out of hours
Helps children who are experiencing emotional or psychological difficulties, in partnership with parents and relevant professionals. Subsidised fees on sliding scale.

## Educational Special Needs

See **Pre-school** chapter.

## NSPCC (National Society for the Prevention of Cruelty to Children)

www.nspcc.org.uk, info@nspcc.org.uk
Child Protection Helpline 0808 800 5000 24hr
Textphone 0800 056 0566 24 hr
020 7825 2775 (Public enquiry point)
Provides counsellor based helpline and range of community based projects (phone public enquiry point number above or see website). The NSPCC fights to end cruelty to children.

### NSPCC Asian Child Protection Helpline

0800 096 7719          Mon-Fri 11am-7pm

# ADOPTIVE, FOSTER, STEP & ONE PARENT FAMILIES

## Adoption UK

46 The Green, South Bar St, Banbury, OX16 9AB
01295 752240
www.adoptionuk.org
**Helpline** 0870 7700 450  10am-4pm
Office: 01295 752240

Supporting families before, during and after adoption or long-term fostering. Online community provides information and support.

## Bristol Family Placement Team (Recruitment)

Social Services, Avonvale Road, Redfield, BS5 9RH
www.bristol-city.gov.uk/fostering
0117 954 8545

This team offers information, training and support to anyone interested in fostering children or young people. They welcome applicants from all sections of the community.

## Child Support Agency (CSA)

www.dss.gov.uk/csa
National enquiries 08457 133 133 (Mon-Fri 8am-8pm, Sat 9am-5pm).
Textphone 08457 138924

Aims to support families with the cost of raising children, while recognising that the primary responsibility rests with parents.

## Gingerbread - One-Parent Families' Services

255 Kentish Town Rd, London, NW5 2LX
www.gingerbread.org.uk
or www.oneparentfamilies.org.uk
Helpline 0800 018 5026
info@gingerbread.org.uk
or info@oneparentfamilies.org.uk

Provides help and advice for lone parents on benefits, work, education, relationship breakdown, child maintenance, local activities, children and holidays.

253

## Our Place

139 Fishponds Road, Eastville, Bristol, BS5 6PR
www.ourplacebristol.org.uk
ourplace1@btconnect.com
0117 951 2433

Offering foster and adoptive families the opportunity to mix with others and share experiences. Fun activities, seminars and workshops run by professionals, no charges.

## Single Parent Action Network UK (SPAN)

Millpond, Baptist St, Easton, BS5 0YW
www.spanuk.org.uk, info@spanuk.org.uk
www.singleparents.org.uk (interactive site)
0117 951 4231 (Mon-Fri 9:30am-4:30pm)

Group run by single parents, which campaigns to improve the lives of one parent families. Supports development of single parent self-help groups around the UK.

### SPAN Study Centre

0117 952 2712      Mon-Fri 9am-5pm
studycentre@spanuk.org.uk

Focuses on training and support for single parents, further education and employment. Offers free creche for under 5's.

## South West Adoption Network (SWAN)

The Park, Daventry Rd, Knowle, Bristol. BS4 1QD
0117 373 0265
www.swan-adoption.org.uk
admin@swan-adoption.org.uk

A post-adoption centre offering advice, counselling, support groups and workshops.

# YOUNG PEOPLE & YOUNG PARENTS

## Brook Young People's Services

1 Unity Street, College Green, Bristol, BS1 5HH
www.brook.org.uk, 0117 929 0090
Helpline  0800 018 5023          Mon-Fri 9am-5pm
Mon-10am-6pm, Tue 1pm-6pm, Wed 12:30pm-2:30pm & 4pm-6pm, Thur 4pm-6pm & Sat 10am-2pm.

Expert counselling and advice on sexual health for under 25's. Provides all methods of contraception and emergency contraception; screening and testing. Connexions advice, and ACCSEX — a project aimed at young disabled people. Extremely informative website.

## Off the Record

2 Horfield Road, St Michael's Hill, Bristol, BS2 8EA
www.otrbristol.co.uk
Helpline 0808 808 9120
Office 0117 922 6747
Mon 9:30am-5pm, Tue & Wed 9:30am-8pm.
Drop in: Mon, Tue & Wed 11:30am-5:30pm.

Free, confidential information, advice and informal support for all ages. Free, counselling via appointments for 11-25's.

## The Young Mothers Group and Information Project

c/o The Mill Youth Centre, Lower Ashley Rd, BS5 0YJ
group@ymgt.fsnet.co.uk
0117 935 5639

Offers advice, support and out-reach visits to mothers under 25yrs. The Information Project is peer-led: trained volunteers talk in schools, colleges & youth clubs about the realities of young parenthood.

### Young Mothers' Group Trust

Kilburn Court, 3 Owen St, Easton, Bristol. BS5 6AP
0117 954 0020, www.ymgt.org.uk
info@ymgt.org.uk

Provides housing and advice for single homeless mothers (16-24yrs) or those facing homelessness.

See **Parent & Baby/Toddler** page 113

# RELATIONSHIPS

## The Bridge Foundation

12 Sydenham Rd, Bristol, BS6 5SH
0117 942 4510, www.bridgefoundation.org.uk
info@bridgefoundation.org.uk

A consultation and therapy service for couples, young children and families. Fees are charged but are discretionary for some.

## Bristol Family Mediation

Alexander House, Telephone Av, Bristol, BS1 4BS
www.bfmbristol.co.uk, 0117 929 2002
mediation@bfmbristol.co.uk

Help pre or post-separating/divorcing couples make mutual decisions or resolve issues. A not-for-profit organisation. Outreach offices in Bath and Weston-super-Mare, see website.

## Marriage Care

141 Whiteladies Road, Clifton, Bristol. BS8 2QB
www.marriagecare.org.uk, 0800 389 3801
Fees by donation

Free, confidential counselling service for adults, whether single or in relationships.

## Relate Avon

133 Cheltenham Rd, Bristol, BS6 5RR
www.relate-avon.org.uk, 0117 942 8444
Fees on a sliding scale.

Counselling people with relationship difficulties, along with psycho-sexual therapy for people in committed relationships.

### Also see:

**Narcotics Anonymous**
www.ukna.org.uk
National Helpline 0845 373 3366 or
020 7730 0009
0117 924 0084 (Bristol branch)

A non-profit fellowship of men & women, for whom drugs have become a major problem. Recovering addicts meet regularly to help each other stay clean. Information on fellowship meetings throughout the West Country and Wales, as well as nationally. Check website for meetings.

# DRUGS AND ALCOHOL

All the groups below offer advice and counselling. Contact for more details.

## Advice and Counselling on Alcohol and Drugs (ACAD)

15/16 Lower Park Row, Bristol, BS1 5BN
www.acad.org.uk, 0117 929 3028

For people directly or indirectly affected by alcohol-related problems.

## Al-Anon Family Group

61 Great Dover St, London, SE1 4YF
www.al-anonuk.org.uk, enquiries@al-anonuk.org.uk
Helpline 0207 403 0888          Daily 10am-10pm

For family and friends of problem drinkers. Details of local support groups.

**Alateen-** 0207 403 0888 (Helpline)
Service for young people (12-20yrs) who have been affected by someone else's drinking.

## Alcoholics Anonymous

Alcoholics Anonymous, PO Box 42, Bristol, BS99 7RJ
www.alcoholics-anonymous.org.uk
0117 926 5520/926 5926 24hr Helpline 0845 769755

Frequent meetings held in various parts of Bristol. Free to join, the only requirement for membership is a desire to stop drinking.

## Bristol & District Tranquilliser Project

88 Henleaze Road, Bristol, BS9 4JY
Helpline 0117 962 8874          Mon-Thu 10am-4pm

For people taking prescribed psychotropic medication and for people who have used drugs in the past. Runs withdrawal groups and individual counselling.

## Bristol Drugs Project

11 Brunswick Square, Bristol, BS2 8PE
0117 987 6000, www.bdp.org.uk, info@bdp.org.uk
Drop-in &/or needle exchange:
Mon-Fri 9:30am-5pm, Sat 9:30am-12:30pm.

Free and confidential advice and counselling for anyone concerned about drug use. Crèche facilities on Wednesday mornings.

# BEREAVEMENT

## ARC - Antenatal Results and Choices

73 Charlotte St, London, W1T 4PN
www.arc-uk.org
info@arc-uk.org
Helpline 0207 631 0285          Mon-Fri 10am-5:30pm

Antenatal Results and Choices provides information and support through the ante-natal testing process and when an abnormality is diagnosed; impartial help when making a decision about a pregnancy's future.

## Cruse Bereavement Care

9A St James Barton, Bristol, BS1 3LT
www.crusebereavementcare.org.uk
National Helpline          0844 477 9400
0117 926 4045          Mon-Fri 10am-2pm
Answerphone out of hours
helpline@cruse.org.uk

Provides free 1:1 or family counselling for those suffering from a bereavement.

## FSID - Foundation for Study of Infant Death

Artillery House, 11-19 Artillery Row,
London, SW1P 1RT
www.sids.org.uk
helpline@fsid.org.uk
Helpline 020 7233 2090 (Mon-Fri 9am-6pm & every day of year 6pm-11pm).
General enquiries: 020 7802 3200

Foundation for the Study of Infant Death funds research, promotes baby health and supports grieving families.

## Miscarriage Association

c/o Clayton Hosp, Northgate, W Yorkshire, WF1 3JS
www.miscarriageassociation.org.uk
Admin 01924 200 795
Helpline 01924 200 799          Mon-Fri 9am-4pm
(Answerphone out of hours)

Support for those who have suffered a miscarriage or are worried that they might. Newsletters, leaflets and local contacts.

## SANDS - Stillbirth and Neonatal Death Society

28 Portland Place, London, W1B 1LY
www.uk-sands.org
helpline@uk-sands.org
Enquiries 0207 436 7940
Helpline 0207 436 5881          Mon-Fri 9.30am-5.30pm

Supports parents who are faced with the loss of a baby before, during or after birth.

## The Compassionate Friends

53 North St, Bristol, BS3 1EN
www.tcf.org.uk
helpline@tcf.org.uk
Helpline 0845 1232304 24hr
Admin 08451 203785          10am-4pm & 6.30-10.30pm

Self-help befriending organisation offering support to families after the death of a child.

## Twins and Multiple Birth Association (TAMBA)

2 The Willows, Gardner Rd, Guildford, GU1 4PG
www.tamba-bsg.org.uk
Helpline: 0870 770 3305

Runs a support group led by parents who have themselves experienced a loss with a multiple birth.

## Winstons Wish

Westmoreland House, 80-86 BathRoad, Cheltenham, Gloucestershire, GL53 7JT
www.winstonswish.org.uk
Helpline: 08452 03 04 05 (Mon-Fri 9am-5pm, Sat 9:30am-1:30pm & answerphone out of hours).
General enquiries: 01242 515157

Helping bereaved children and their families rebuild their lives. Also assists schools and carers with the needs of bereaved children.

If you think you could benefit from 1:1 professional counselling see **Family Health.**

# FOR WOMEN

## WOMEN'S HEALTH

### Wellwomen Information

6 West Street, Old Market, St Philips, BS2 0BH
0117 941 2983, www.wellwomeninformation.org.uk
services@wellwomeninformation.org.uk

Drop-in and helpline available for women in distress or other health problems. Counselling for women on low incomes. Health talks & workshops in Asian languages.

Mon 10am-12:30pm & Tue 11am-12:30pm.

**Sehatmand Aurat (Asian Women's Health Project)**
6 West Street, Old Market, St Philips, BS2 0BH
0117 941 2983

Complementary therapy sessions fortnightly, Mon 10am-12.30pm.

### Womankind

3rd Floor, Brunswick Court, Brunswick Sq, BS2 8PE
0845 458 2914, www.womankindbristol.org.uk

Provides women in the Bristol area with free or affordable professional counselling, psychotherapy and on-going support. There is a Helpline for women in distress and women suffering domestic abuse, and a befriending service for women with enduring mental health issues living in South Gloucestershire. Also offers training for volunteers and professionals.

## PRECONCEPTION & ANTENATAL

### Pre-conception care

GPs give advice on pre-conception and fertility problems, and will refer you to specialists if necessary. There are also organisations that help with pre-conception healthcare outside the NHS.

### Foresight

178 Hawthorn Rd, W Bognor, W Sussex, PO21 2UY
www.foresight-preconception.org.uk
01243 868 001

Offers dietary & life-style advice and general support to help couples conceive. For further information send an SAE (35p) or see website.

### Life

1 Mill St, Leamington Spa, Warwickshire, CV31 1ES
www.lifeuk.org, Helpline 0800 915 4600
Free/donations welcome

Pro-life counselling service for women facing unplanned pregnancy, termination, miscarriage, still birth or infertility.

### National Childbirth Trust (NCT)

The NCT, Alexandra House, Oldham Terrace, Acton, London, W3 6NH
www.nct.org.uk
Pregnancy & Birth Line: 0300 3300 772
Breastfeeding Line: 0300 33 00 771
Enquiries Line: 0300 33 00 770
Bristol Branch: 0844 243 6063

Information and support in pregnancy, childbirth and early parenthood. See listing in **Family Health** for ante-natal classes, and breastfeeding counsellors.

### The National Endometriosis Society

50 Westminster Palace Gardens, Artillery Row, London, SW1P 1RR
0207 222 2781
www.endometriosis-uk.org
enquiries@endometriosis-uk.org
Helpline 0808 808 2227      7pm-10pm

Provides support, information and local branch phone numbers.

## Well-Being Eating for Pregnancy Helpline

www.eatingforpregnancy.co.uk, 0845 1303646

The helpline offers scientifically valid information on nutrition for women who are pregnant, planning to be or are breast-feeding.

# MATERNITY RIGHTS

### ACAS

0117 946 9500, www.acas.org.uk

An independent and impartial service to prevent and resolve disputes and to build harmonious relationships at work.

### Department of Trade and Industry

0870 1502500, www.dti.gov.uk

Information about parental leave and maternity rights. Parental leave is available to employees who have, or expect to have, parental responsibility for a child, and have worked for their current employer for a year.

### Direct Gov

www.direct.gov.uk

Information about all maternity and baby entitlements, such as payments, grants and free milk.

### Maternity Alliance

Third Floor West, 2-6 Northburgh Street, London, EC1V 0AY
020 7490 7638, www.maternityalliance.org.uk

Supports pregnant women and parents-to-be, working to ensure that all babies have the best possible start in life.

## Health in Pregnancy Grant

A one off, tax-free payment from H M Revenue & Customs (HMRC) if you're a mum-to-be who's at least 25 weeks pregnant. The payment is called 'Health in Pregnancy Grant' and is to help you prepare for the birth of your baby. Your midwife should give you the forms but if they don't, call: 0845 366 7885

# POSTNATAL ILLNESS

## Association for Post Natal Illness

145 Dawes Rd, London, SW6 7EB
www.apni.org
0207 386 0868                    Mon-Fri: 10am-2pm

Telephone one-to-one support for mothers with post-natal illness. Callers are matched with a local volunteer who has experienced the illness. The line is very busy, but do keep trying, answerphone messages are responded to within 24hrs.

## Hopes Place

0117 968 6303, www.hopesplace.org.uk

A local Christian charity promoting emotional healing and wholeness for women and young people through offering free counselling, listening and education services.

## Meet A Mum Association

54 Lillington Rd, Radstock, BA3 3NR
www.mama.co.uk, National Helpline 0845 120 3746
Mon-Fri 7pm-10pm

Offers moral support, friendship and practical help (local groups) to women suffering from post-natal illness, or who feel lonely or isolated after birth of a child.

## Mothers for Mothers

PO Box 1292, Bristol, BS99 2FD
www.mothersformothers.co.uk
Helpline: 0117 975 6006 (Mon-Thurs).
9.30am - 12.30pm & Crisis line 2.30-9pm.

Befriending and support for women suffering post-natal illness. Holds coffee mornings for mothers to meet. Counselling and home visits available.

## IN CRISIS

### Avon Sexual Abuse Centre

PO Box 665, Bristol, BS99 1XY
www.napac.org.uk
National Helpline 0800 0853 330
0117 935 1707
(Mon/Wed/Thu 9.30am-4pm
Answerphone at all other times)

A free and confidential counselling service available to adults, children and their families.

### Bristol Crisis Service for Women

PO Box 654, Bristol, BS99 1XH
www.selfinjurysupport.org.uk
bcsw@btconnect.com
Admin 0117 927 9600
Helpline 0117 925 1119
Fri, Sat 9pm-12.30am. Sun 6-9pm
Answerphone out of hours

Support for women in any emotional distress; specialises in helping people who have suffered childhood abuse, and those who self injure.

### Gloucester Rape Crisis Centre

P O Box 16, Gloucester, GL4 0RU
Helpline 01452 526770
(Mon-Wed 7:30pm-12:30pm
Fri 7:30pm-8:30pm).
www.rapecrisis.org.uk

Telephone advice and counselling service for women and children who have been raped or sexually abused.

### Next Link Domestic Abuse Services

5 Queen Sq, Bristol, BS1 4JQ
0117 925 0680
www.nextlinkhousing.co.uk
enquiries@nextlinkhousing.co.uk
Mon-Fri 9am-5pm, answerphone out of hours

Safe temporary accommodation for women and children who are experiencing and fleeing domestic abuse. Offers other support services including resettlement and tenancy.

## FOR MINORITY GROUPS

## GENERAL SUPPORT

### Bangladesh Association

Bangladesh House, 539 Stapleton Rd, Eastville, Bristol, BS5 6PE
0117 951 1491
www.bangladesh-association.org
team@bangladesh-association.org

Advice, information and library service for the Bangladeshi community in English and Bengali.

### Bangladeshi Women's Group

Bangladesh Centre, 35 Mivert Street, Easton, Bristol. BS5 6JF
0117 951 9777
bbawg@tiscali.co.uk

Classes held for Bangladeshi women & children living in the Bristol area. Classes include sewing, English classes & mother tongue classes (Bangla) for children, (boys aged 6-14yrs & girls 6-16yrs). Creche provided for children up to 5 years.

### Bristol & Avon Chinese Women's Group

St Agnes Church, Thomas St, St Pauls, BS2 9LL
www.bacwg.org.uk
bacwg2@onetel.com
0117 935 1462      Mon-Fri 9.30am-4.30pm, Fri 4pm

Provides support, advice and information to Chinese women living in Bristol.

### Bristol Gay & Lesbian Switchboard

8 Somerville Rd, Bishopston, Bristol, BS7 9AA
www.bristolblags.org. uk
email@bristolblags.org.uk
0117 922 1328      Mon-Thur 8pm-10pm

Provides information and support to gay, lesbian, transgender and tranvestite people.

## Bristol Pakistani Women's Organisation

454 Stapleton Rd, Easton, Bristol, BS5 6PA
0117 952 3031

Organises social, cultural, educational, religious and recreational activities especially for women and children.

## Bristol Racial Equality Council

Colston House, Colston St, Bristol, BS1 5AQ
0117 929 7899

Advice on racial discrimination. Produces a directory of organisations and contacts for black and other ethnic minority groups, and a monthly newsletter and weekly news bulletin.

## KHAAS

St Werburgh's Community Centre, Horley Rd, BS29TJ
0117 955 4070
khaas_bristol@yahoo.co.uk

Provides services to Asian families who have children with disabilities and special needs.

## Overseas Chinese Association

11-13 Lower Ashley Rd, St Agnes, BS2 9QA
info@oca888.org
0117 955 5225

Support for the local Chinese community. There is a club for the elderly, a Chinese language group, courses and workshops.

## Support Against Racist Incidents (SARI)

PO Box 2454, Bristol, BS2 2WX
www.sariweb.org.uk, sari@sariweb.org.uk
0117 952 0060

Support for people under racial attack or suffering harassment.

## Unity Group

Fulford Family Centre, 237-239 Gatehouse Ave, Withywood, BS13 9AQ
0117 978 2441
fulford.family@barnardos.org.uk
Thu 1-3pm

Informal support group with crèche, for black multi-racial families living in Hartcliffe, Withywood, Highridge and Bishopsworth.

# MEDICAL CONDITIONS & SPECIAL NEEDS

## GENERAL SUPPORT GROUPS

### Break

1 Montague Rd, Sheringham, Norfolk, NR26 8WN
www.break-charity.org, office@break-charity.org
01263 822161 (Mon-Fri 9am-5pm & answerphone out of hours).

Provides special care services for children, adults and families with special needs, including subsidised holidays and respite care.

### Bristol Family Link Scheme

Family Placements, Avonvale Rd, Redfield, BS5 9RH
www.bristol.gov.uk (Search: family link).
0117 353 4086

Family-based short breaks for disabled children and young people.

### Contact a Family

209-211 City Rd, London, EC1V 1JN
www.cafamily.org.uk, info@cafamily.org.uk or helpline@cafamily.org.uk
Admin 020 7608 8700
Helpline 0808 808 3555
Textphone 0808 808 3556

Supports families with disabled children, including those with health conditions and rare disorders. Supplies information on eductional needs, benefits and local support.

### Living Bristol

(Formerly 'Disabled Living Centre').
The Vassall Centre, Gill Ave, Fishponds, BS16 2QQ
www.thisisliving.org.uk
info@thisisliving.org.uk
0117 965 3651 (also Minicom)
For appts: Mon-Fri 10am-4pm & Sat 10am-1pm.

Consultation by appointment providing professional, impartial information and advice on products and equipment to aid independent living. Also has a Multimedia Resource Area, coffee shop and garden.

## Disabled Parents Network

81 Melton Rd, West Bridgford, Nottingham, NG2 8EN
www.disabledparentsnetwork.org.uk
0300 3300 639
information@disabledparentsnetwork.org.uk

A national network of disabled people who are parents or hope to become parents. Peer support, information, advice, contact register, a quarterly newsletter and a helpline. Local and national events.

## Hop Skip & Jump

Grimsbury Road, Kingswood, Bristol, BS15 9SE
www.hopskipandjump.org.uk
0117 967 7282
Mon-Fri: 9am-5.30pm, (Thur 10am-3pm) & Sat 10am-4pm

Donations welcome

Charity-run play centre for children, 0-16yrs, with special needs, where parents can relax while children are looked after by qualified care workers, siblings welcome.

## Parkway Parent and Child Project

Parkway Methodist Church, Conduit Place,
St Werburghs, BS2 9RU
info@parkwaypcp.org
0117 935 0205

Playgroup, crèche, parent and toddler sessions. Informal advice and counselling, courses and workshops.

## The Care Forum

The Vassall Centre, Gill Ave, Fishponds, BS16 2QQ
0117 965 4444 (Mon-Thur 9am-5pm & Fri 9am-4:30pm).
www.thecareforum.org.uk
admin@thecareforum.org.uk

Provides support, co-ordination and information services for voluntary groups enabling them to deliver local health and social care services. Direct services includes The Complaints Procedure Advocacy Service (CPA), complaints about Social Services; The Disability Information Service (DIS).

### Purple Pages Helpline

www.thecareforum.org.uk
info@purplepage.org.uk
0808 808 5252          Mon-Fri 9.30am-4.30pm

A friendly and up-to-date helpline for disabled people, older people, carers and their friends, family and professionals in Bristol and the surrounding areas. Provides contact information on local organisations and groups that help with health, care and well-being.

## The Yellow Book

Consumer Services Manager at South Gloucestershire Council
www.southglos.gov.uk
cis@southglos.gov.uk
01454 866 008

A definitive guide book giving information on services relevant to caring for children with special needs in South Gloucestershire. Download guide from website.

## Time 2 Share

Unit 37, Easton Business Centre, Felix Rd, BS5 0HE
www.time2share.org.uk, hello@time2share.org.uk
0117 941 5868          Mon-Fri 10am-4pm
Answerphone out of hours

Support for families who care for children with learning difficulties. Provides sitters and caters for individual needs. Families are matched on a one to one basis with a volunteer; support and training is available.

## West of England Centre for Disabled Living

The Vasall Centre, Gill Ave, Fishponds, BS16 2QQ
www.wecil.co.uk, reception@wecil.co.uk
Helpline & Minicom 0117 903 8900
Admin 0117 983 2828

Phone service provided by disabled people, offering free, confidential advice covering all aspects of disability — especially welfare rights, DLA and AA form-filling service.

# A-Z SUPPORT FOR SPECIFIC NEEDS & MEDICAL CONDITIONS

## ALLERGIES

### Allergy UK

www.allergyuk.org, helpline 01322 619 898

Aims to increase understanding and awareness and assist in allergy management. Information, advice and support.

## ARTHRITIS

### Arthritis Care South England

www.arthritiscare.org.uk, Helpline: 020 7380 6509
24hr Information Line: 0845 600 6868

Aims to empower people with arthritis to take control of their arthritis and their lives.

## ASTHMA

### Asthma UK

www.asthma.org.uk, Advice Line 020 7786 4900
Helpline 08457 010203          Mon-Fri 9am-5pm

Helpline staffed by asthma nurses. Publishes fact sheets and lists of support groups.

## AUTISM

### Autism (National Autistic Society)

www.nas.org.uk, local contact 0117 974 8460
Helpline 0845 070 4004          Mon-Fri 10am-4pm
Minicom: 0845 070 4003

Impartial, confidential advice and support to people with autism spectrum disorders and their families. The local group meets regularly.

## BED WETTING

### ERIC Education & Resources for Improving Childhood Continence

36 Old School House, Brittania Rd, Kingswood, BS15 8DB
www.eric.org.uk, 0845 370 8008 Mon-Fri 10am-4pm

Advice and information on bedwetting, daytime wetting, constipation and soiling.

## BIRTH DEFECTS

### Newlife Foundation for Disabled Children

www.bdfcharity.co.uk, www.newlifecharity.co.uk
Helpline 01543 462777          Mon-Fri 9.30am-5pm
Answerphone out of hours

Dedicated to improving child health by combating birth defects and supporting those affected or at risk. Help, support & advice for disabled & terminally ill children & carers.

## BLOOD DISORDERS

### Haemophilia Society

www.haemophilia.org.uk, Admin 0207831 1020
Helpline 0800 018 6068          Mon-Fri 10am-4pm

Patient group for people with haemophilia, von Willebrand's and related bleeding disorders. Information and advice.

### OSCAR (Sickle Cell and Thalassaemia Centre, Bristol)

256 Stapleton Road, Easton, Bristol, BS5 0NP
www.sicklecellsociety.org, 0117 951 2200

Information, support and counselling.

## BRAIN INJURIES

### Cerebra

13 Guild Hall Sq, Carmarthen, Wales, SA31 1PR
www.cerebra.org.uk, 0126 724 4200

Information, contact and support network for families and carers of brain-injured children.

# CEREBRAL PALSY

## Cerebral Palsy Plus

Unit 13 The Greenway Centre, Doncaster Rd,
Southmead, Bristol. BS10 5PY
www.cerebralpalsyplus.co.uk
0117 950 5099        Mon-Thu 9am-3pm, Fri 9-12am
Answerphone out of hours

Advice, support, information & financial
help to people affected by Cerebral Palsy &
their families. Run parent group, swimming
sessions, evening club & organise trips.

## Scope

www.scope.org.uk, 0808 800 3333 (Helpline 9am-
7pm weekdays & 10am-2pm Saturdays).

Offer advice, support & information to people
with cerebral palsy & their families & carers.

# CLEFT LIP & PALATE

## CLAPA (Cleft Lip and Palate Association)

www.clapa.com, 020 7833 4883, answerphone out
of hours.
Branch chair: Samantha Jones: 07974 597 548

Information and support. Specialist feeding
bottles, leaflets, and lists of local contacts.

# CYSTIC FIBROSIS

## Cystic Fibrosis Trust

www.cftrust.org.uk, enquiries@cftrust.org.uk
Helpline 0845 8591000, answerphone out of hours

Information, advice and support for those
affected by CF and their families and carers.
Lists of local contacts.

# DEAFNESS

## Acorns Resource for Families of Deaf Children

Elmfield House, Greystoke Ave, W-o-T, BS10 6AY
sue_horne@bristol-city.gov.uk
Voice/minicom 0117 903 8442

For families with pre-school deaf children.
Drop-in centre for parents, access to advice
on sign language and communication. There
is a crèche, Wed in term time.

### BUDS Group

Sensory Support Service (0117 903 8442)

Beginning to Understand Deafness for
families with newly-diagnosed,
hearing-impaired children.

## Bristol Centre for Deaf People

16-18 King Sq, Bristol, BS2 8JL
www.centrefordeaf.org.uk
0117 924 9868      Mon-Fri 8.30am-5pm
Minicom 0117 944 1344

Support, information and advice for deaf
children and their families. Sign language and
lip-reading taught to hearing-impaired parents
or to those with hearing-impaired children.

## Family Centre (Deaf Children)

Family Centre (Deaf Children), Frome House,
Cranleigh Court Rd, Yate, BS37 5DE
www.fcdc.org.uk, Minicom 01454 315405
01454 315404            Mon/Wed-Fri 9am-5.30pm
answerphone out of hours, (voice phone users dial
18002 before minicom number).

Support, information, educational and social
activities for hearing families with deaf
children across Bristol.

## Sense (The National Deafblind and Rubella Association)

The Woodside Family Centre, Woodside Rd,
Kingswood, BS15 8DG
www.sense.org.uk, 0117 967 0008

Support to the families of multi-sensory
impaired children. Running groups
for babies, toddlers and children. Facilities
include toy library, crèche and sensory
stimulation room.

## Sensory Services Supporting People Team

Health & Social Care, RNIB, 10 Still House Lane, Bedminster, Bristol. BS3 4EB
0117 914 1440, Minicom 0117 914 1443

Advice and social work services for deaf and hearing-impaired people.

# DIABETES

## Diabetes UK

www.diabetes.org.uk, info@diabetes.org.uk
0207 424 1000                    Mon-Fri 9am-5pm
Care line 0845 1202960
Local: 01823 324 007 south.west@diabetes.org.uk

Advice to people with diabetes.

# DOWNS SYNDROME

## Downs Syndrome Association

www.downs-syndrome.org.uk
0845 230 0372 - Mon-Fri 10am-4pm

**South West Development Officer**
vr_dsasouthwest@hotmail.com, 01275 858230

**BADSS (local parent support group)**
www.dsa-bristol.org.uk, info@badss.org.uk
01454 315 649 - Andrew King 0845 642 2377
Information library, parents support network and mother & toddler group. Outings, events.

# DYSLEXIA

See **Pre-schools** chapter.

# EPILEPSY

## Epilepsy (British Epilepsy Association)

www.epilepsy.org.uk, helpline@epilepsy.org.uk
Admin 0113 210 8800 admin
Helpline 0808 800 5050          Mon-Thu 9am-4.30pm
                                Fri 9am-4pm

Information, local support groups and a newsletter.

# HIV

## Aled Richards Centre

8-10 West St, Old Market, BS2 0BH
0117 955 1000 (10am-4pm), www.tht.org.uk

Wide range of publications and information on HIV, AIDS and sexual health for professionals and the public.

# HYPERACTIVE CHILDREN

## Hyperactive Children's Support Group

71 Whyke Lane, Chichester, Sussex, PO19 7PD
www.hacsg.org.uk, hacsg@hacsg.org.uk
01243 539966                    Mon-Fri 10am-1pm

Including allergic/ADD children. Advice and support with a dietary and nutrition approach for parents, carers and professionals.

# LEARNING DISABILITY

## MENCAP Avon North

Kingswood House, South Rd, Kingswood, BS15 8JF
www.avonnorthmencap.org.uk
0117 961 4372, avonm@btconnect.com

Support, advice and information for people with learning disabilities and their families.

# LIMB DISABILITIES

## Reach

www.reach.org.uk, 0845 130 6225 Mon-Fri 9am-5pm

Association for children with hand or arm deficiency. Parent support group offering information and lists of local contacts. Membership approx £20 per year.

## STEPS

www.steps-charity.org.uk, info@steps-charity.org.uk
Helpline 0871 7170044, Mon-Fri 9:30am-4pm

Association for people with lower limb conditions which offers information and support with local contacts.

# MENINGITIS

## Meningitis Research Foundation

Midland Way, Thornbury, Bristol, BS35 2BS
www.meningitis.org, Helpline 0808 800 3344 24hr
Children's helpline: 0808 801 0388

Funds vital scientific research into the prevention, detection and treatment of meningitis and septicaemia. Offers support through in-depth information and befriending.

## The Meningitis Trust

Fern House, Bath Rd, Stroud, GL5 3TJ
01453 768 000 (admin and info) Mon-Fri 9am-5pm
www.meningitis-trust.org, Helpline 0800 0281828

Financial, emotional and practical support to sufferers and their families. Information and local contacts available on admin line.

# MENTAL HEALTH

## Mind

35 Old Market St, Bristol. BS2 0EZ
www.bristolmind.org.uk
Mindline 0845 766 0163 (Mon-Fri 9am-5pm).

Drop-in, advocacy, information services and helpline for those with mental health or emotional support needs.

# METABOLIC DISEASES

## CLIMB (Metabolic diseases)

www.climb.org.uk, 0845 241 2172
Helpline 0800 6523181 Mon-Fri 10am-4pm.

Information to parents, carers and professionals. Local contacts and magazine.

# PREMATURE BABIES

## BLISS (The Premature Baby Charity)

www.bliss.org.uk, Parent Support Line 0500 618 140
Mon-Fri 10am-10pm, Answerphone out of hours

Support and information for parents and families with babies on, or recently returned home from, special care baby units.

# SKIN DISORDERS

## National Eczema Society

Hill House, Highgate Hill, London, N19 5NA
www.eczema.org, info@eczema.org
Helpline 0800 089 1122          Mon-Fri 8am-8pm

Help and support for people affected by eczema. Provides list of local support groups.

## Psoriasis Association

7 Milton St, Northampton, NN2 7JG
www.psoriasis-association.org.uk, 0845 676 0076
Mon-Thu 9.15am-4.45pm, Fri 9.15am-4.15pm

Offers support and advice to children and adults suffering from psoriasis.

# SPINA BIFIDA & HYDROCEPHALUS

## ASBAH

Asbah House, 42 Park Road, Peterborough, PE1 2UQ
0845 450 7755, www.asbah.org, helpline@asbah.org

Information, support and practical help. Local group contacts.

# VISUALLY IMPAIRED & HEARING LOSS

## RNIB Bristol

10 Stillhouse Lane, Bedminster, Bristol, BS3 4EB
www.rnib.org.uk, rnibsouthwest@rnib.org.uk
National Helpline 0303 123 9999 Mon-Fri 9am-5pm.
Local Helpline: 0117 - 914 1440
Voice/minicom 0117 914 1443
Mon-Fri 10am-4pm

Support and facilities for those with any level of visual impairment, including combined sight and hearing loss. Sells a range of equipment, offers information (education and employment issues — New Deal, Access to Work) on cds and leaflets. Many other services.

# SERIOUS & TERMINAL ILLNESSES

## ACT (Association for Children with Life Threatening or Terminal Conditions and their Families)

Brunswick Court, Brunswick Square, Bristol. BS2 8PE
www.act.org.uk, info@act.org.uk
Helpline 0117 916 6422 or 0845 108 2201    Mon-Fri 8.30am-5pm Answerphone out of hours

Information on support services available for families with a child suffering from life limiting/life threatening illness. ACT campaigns for the development of children's palliative care services. Online discussion group.

## CLIC Sargent (Cancer and Leukaemia in Childhood)

Abbeywood Business Park, Bristol, BS34 7JU
www.clicsargent.org.uk, helpline@clicsargent.org.uk
0117 311 2600                    Mon-Fri: 8.30am-5pm
Helpline 0800 197 0068           Mon-Fri 9am-5pm
Answerphone out of hours

Provides specialist clinical care, family support, family accommodation close to paediatric oncology centres, holidays, financial help and advice, research.

## Leukaemia Care Society

1 Birch Court, Blackpole East, Worcester, WR3 8SG
www.leukaemiacare.org.uk
01905 755 977                    Mon-Fri 9am-5pm
Helpline 0800 169 6680 24hr

Support through a national befriending scheme. Provides information, limited financial assistance and organises caravan holidays. Lists local contacts. Helpline staffed by those with direct experience of leukaemia.

## The Jessie May Trust

35 Old School House, Kingswood Foundation Estate, Britannia Rd, Kingswood, Bristol, BS15 8DB
www.jessiemaytrust.org.uk
info@jessiemaytrust.org.uk
Admin 0117 961 6840
Care Team 0117 958 2172

Providing a palliative care service for children and young people who are not expected to live beyond the age of 19. Respite, support, advice, terminal nursing care and bereavement support.

## The Rainbow Centre

27 Lilymead Avenue, Bristol, BS4 2BY
www.rainbowcentre.org.uk
0117 985 3343, contact@rainbowcentre.org.uk

Aims to provide the highest quality support and help to children, and the families of children, with life-threatening illness. Also bereavement support, art and play therapy, and complementary therapies.

# LEGAL & FINANCIAL ADVICE

## ADVICE ON ALL ISSUES

### Citizens Advice Bureau

www.citizensadvice.org.uk

Free, confidential, impartial and independent advice on almost any subject including: debt, benefits, employment, housing problems, relationship breakdown and immigration. Operates on a first-in-line basis.

**Bristol CAB**
12 Broad Street, Bristol BS1 2HL
0844 499 4718
Open Mon-Fri 9.30am-1pm, Sat 9.30am-12pm (appointment only).
See Bristol CAB website for full list of CAB services.

**Outreach:**
The Meeting Rooms, 105 Greystoke Avenue, Southmead, Bristol. BS10 6AS
Wed 10am-1pm (drop-in only)

### South Gloucester (Yate) CAB

Kennedy Way, Yate, BS37 4DQ
0870 121 2019

**Outreaches:**
Town Hall, 35 High St, Thornbury
Patchway Community Centre, Rodway Rd, Patchway,
BS34 5PE

**Keynsham CAB** Town Hall, Keynsham, BS31 1EF

**Cadbury Heath Hall,** School Road, Cadbury
Heath, BS30

## North Bristol Advice Centre

2 Gainsborough Square, Lockleaze, Bristol, BS7 9XA
www.northbristoladvice.org.uk
0117 951 5751
Minicom 0117 952 7681
team@northbristoladvice.org.uk

Free, independent and confidential legal
advice and assistance in social welfare law
and general advice on debt, housing and
employment issues. Drop-in and appointment
advice sessions available throughout the week
in Lockleaze, Southmead, Horfield, Patchway,
Little Stoke, Lawrence Weston and Sea Mills.

## South Bristol Advice Service

Leinster House, Leinster Avenue, Knowle, BS4 1NL
Minicom 0117 909 9705
0117 985 1122 answerphone out of hours
www.southbristoladvice.org.uk

Advice, representation, specialist debt and
benefit services. Advice points across south
Bristol. Home visits for house-bound clients.

## St Pauls Advice Centre

146 Grosvenor Rd, St Paul's, Bristol, BS2 8YA
stpaulsadvice@btconnect.com
0117 955 2981
Mon-Fri (closed Wed) 10am-12pm, appt or drop-in
www.advicecentresforavon.org.uk (search: St Pauls
Advice Centres).

Advice on benefits, housing, debt and rights
issues. Tribunal representation available.

# DEBT

## Bristol Debt Advice Centre

2nd Floor, 48-54 West Street, St Philips, BS2 0BL
www.bdac.org.uk, mail@bdac.org.uk
Helpline: 0117 954 3990
Minicom 0117 954 3991
Telephone advice - Thurs 9:30am-12pm, (see
timetable for full list of sessions).

Free professional advice over the phone to
people in debt. Also sessions in Lawrence
Weston, Knowle West, St Pauls & Lockleaze.
Appointments for more complex problems.

# HOUSING

## Bristol City Council Housing Services

www.bristol.gov.uk (Search: Housing services).
General enquiries: 0117 922 2000

Advice to council tenants on housing problems
including homelessness and money advice.
See website for further information.

## Shelter Housing Aid Centre

Kenham House, Wilder St, Bristol, BS2 8PD
www.shelter.org.uk
National Helpline: 0808 800 4444 or Local Helpline:
0844 515 1414
Mon-Fri (closed Wed) 10am-1pm

A drop-in and telephone service providing
advice and help on housing issues.

## South Glos and North Bristol Housing Aid Centre

Callicroft House, Rodway Rd, Patchway, BS34 5DQ
www.england.shelter.org.uk
0844 515 1705

A drop-in and telephone service providing
advice and help on housing issues.

## The SPACE Trust

The Assisi Centre, Lawfords Gate, Bristol. BS5 0RE
www.spacetrust.org.uk
heather@spacetrust.org.uk
Enquiries 0117 907 5355
Outreach/children's work 0117 907 3012

Christian charity working with families

(from all cultures) housed in temporary accommodation. Organises outreach clubs in hostels and finds families free furniture and household goods when rehoused.

## LEGAL

### Avon and Bristol Law Centre

2 Moon St, Stokes Croft, BS2 8QE
www.avonandbristollawcentre.org.uk
0117 924 8662 Mon-Fri 9am-5pm
mail@ablc.org.uk

Free legal advice and advocacy service. Advice on immigration, employment (including discrimination), housing, debt, welfare benefits and community groups. By appointment only.

### Resolution (First for Family Law)

PO Box 302, Orpington, Kent, BR6 8QX
www.resolution.org.uk
01689 820 272 - 9am-5:30pm.
info@resolution.org.uk

Provides local lists of solicitors who are members of the Association. Promotes non-confrontational resolutions to family problems.

### The Law Shop

48 Gloucester Rd, Bishopston, BS7 8BH
www.lawshopbristol.co.uk
0117 944 1966
Mon-Fri 9am-5pm, Sat 9.30-12.30am
Duty solicitor: £6 per 5 minutes

Provides support to people handling simple legal matters themselves. Services include legal forms, books and CDs. Provides free access to the legal library, workstations for people who want to do the work themselves (which can be checked by the duty solicitor) and low cost internet access. The Law Shop does not give advice by phone or email.

## SOCIAL SECURITY & TAX

### Citizens Advice Bureau

Provides free, confidential, impartial and independent advice on social security and tax issues. See listings above.

### Inland Revenue

www.hmrc.gov.uk
See telephone book for full range of helplines

**Child Benefits**
0845 302 1444                    Daily 8am-8pm
Textphone 0845 302 1474

**Working Tax Credit**
Textphone 0845 300 3909
0845 300 3900                    Mon-Fri 8am-8pm

**Self assessment**
0845 900 0444                    Daily 8am-8pm

**Bristol & North Somerset area**
Norfolk House, Temple Street, BS1 6HS
0845 302 1443    Mon-Fri 8am-8pm, Sat 9am-4pm

Local office providing help and advice.

### Social Security

www.hmrc.gov.uk, 0117 938 8200
Central Jobcentre Plus, Eagle House, St. Stephens, Bristol. BS1 1EN
Jobseeker Direct 0845 60 60 234
Textphone 0845 605 5255
Mon-Fri 8am-6pm, Sat 9am-1pm

Jobcentre Plus offers help for those seeking work, also with Jobseeker's Allowance, social security benefit and NI number applications.

| | |
|---|---|
| Benefit enquiry line | 0800 882 200 |
| (Textphone | 0800 24 33 55) |
| Disability Living Allowance | 0845 712 3456 |
| Textphone | 0845 224 433 |
| Attendance Allowance | 0845 712 3456 |
| Textphone | 0845 224 433 |
| National Insurance enquiries | 0845 302 1479 |
| Carers' Allowance | 01253 856123 |

# Maps

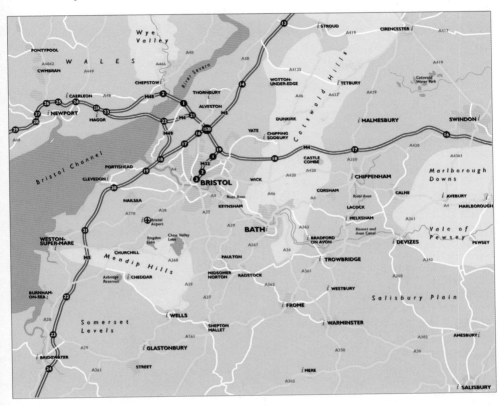

We have included five maps of Bristol and the West in this guide for general orientation purposes only. Three can be found here, one in **Beaches** and one in **Family Holidays and Weekends Away**. Many excellent maps can be found by looking at the following:

Google Maps - maps.google.co.uk

AA Route Finder - www.theaa.com

Bristol City Council's Website - www.bristol.gov.uk

By visiting Bristol's Visitor Information Centres.

Or by purchasing an A-Z map - www.a-zmaps.co.uk

Thank you to Visit Bristol for the use of their maps. Have a look at their excellent website, packed full of information about Bristol and the West: www.visitbristol.co.uk

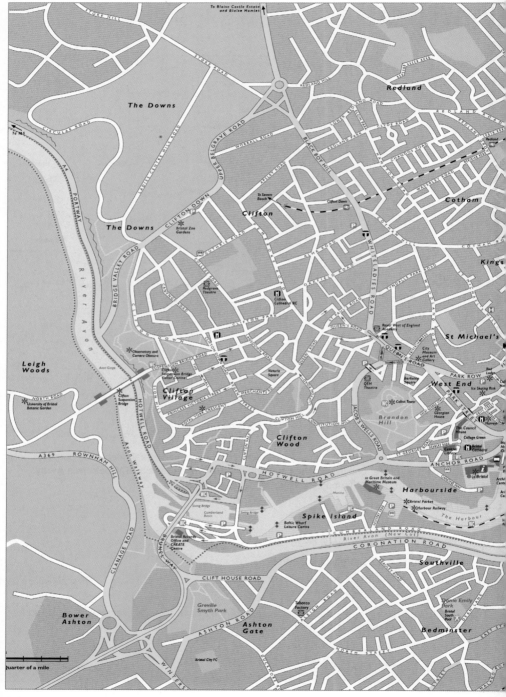

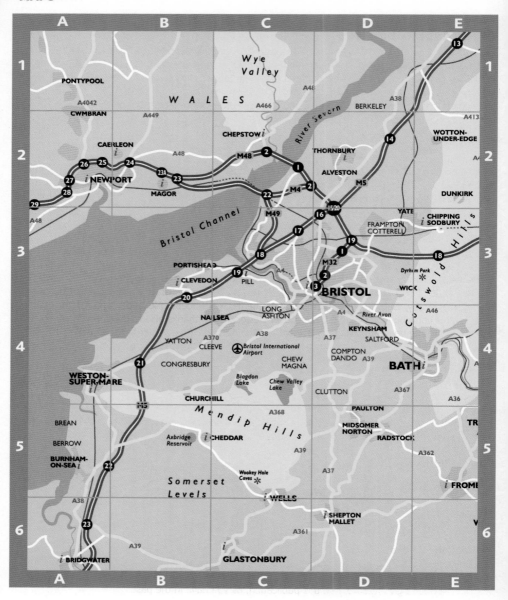

# ACKNOWLEDGEMENTS

Putting this book together is a mammoth task, one that can only be fully realised once you have lived and breathed every second of it. The admiration that I feel for those who have gone before me is immense. As always, it is impossible to credit the thousands of contributors to Titch Hikers' over the last 26 years, but we are particularly grateful to Tricia Phoenix and Sally Stanley who came up with the original idea back in the early 1980s, and Lindsey Potter whose leadership on the 9th and 10th Editions of the book moved us into the 21st century.

## Chapter Introduction Design

Dominic (Christ Church), **Pregnancy & Birth**, **Family Health**, and **Art, Craft & Cookery**; Lexie and Elinah (Christ Church), **Courses for Parents**; Anna (The Clifton Children's House Montessori), **Shopping**; Wren (Christ Church), **Travelling Around**; Ibrahim (Barton Hill) **Animals**; Iqra (Barton Hill) **Walks, Woods & Nature Reserves**; Zai (Christ Church) **Get Physical**; Ibtsian (Barton Hill), **Childcare**; Ilsan (Barton Hill), **Parks**; Millie (Little Monster Baby & Toddler Show), **Pre-schools and Early Education**; Lucas (Christ Church), **New Opportunities**; Ed (Christ Church), **Advice & Support**; Isabelle (Christ Church), "me, my sister, my mum & my daddy", **Performing Arts**;  Emily (Christ Church), **Children's Theatre**; Mikael (Barton Hill), **Reading & Storytelling**; Santiago (Christ Church), "me, my mum & dad & my brother & sister playing in the sunshine", **Parties**; Maisie (Greenfield), **Family Holidays & Weekends Away**; Kirk (Greenfield), **Beaches**; Victoria (22 months, Little Monster Baby & Toddler Show), **Parent & Baby/Toddler**; William (Christ Church), **Eating Out**. Ruby, Isabelle, Amara, Emilia, Joe, Charlie, Nia, Phoebe, Alexander, and A.J. for their considerable contributions to the Chapter Cover Designs. With thanks also to the children who contributed to the beautiful collage in **Bristol Visitor Atttractions**, courtesy of Brunel's ss Great Britain. Also to Mrs Shires' class, Christ Church, for the art in **Out & About West**.

## Artwork within the sections

The pages sparkle with the artwork of many students of Barton Hill Primary (Year 1/2); Christ Church (Reception and Art Club); Greenfield Primary (Nursery, Year 1, 2 and Year 5); and St Werburgh's (Year 1), and also the Little Monster Baby and Toddler Show 2009. These children have made the book extraordinarily vibrant, for which we are most thankful. A special thanks should go to Mrs Richardson, Miss Thomas, and Iris for their inspiration and enthusiasm.

## Photographs

Dreamboats image, **Bristol Visitor Attractions** - Shawn Spencer-Smith. 'Ready for launch' image, **Travelling Around Bristol & the West** - Luke Jerram.

## Personal thanks

To my four children, William, Dominic, Anna and Ollie. And to Ben.

## Parents and Carers

A huge debt of gratitude is owed to all the parents and carers who have kept the Titchhikers' team abreast of new developments for families in Bristol not just this year, but for the past twenty six years. Please continue to give feedback on this publication, as you have in the past.

# INDEX

# My family record

Why not stick photos, train tickets, or other souvenirs here and use this space to keep a record of your days out in and around Bristol.

# My family record

Why not stick photos, train tickets, or other souvenirs here and use this space to keep a record of your days out in and around Bristol.